I ... enjoy the ...
" Sua Sponte "

Jerry Bussl

8.8.05

P/s if you are a
friend of Ray Frame
you are a friend of mine

OF
THEIR OWN
ACCORD

GARY DOLAN

"I have long waited for someone to step forward and give a realistic account of what it was like being a Ranger in combat in Vietnam. Gary Dolan has magnificently accomplished this task. His book is "superb"... a fascinating, accurate, human portrait of Vietnam Rangers in combat. I know...I was there as his front seat pilot. "

Colonel Jerry Bussell (Retired)
Homeland Security Advisor to the State of Nevada
Ranger and 0-1 Birddog Pilot

"I am proud and honored to have been asked to write the introduction to this outstanding work. Gary Dolan has written an unqualified tribute to his men and to his nation, a success story in an unsuccessful war. It should be required reading for every young, aspiring officer entering the military today."

Gary A. Linderer
Nationally known author and publisher of *Behind the Lines*
F Co., 58th Inf. (LRP)
L Co., 75th Inf. (Ranger)

"Gary Dolan has written a profound tribute to all of us who served in Charlie Rangers. In his book he teaches how the Rangers employed their special art of warfare, and he does so with discipline, compassion, humor and courageous self-examination. I am proud to have been in Charlie Rangers; I am proud to have served my country; I am proud to have been inducted into the Ranger Hall of Fame. I am proud of Gary Dolan's book. It brilliantly tells our true story."

Ronald Leslie, Ranger Hall of Fame
Team Leader, Co C (Ranger), 75th Infantry (Airborne)

"This is a profound story of Brave Young Warriors who fought the fight, did their best and served our great country, as only Airborne Rangers would challenge. My son, Rex Marcel Sherman was 18 years old when he was Killed in Action with Charlie Rangers in Vietnam, a country he believed in defending. I believe in the 75th Infantry Regiment, their principals, their leaders and their Creed. Rangers Lead The Way. As the National President of the American Gold Star Mothers, I will 'Lead The Way' for other mothers who are left behind, sons who never returned and those who did return and need to know that we love them and know that they are all Heroes. This is why I thank you for the opportunity to endorse this book, this great truth. Well done, Gary!"

Ann Y. Sherman Wolcott
National President
American Gold Star Mothers, Inc.

"My Brother, my brother—here is some more infantry blue for YOU!! Great dadgummed read. I felt like I was along, actually there, on each mission... You captured the blood, guts, glory, fear, and character of our guys that was not too painful or boastful concerning our mission, style of warfare, and way of life...I would follow YOU into hell and tell the devil to turn up the heat!! CHARLIE RANGERS Lead The Way! Sua Sponte! Your Friend and Combat Brother, GRN

Gary R. Norsworthy
Team Leader, Co C (Ranger)
75th Infantry (Airborne)

OF
THEIR OWN
ACCORD

GARY DOLAN

THE WRITERS' COLLECTIVE
Independent Books for Independent Readers

Of Their Own Accord
© 2005, Gary Dolan. All rights reserved.

ISBN-13: 978-1-59411-026-9
ISBN-10: 1-59411-026-3

Cover Designer: Barbara Hodge
Interior Designer: Barbara Hodge

Printed in the United States of America

10 9 8 7 6 5 4 3 2 1

LCCN: 2003110381

Published by the Writers' Collective • Cranston, Rhode Island

I dedicate this book to all combat veterans, especially those who served in the ignoble conflict of Vietnam, and to the glorious Brotherhood of past, present and future generations of Rangers. Most notably, I dedicate this book to the valiant, courageous, and worthy warriors of Company C (Ranger), 75th Infantry (Airborne), known as "Charlie Ranger." *Rangers Lead The Way!*

My deep appreciation to Gary A. Linderer, F Co., 58th Inf. (LRP), L Co., 75th Inf. (Ranger) for contributing the Afterword.

PROLOGUE
Memorial Day, 1970

W E GO BACK! WE GO BACK! NO GO THAT WAY! Boo Koo NVA! Boo Koo NVA!" Trang shook his head, "No!" Transferring the M-16 to his left hand, he raised his right hand to just above his waist, palm out and vigorously shook the hand back and forth in a blurred stop sign.

Rusky had never seen Trang so unnerved. *Was Trang sweating?*, as he had never seen Trang sweat. The whites of Trang's Asian eyes appeared to be bulging out of their sockets as a single bead of sweat trickled down his camouflaged cheek.

When the team of Rangers suddenly emerged from the dark, dense, thorny brush, they unexpectedly discovered a camp nestled between the "V' formed by two divergent trails. Like ghosts, they slipped back into the brush and silently waited in the eerie stillness as they observed their surroundings for over an hour. Then the team leader sent Rusky and Trang to get a more precise estimation of the base. The two men barely crept inside the perimeter of the camp when Trang insisted they go back.

"The north trail is the way to go," said The Mad Swede, ignoring his Kit Carson Scout. "It's clear the fuckers went that way when they left this base."

"No! I no go. You *dien cai dau*. This tee tee camp. Many big camps with boo koo NVA that way. They come back. We die! *Di di mau!*"

"Listen to Trang, boss." Even Rusky's whisper sounded peculiar due to his accent. "There's no evidence this camp was deserted in a hurry or because of us. Looks to me, boss, like they'll be back."

"I don't know," mused The Mad Swede.

"Just because it's Memorial Day doesn't mean we should go and get ourselves whacked," Rusky continued. "I agree with Trang. If we go that way or even if we stay here, we're gonna get into some deep Kim chi. Remember, they dropped us so far into Cambodia that we got no arty

support. I don't know about you, boss, but I'd like to be around to celebrate Memorial Day in The World next year."

"Alright, fuck it!" retorted The Mad Swede. "But we're gonna have
to booby trap this base before we leave. Shortround, set up a defensive
position and watch our ass on that trail to the left. Hilltopper, take your
M-60 and set up where you have a good view up that northern trail.
Rusky, you fucking stay here with BJ on the radio, but take your claymores out of your pack. Trang, you and I are gonna rig some explosives
for when those fuckers get back."

The team leader's decision did not appease Trang, who continued to
glance at the northern trail where Hilltopper was setting up the machine
gun. Like a prospector with his beast of burden stealing into a rival's
claim, the diminutive scout led the massive American into the deserted
base camp of eleven empty hooch. Trang was careful not to disturb
anything that would announce their presence. Silently, he went to work
hiding grenades primed to explode as a result of pressure or movement
associated with normal activities. Next, Trang carefully placed, aimed
and camouflaged the claymore mines. After that he spent precious time
stretching out and hiding the trip wires that would detonate the mines.
All the while he worked, he furtively stole glances toward the northern
trail and kept alert to any telltale noise or smell. After an hour and a
half of painstakingly careful effort, Trang turned to The Mad Swede,
who held even more munitions.

"We go now. All done. Boo Koo NVA come soon. We go now."

"Yeah, Trang, we fucking go now," said The Mad Swede as he silently
signaled for the team to reassemble at the radio with BJ and Rusky. As
the two men retraced their steps out of the camp, Trang meticulously
erased any evidence of their retreat.

"I called in the location of this gook base camp to X-ray when I made
the last commo check," said Rusky. "I also alerted them that we may
need some gun ships before the night is over."

"We go now! *Di di mau!* We go!"

"Fucking-A, Trang." The Mad Swede was easily annoyed. "We're not
humpin' that trail. Get a hold of yourself. We're going due south up
the goddamn mountain... shit... these shitty vines are thick and dirty.
Christ... it's gonna take us a long time to get clear of this fucking area,
and it's already late! Rusky, take point. Trang, you take slack so you can
clean up our tracks. Rusky, in about two hours, before it gets dark, look
for a place to hole up in for the night."

It was well over an hour before they reached the summit, which was
less than two hundred meters from the enemy's bivouac camp. Through
a small clearing was revealed the Srepok River far below meandering
through the distant valley that led towards Viet Nam. The luscious, deep
green forest blanketed the earth farther than the unassisted eye could
view in the twilight sun and unlike the exfoliated scars of its neighbor,

the Cambodian jungle was vibrant and harmonious with nature and, so far, unblemished by man's war. However, the six Rangers had not the time, the energy nor the inclination to notice the natural beauty surrounding them.

KABOOM!

"Claymore," said Rusky. "Listen. You can hear them."

"*Chet bat dac ky tu;chet treo. Chet mét cach vinh quang. GI, you die tonight! Caca dau!*" The meaning of the distant screams and curses reached their intended audience.

"We go fast now! Boo koo NVA!" Normally, an implacable Trang was comfortable with the excruciatingly deliberate pace that allowed him to straighten any bent twigs and cover their tracks. However, ever since they had begun their climb, he had been imploring them to speed up.

"Fuck! Trang's right. We've got less than an hour of light to get as far away as we can. Let's go!" The Mad Swede urged.

The descent through the thorny vines and moss-covered rocky surfaces was every bit as difficult as the climbing had been. In varying degrees, the men were all suffering from heat exhaustion, fatigue and thirst, but the real, unabashed fear exhibited by their normally intrepid scout, drove them on.

After they had traversed another hundred and fifty meters, The Mad Swede stopped them. "Shortround, go ahead at least fifty meters with Rusky and find a place for us to hide. Hilltopper, you and Trang set up some claymores with trip wires. Make sure you fucking spread them way out. BJ, how's our commo?"

"Commo is five by. No birds in the air right now."

"That means it'll take at least an hour for them to get us any air support. Fuck! I should have scrambled them when the claymore blew," The Mad Swede censured himself.

"Think we need it, Swede? Trang was talking about us dying. He said they were yelling that they knew we were out here and that they were going to find and kill us," BJ said.

"BJ, when it turns dark, you won't be able to see your goddamn hand pressed against your nose. Nothing but fucking insects will bother us tonight. Pass me the goddamn handset," said an impatient, yet worried Swede.

BLAMM!

"What was that?" BJ asked.

The Mad Swede responded tersely, "One of the grenades Trang set. Too bad all of 'em didn't explode."

"X-ray, this is Foul Tip Two Four." The team leader said urgently as he depressed the squelch button on the radio handset. "Scramble gunships. No contact. I say again. No contact. Unknown number of unfriendly set off surprise packages we left for them. Scramble to coordinates previously sent. How copy? Over."

"Foul Tip Two Four, this is X-ray. Lima Charlie. Stand by. Over."

Since the twilight blurred outlines and tricked their vision, the two men strained to hear any foreign sound that might be muffled by the leafy layers of the jungle. Occasionally, they detected a distinctive high pitch that emanated from a distant Vietnamese yell. Also they heard a closer sound of a disturbed bush and silently prayed it was from one of their own or a small forest critter. More than forty minutes passed before the familiar sound of the radio interrupted their purposeful watch.

"Foul Tip Two Four, this is X-ray. Over."

"This is Two Four. Over."

"Foul Tip Two Four, this is X-ray. Be advised a flock of six Intruder helicopters are near your Alpha Oscar. They are fully armed and anxious to go hunting. You should be able to hear them any minute. Over"

"Roger, X-ray. Let them know that Foul Tip Two Four is more than three hundred Mikes south of unfriendly base. Out."

Above the canopy of the jungle, the green earth basked in the amber hues of the setting sun. Below the canopy, darkening shadows quickly devoured the receding shade.

"Hey, boss," whispered Rusky, who had reappeared with Shortround, "we found a spot with large boulders surrounded by thick, thorny bushes. It's perfect and nobody would want to go through there. Hey! Choppers. I hear choppers!"

"Yeah, gunnies from the 281st are gonna fuck up our neighbors."

Hilltopper with Trang, whose trained eyes still revealed considerable fear, joined the reassembled team.

"Good, we're all here," said their team leader. "Rusky, take us there before it gets too damn dark to see anything. When we get settled for the night, maybe the Intruders will provide us with a display of Memorial Day fireworks."

The team hoisted their individual rucksacks onto their backs and silently fell into line behind Rusky, who strode with renewed confidence. They had barely gone twenty meters before the forced quiet of their stealth was shattered by the distant roar of hell from above being visited upon the ground inhabitants, who fired back their fury into the heavens. The unmistakable brap sound of the miniguns meant the gunships were hot. The huge amount of distinctive "popping" sounds of the AK-47s meant the gunships also received a hot reception.

"I feel like fucking cheering," said BJ.

"Shut the fuck up and keep going. Go!" the team leader commanded.

When the team finally reached its objective, each man had to crawl through a ten-foot expanse of thorny bushes to reach the interior fortress of rock boulders. Hilltopper struggled the most with the burden of his M-60. Unable to pull his bandana free from the vines that had ripped it from his head, he finally hacked it loose with his K-bar and buried it on the spot. The crown of thorns was worthless to him.

For the next half hour, the cacophony of ferocious battle they had orchestrated blasted around them. Missiles whistled, rockets swooshed, rifles popped, large caliber weapons in the air and on the ground rattled, and the constant cymbal clapping of explosions thundered, nearly always drowning out high-pitched screams... nearly always.

By now, darkness had completely engulfed the dense forest all around them. The small clearing above the soldier's fortress of large boulders, allowed some starlight to lessen the blackness of their immediate position.

The Mad Swede took the handset from BJ and then informed his men of the transmission. "X-ray says that Wolfpack found three fucking large enemy base-camps not far from the small one we spotted. They said there were hundreds of enemy with all kinds of shit. Two of their birds were badly damaged and one crewman shot... X-ray doesn't know how badly. Anyway, they fucking dumped all their payload on those fuckers."

"We should call for an extraction," interjected Hilltopper.

"No can do."

"Why not?" BJ interrupted. "We should get the fuck out of here!"

"The Old Man made an agreement with the chopper command. No more night extractions."

"That's horseshit. Major Holden would never leave us out here with our dicks waving in the breeze," insisted BJ.

"That's right. If necessary, they'll provide us gunships and flares all night long," assured The Mad Swede.

"Then why wouldn't they just pull us the fuck out?" asked BJ.

"Because it's too fucking dangerous," said The Mad Swede. "The last night exfill was just outside of Phan Thiet. When light from the flares went out, a chopper's rotor hit a fucking tree or the ground. Anyway, it crashed, killing three of the crew and a Ranger. So, no more fucking night extractions! We'll get pulled out at first light. Till then, those fuckers don't know where we are, so just stay cool."

"This bad. NVA come. This very bad," insisted Trang.

"Trang, I don't want to hear any more of your shit. You've been spooked this whole mission. Let's all just cool it now," ordered their leader.

Noise from the distant enemy camp continued unabated until well past midnight and none of the Rangers expected or intended to sleep that night. Without any prompting by their team leader, they each kept a vigilant ear for any potential warning sound.

Thump...Thump...Thump...Thump. Though distant, that sound was unmistakable.

"Mortars," whispered Rusky.

CARUMP! CARUMP! CARUMP! CARUMP!" They couldn't tell where the explosions landed, only that they sounded as if they were all around them.

"X-ray, this is Foul Tip Two Four. Scramble Spooky and Shadow. We are being probed by mortar fire. Over."

"Foul Tip Two Four, this is X-ray. Roger. Over."

Off and on over the next half hour, the maddening THUMP of the mortar being fired interjected renewed apprehension. The resulting CARUMP explosions always sounded closer and louder.

"Foul Tip Two Four, this is X-ray. Be advised that Spooky and Shadow with SLAR are heading your way. Over."

"X-ray, this is Foul Tip Two Four. Roger. Out."

The Side Looking Airborne Radar could locate and pinpoint the enemy better than daylight observation. This allowed the Spooky gunship to obliterate the enemy because of its ability to concentrate a heavy dose of defensive fire into a surgically determined area.

Suddenly, the heavens erupted again. The shouts and cries of the approaching enemy being raked by the venomous fire from Spooky sounded ominously closer than did the earlier distant screams evoked by the Intruder Wolfpack gunships.

The Spooky pilot circled slowly as three, multibarreled 7-62mm machine guns fired 18,000 rounds per minute from the door and two windows in the port side of the passenger compartment. The aircraft was called "Puff" because it resembled a dragon overhead with flames billowing from its guns.

"It's 'Puff the Magic Dragon,' that's awesome, boss!" exclaimed an excited Rusky.

"The new version of Puff is called 'Spooky,' Rusky," corrected the team leader. "Thank God...fucking just in time, too!"

The hellish racket of war ended as abruptly as it had begun after a raucous fifteen minutes. Evidently, it was long enough to forestall any further southern excursions toward the hiding Rangers.

In the early morning twilight, two Intruder Bandit slicks each pulled out three relieved Rangers on a McGuire rig. Two sister sets of Wolfpack gunships covered their extraction. There were no friendly injured.

At about the same time that the Rangers were being lifted by rope to safety, in an eleven hour earlier time zone, two hundred champagne glasses were being lifted in a toast to newlyweds, 2LT Joseph Dunn and his bride, Marie.

The Memorial Day wedding could not have been scheduled on a more beautiful day. The sun shining brightly in a sky over West Point, was unblemished by even a cloud. The reception was held in the Main Ballroom of the Thayer Hotel. At one end, a wall of glass windows overlooked the Hudson River, which meandered from the pristine, forested mountains of the New York highlands to flow past the man-made jungle known as New York City.

"A toast," announced the best man, 2LT Matt Wheeler. "May Joe and Marie enjoy a life filled with love, happiness and many children, and may Joe spend his next year with a terrific unit and come home safely to us so he can enjoy making all those beautiful children!"

1
Reminiscing on the Flight

T HE SUN HAD JUST COME UP BUT WAS NOT YET visible due to overcast skies, the early morning mist coloring the new day a light ethereal gray. First Lieutenant Joseph Dunn led the walk outside from the confines of the staging area at McGuire Air Force Base to the tarmac and a lone waiting civilian jet. The group of men behind him looked strac, very military in the by-the-book sense. All were dressed smartly in their jungle camouflage fatigues with shirtsleeves rolled precisely above the forearm. They looked ready and were ready.

Dressed in a lightweight, short-sleeved khaki shirt, Dunn shivered. But he remained staunchly silent as he stepped along with everyone else. Even though it was July 28, the surroundings reminded him of West Point during winter. At the Academy, it had seemed everything during the winter was depressingly gray-the uniforms, buildings, sky, and even the moods of the men. The wind whipping off the Hudson always made one feel as if the air was pummeling you with little, icy, sharp needles that made your body feel as if it were being used as a reluctant pincushion. Maybe it was a stretch to say these men were being herded, but while at West Point, he had always felt as if everyone was being herded-even at evening chow. Oh, how he loved hating that place! *Well, at least it's not windy,* he thought as he ambled with the group.

Not only had they been ordered to bring only one duffel bag but were further given precise instructions on what specific items to pack. As he watched an airman pitching duffel bags from a huge mound of identical bags into the belly of the plane, he mused, *If the white name tag is somehow torn off, I'll have a hell of a time locating my bag.*

"WWWHEET, WWWHEEUU!" a wolf whistle rang out. "This man's army is all right!" shouted a trooper. "We're goin' to 'Nam in style."

Even Dunn was surprised when a smartly dressed stewardess stepped out from inside the plane onto the landing at the top of the stairs. He knew the army chartered civilian aircraft to shuttle troops to Viet Nam, but never in his wildest imagination had he expected *civilian* stewardesses.

With a beautiful, welcoming smile, another pretty, uniformed attendant announced that the first ten rows were for officers and that the rest was open seating. Delighted to find an aisle seat in the fifth row, Dunn quickly slid into the waiting seat. Next to him by the window, was another first lieutenant who was already fluffing a pillow against the closed window in preparation for a long sleep. All the catcalls and sexual innuendos directed towards the stewardesses seemed crass to Joseph, but they did not appear to object. In fact, they seemed to enjoy the flirting and treated each soldier as if he were special.

Joe could not help but make a mental analogy to the time of the Roman gladiators, who, when saluting and paying tribute to their emperor pledged, "We, who are about to die, salute you!"

Were the warriors on this plane being treated special because they were being carried to an arena of death? He further mused, *Strange... that just before boarding the plane, reveille had sounded and all of us immediately had turned to face the American Flag or toward the sound of reveille, snapped to attention and raised our hands in salute. That was the standard military start to a new day... but also a fitting farewell gesture...*

Too soon, and not yet ready to think or face what was ahead of him, Dunn settled into his seat and welcomed his mind's wandering over the special and delightful events of the past few months. He had just gotten married to his beautiful and lovely soul mate, Marie, and as he had been able to amass quite a number of leave days, they had been able to enjoy a wonderful, once-in-a-lifetime, forty-day honeymoon.

Being terribly in love and missing his Marie, he thought back to the very first moment he had laid eyes on Marie and how, in storybook fashion, had fallen madly in love with her almost immediately. Instinctively he had known he wanted to share the most intimate details of his present life and future with her.

Dunn looked forward to nothing more than freedom from West Point... a guy who simply wished to become his own man. He chose the Infantry as his branch and requested to go to Airborne and Ranger Schools and even volunteered to go to Viet Nam. His rationale was he probably would remain a bachelor for at least another ten years because he doubted he would find the right woman. Well... fate had stepped in. He found and promptly married her.

A soft whisper interrupted his reverie a little while after takeoff, "Can I get you some coffee or something to drink? It's amazing that almost everyone else has already fallen asleep," said the smiling stewardess.

"Yes, thank you. Coffee, black, please."

Normally, he, too, would have been asleep, as he had learned that sleep was a way of escape. The Army could order his body to be at a designated place at a designated time, but whenever he was asleep, his spirit was free to be anything, roam anywhere, and to be with anybody. He could even fall asleep on one of the hard, drop-down, benches in the back of a deuce-and-a-half truck during a fifteen-minute ride on an unimproved road.

Whenever his schedule provided a half-hour break at the Point, he hurried back to his room, not to study but to sleep. His roommates could never fathom why he bothered to undress, get in bed and then have to redress, plus have to redo the bed in strict military fashion. But while his roommates were feeling stressed, Joe usually felt refreshed from a mini-vacation. Sleep was his recharger.

If he had a break of at least an hour or more during the winter months, he would change into ski gear and catch the shuttle to the Cadet slopes; skiing for him was another form of escape and regeneration. While skiing, one did not think about anything except the task at hand. Skiing was a form of entertainment that Joe considered almost better than sex. He could do it all day long, and not even be aware of aches or pains; plus, he was surrounded by gorgeous, pristine scenery. Then, when he was finished, he would be totally exhausted and spent... yet at the same time totally relaxed.

Too bad Marie has never been skiing, his thoughts continued. *I will have to teach her, and then I can have sex and skiing! Could life really get that good? One thing was for certain, there won't be any skiing, or sex for that matter, where I'm now headed.*

Another reason he would not allow himself to fall asleep was he feared having another of his recurring nightmares. The first time he had had that ugly dream was a month before his wedding on a flight up to New York from Ft. Bragg. Originally, he had dismissed it as pre-nuptial jitters, but he had the exact same dream every two or three nights and whenever he stole a catnap.

In his dream, or nightmare, his spirit was flying around inside a gaudy version of the West Point Catholic Chapel. There were bright gold adornments everywhere. Three gold chains suspended a five-foot high golden crucifix over the main altar. A priest in gold robes was eulogizing a fallen veteran. Marie, dressed in black, was bent over sobbing in the front pew while her parents stood in the shadows of the rear vestibule. Joe's spirit frantically kept crying out as it flew round and round inside the chapel, "I'm here! I'm here!" But no one heard.

Each time he awoke from the nightmare, the same hurt washed over him as in the Cadet Mess whenever the Regimental Commander, from the Poop Deck, would announce the names of former cadets who had been killed in action. It was not that Joe was afraid of death nor thought of himself as invincible. But, he also did not think for one moment that he was going to die. Having just married the smartest, sweetest, and the most gorgeous woman in the whole world, he didn't believe for one minute God would present him with such a wonderful gift and not permit him a full lifetime in which to love and be loved.

Marie had never questioned his decision to volunteer, as this was one decision on which Dunn consulted no one. Even if she had not really accepted it, she understood his explanation and simply wanted it to be over so they could get on with their lives and start a family.

Joe explained to Marie, "I have to go to Viet Nam in order to help save lives. The army has spent years and tens of thousands of dollars in training me for this purpose. Too many young lieutenants are just cannon fodder. Many do not have the benefit of my extensive training, as they were drafted out of a college or the ROTC program and were thrust into a situation where they were leading other youngsters. It's bad enough that young lieutenants are getting killed in record numbers, but what is worse is they are too often responsible for the deaths of the brave young men they are assigned to lead."

Dunn suspected that incidents of troops killing their own officers with fragmentation grenades, "fragging," were not always drug related. He often wondered why fragging was never a topic for official discussion in any of his many classes. Instead, the emphasis was about ambushes, snipers and booby traps

Some of the more in-depth discussions Dunn had with the noncom-missioned officers who already served tours in Viet Nam, confirmed his suspicions; the unofficial grapevine accurately described the fragging problem. The NCO instructors in Panama taught him more in their ear-nest, informal, personal discussions than he learned in untold hours of classroom lectures.

"You don't act like no West Pointer," he often heard. It had been meant as a compliment.

West Point graduates expected to spend one year stateside with a line unit before being assigned to a combat zone. Dunn was the first in his class of, The Long Gray Line, to go to Viet Nam. He had won a bid to become platoon leader of the LRRP, Long Range Recon Patrol, 82nd Airborne Division, Ft Bragg, North Carolina. He extracted a promise from the commander to allow him to go to 'Nam, provided Dunn's unit met certain criteria. It did, and four months later he was winging his way to South East Asia, eight months earlier than the required one year tour stateside.

〜

Dark twilight gradually gave way to full light as the stewardesses served breakfast. Dunn had a bad habit of eating too fast and there-fore dispatched his meal too quickly. Once again, he wandered into a semiconscious state. He enjoyed flying as it forced him to relax, read or reflect, about life.

The amenities on this particular westbound flight did not include a movie. Even though the plane stopped at another airbase for over an hour, they had not been allowed to deplane. Additional troops boarded, and the plane was full for the final two legs of the journey. There would be one more refueling stop in the Philippines before the final descent into Saigon.

The lieutenant next to Dunn woke with a loud snore and proceeded to vigorously shake his hand, complaining that it was still asleep. Finally settling down, the lieutenant raised the sliding cover on the window and introduced himself. "Hi, I'm Roger Dowd. I am being assigned to a Graves Registration detachment located in Saigon. Do you have orders telling you to what unit you're going?"

"Joe... Joe Dunn. No, I don't. I am supposed to find out during In-Country indoctrination."

"Well, I hope for your sake it's not some line-company out in the boonies where you can get jabbed by a bamboo booby trap or blown up by your own men." As Roger started to get up he asked, "Do you mind if I slip past you so I can stretch my legs a bit and use the head?"

"No, of course not." Joe slipped out of his seat and stood in the aisle.

Somehow, he knew he wouldn't enjoy passing the time in conversation with Roger. *Just as well since I would much prefer to continue reminiscing about the past few months.*

Instead, he fell fast asleep and didn't wake up until the airline captain announced they were approximately one half hour from touchdown in Saigon and would now begin their descent.

Half awake, Joe let his thoughts idly roam: *I wonder what will be my first impressions of Viet Nam? I have no preconceived notions and no real expectations... but what are my feelings? What am I feeling now? I'm not afraid, not anxious, or nervous. So, what do I really feel... curious? Yes, that's it. I feel curious... about the country, the people, the war, and how I'll fit in. Mainly, though, I'm curious as to what new experiences await me... what new people I will meet... what new customs I will observe... what manmade and natural sights I will behold... what challenges I will face, and how I will react...*

The stoic lieutenant next to him hogged the view out the window, but that was okay as there really wasn't much to be seen from their position over the wing. The landing was uneventful and as they were coasting to a stop, the flight captain announced, "Welcome to Tan Son Nhut Air Force Base, Viet Nam. We look forward to flying each and every one of you back safely to the United States when you complete your tour here. Until then, God speed and protect you. It has been the honor of our staff to have served you on this flight."

2
In Country

WHEN DUNN STEPPED OUT OF THE BELLY OF THE plane, he felt as if someone had sucker-punched him with a furnace blast of hot, humid air. By the time he walked down the stairs, he had perspired through his uniform. Six, olive drab army buses were already lined up, and he could see more approaching. Everywhere he looked, men and machines were in motion. Tan Son Nhut looked just like every other air base he had visited, only the hustle and bustle was much quicker, more determined and focused. Four airmen were unloading duffel bags, and two army sergeants with clipboards were answering questions, directing traffic and giving orders.

"Lieutenant Dunn, sir," barked the sergeant, "please retrieve your gear and proceed to Bus #2." When all the buses were loaded, the sergeants boarded each one in order to announce the itinerary.

"Welcome to 'Nam. I am Sergeant Billings, your official welcoming committee. All of you aboard this Bus #2 are going to Bien Hoa and the In Country Indoctrination Training. Now, I know some of you think you had enough training stateside. Well, I suggest you pay attention because for the next ten days you will be briefed on the latest of 'Charlie's' tricks and what we have learned from recent defectors and prisoners of war. For those of you without orders, which are just about everybody on this bus, that is where you will receive your specific unit assignments. Then, your training will be refined to include tips on surviving the specific terrain of your assigned unit. Any questions? No? Good. Driver, you are off to Bien Hoa."

The name, "Charlie," is the term used to denote the enemy soldier. It derived from the phonetic pronunciation of the letter, "C," in proper military radio procedure. The enemy was the "Viet Cong," or "VC," for short. A radio operator would say, "Victor Charlie for VC," which stood for Viet Cong. Eventually, soldiers started to refer to the Viet Cong as simply "Charlie."

Naturally, Joe and his fellow soldiers were both curious and anxious to get their first looks at their host country, and it didn't take long. Once the bus left, the area outside the gates was not unlike outside any other US. Air Force Base-an inordinate number of bars and strip joints with plenty of "ladies of leisure."

Next, they couldn't help but notice how narrow were the unmarked paved roads. But other than that, they were not otherwise dissimilar to any other paved roads. Soon, it became obvious the streets of Saigon were unbelievably busy and like any other Asian metropolis. Everywhere were seen identical looking black bicycles being pedaled on the streets or parked together en masse. Most vehicles were bicycles, motorcycles or military, but what was surprising were the number of civilian small cars and trucks that darted every which way. The locals were pretty much all dressed alike but woven among them could be seen many U.S. soldiers and airmen in their various tropical and jungle uniforms.

The natives looked as if they were wearing pajamas as the traditional dress of the Vietnamese people tended to be very simple and modest. Men wore brown shirts and black or white trousers. Their headgear was a simple piece of wrapped cloth, and most footwear consisted of a pair of plain sandals.

In feudal times, strict dress codes differentiated the classes of people. Ordinary people were not allowed to wear clothes with dyes other than black, brown or white. Young women wore light brown-colored short shirts with long black skirts, and their headgear was a black turban with a peak at the front. Then, to make their waists look smaller, they tightly fastened a long piece of pink or violet cloth around them.

On formal occasions, these young women wore a special three-layered dress called an "ao dai," which was a long gown with slits on either side. The two long slits allowed the gown to have two, free floating panels-one in the front and the other at the back of the dress. The floating panels exposed a long pair of white silk trousers. To complete the outfit, was an elegant-looking conical palm hat, which was traditionally known as a "non bai tho."

Poetry was written on these hats, and both men and women wore them. This traditional conical hat was particularly suitable for a tropical country such as Vietnam, where fierce sunshine and hard rain were commonplace.

Young children appeared everywhere and seemed to be either just playing or passing the time. While the bus was momentarily stopped, Dunn noticed a group of waving children . Among them was a cute Vietnamese girl, about five years old with long, curly unkempt black hair and two huge brown eyes. A baby boy, not much older than one, was standing with his hands high above his head clenching the hands of his sister, who was squatting directly behind him. The little fellow wasn't shy in the least, with his chubby smiling cheeks and his strategically cutout section of his little pajama trousers showing his all. Obviously, he did not use diapers.

As Joe watched the busy mass of constantly moving humanity, it appeared to him that outwardly, the Vietnamese people seemed impervious to the fact there was a war being waged.

Once outside the city limits, Joe observed that the landscape markedly changed to thick vegetation painted by Mother Nature in every possible shade of green. *Lush*, was the word that popped unbidden into his mind as he assimilated his new surroundings. On the horizon, Mountain ranges loomed in every direction and, except for the occasional burnt remnant of a destroyed vehicle or building and the creative use by locals of discarded military equipment, the ravages and reminders of war and the obvious poverty were far overshadowed by the absolute beauty of the rich, luscious countryside.

On the ride toward Bien Hoa, Joe admired the beauty of the country. He admired and respected the hardworking peasants who tilled the land by hand, using plows pulled by large water buffalo, not shiny new John Deere tractors.

His reverie was broken as the bus halted and the enlisted bus driver announced, "First and last stop," as he rose to push open the doors at the bottom of the two steps. "This will be your home for the next ten days. After that, somebody else will take charge of your tour here in 'Nam."

The In Country Indoctrination Training site was operated by elements of the 25th Infantry Division and was mostly a transient camp, with soldiers constantly arriving and departing.

The quarters for officers and enlisted personnel were the same, long wooden huts, open on the sides with screen mesh and screen doors on each end. Inside there was just slightly more space than what two rows of folding cots needed. The only cinderblock building was the latrine and showers, with an entrance on one side for men and the other for women. Bleachers and firing ranges were used as open classrooms for the conducting of hands-on training and demonstrations.

Surrounding the compound was a double wire, mesh fence with reinforced pillars every four feet. The gate was an open roadway flanked on both sides by a sentry guardhouse covered with sandbags. Every morning and evening a line of Vietnamese civilians, mostly women, were casually inspected and ushered through the open gateway.

Indoctrination, Joe thought, *what a strange term for the army to use to describe my first look at a camp in a combat zone. Well, maybe the time here will allow my body to become better acclimated to this oppressive heat. It's an effort just to breathe. From the looks of this place, I am sure there is no air-conditioning to be found anywhere. I guess we'll be lucky just to have electricity.*

"All officers, follow me, sirs," intoned a Buck Sergeant. "You will all be housed in Building #218. Pick a cot and stow your gear. Then, please stand by until I come by and collect your name and cot number. After that, you are free to wash up and chow down at the mess hall located to the south of the gate where you entered. At 1300 hours, you are to be seated in the main bleachers located directly behind the mess hall. The Camp Commander, Lieutenant Colonel Wright, will welcome you and introduce your instructors. Dress for everything here is cammies, meaning camouflage fatigues. This way, please, sirs."

"Hey, Sergeant," a voice from the group rang out, "when will we receive our unit orders?"

"Sir, orders will be delivered to your cot. Some of you will have them by tonight. All of the orders will be distributed within 72 hours. The address of your unit is what you will use when you notify your loved ones as to your new mailing address. All outgoing mail can be dropped in the box at the mess hall. Mail pickup is at 1000 hours. Any other questions?"

"What about stamps?"

"One of the perks of being in 'Nam, sir," the sergeant responded, "is that Uncle Sam pays your postage while you are in a combat zone. Simply write the word, 'free,' where you would normally put the stamp."

The group followed the sergeant past rows of huts and then into their designated quarters. Dunn selected an empty cot next to a friendly looking fellow who was stretched out shirtless on his cot and reading an Army Times.

Upon seeing Dunn, the fellow introduced himself. "Hi, I'm Henry Berry, Lieutenant. My friends always call me 'Hank.' Where are you from?"

"Hi, Hank, I'm Joe Dunn. Well, since my wife is in New York, I guess that's where I'm from. My last assignment was with the 82nd at Fort Bragg. How about you, Hank?"

"Home for me is and always will be Montana; even though I haven't spent more than one week in my home state these past five years. I take it this is your first day In Country but I've already wasted six days in this hole, and it has seemed like I've been here an eternity. Never figured I'd be one to complain about hot weather, but this place has got to be as hot as hell itself. Sure will be glad to join my unit tomorrow. I don't know what awaits me, but it has to be luxury in comparison to this place. One thing I know I can count on from a unit with pilots is creature comforts at their home base, at least. We'll head over to the mess hall when you're ready."

When Hank stood up and reached to put on his shirt, was when Dunn realized that Hank was a Captain. "Sir..." he began.

"Can the 'sir' crap," interrupted Hank. "When it's just the two of us we can forget the Mickey Mouse military stuff. Besides, someday you might just be glad you have a pilot that's a friend instead of some 'sir' to pull your infantry butt out of Charlie's jungle."

"Okay, Hank. Let me write a quick note to mail home while I wait for the sergeant to take my info. Then, I would love to join you in feasting on some delicious army chow," Dunn said sarcastically. He sure hoped he would have the opportunity to work with guys in the Army Aviation, especially if they were all like Hank.

As the two men walked towards the mess hall, Joe was amazed at the number of Vietnamese men and woman working in various capacities around the camp. *This area of the country must be pretty safe, because there doesn't seem to be much concern for security,* he thought.

Other than the mess sergeant and two GI's, all the workers in the mess hall were locals. The Vietnamese language was stranger sounding than Joe had expected, with high pitches and many "ng" sounds. The delivery was so rapid that he couldn't discern separate words. Even though he prided himself on his linguistic ability, this was one language he doubted he would learn many words. Beckoning to one of the girls serving food, he motioned towards the First Lieutenant insignia on his shirt. "Lieutenant. This is Lieutenant. How do you say Lieutenant in Vietnamese?"

"You *'Trung u".'* (Lieutenant). Him *'Dai u".'* (Captain). *Sù ta an* (Thank you)." said the slim young Vietnamese girl with a quick smile. She had pointed to each of them as she spoke. Then, she giggled, covered her mouth with both her hands, bowed slightly and quickly went back to her chores.

As they ate their hamburgers, Hank explained, "I am rated to fly the military equivalent of the Leer Jet, and I sure hope I'm not going to be stuck flying diplomatic shuttles or courier dispatches. My biggest fear is that I'll be assigned as a babysitter for some general or other VIP on flights to R & R destinations.

"I am also rated as a rotary head, meaning that I can handle any helicopter that Huey, Bell or Boeing makes. So, there's a good chance I'll have my own UH-1H Huey utility helicopter with M60D 7.28mm door guns on M23 armament subsystem. That just means I'd be a machine gun toting taxi for you grunts. However, my first love is fixed wing, not rotary," said Hank between bites of hamburger and fries. "What I really want is to pilot the 0-1 Birddog, a fixed wing, two-seater built by Cessna. That baby is ideally suited for C & C, Command and Control. Also, it can carry up to eight rockets. Of course, there is the remote chance some stuck-in-the-mud grunt like you would be occupying my backseat."

"Sounds like real fun, but this man's army spent a ton of money training me to be the ultimate weapon as a ground-pounder. Since I don't know a thing about air warfare, I agree there's not much chance you'll have to worry about me being your backseat," laughed Dunn.

"'Ultimate Weapon,' my ass! You obviously have never witnessed the fire power of the Cobra Attack Helicopter up close and personal," Hank retorted.

Dunn quickly finished his burger, but the heat caused him to lose his appetite for the fries. As he rose to leave Joe said, "Hank, I need to excuse myself as I need to prepare for the commander's welcome briefing."

"Make certain you pay attention to the class on booby traps. It's the best class they give here and the sergeant that gives it is a real pro. Besides, I'd hate for us to lose our 'Ultimate Weapon' to some bamboo stake." Hank nodded to him and then pulled out the Army Times from the lower leg side pocket of his cammies. "See you tonight."

LTC Wright gave a less than inspiring, ten-minute address to the hundred plus soldiers who had been waiting for more than fifteen minutes in the uncomfortable heat. Since the sweltering sun was to their backs, many had draped handkerchiefs under their hats in order to give some protection to their neck.

Everything here is so casual and informal, thought Dunn. *Back at the Academy and at all the stateside units; there is zero tolerance for any disregard of military dress or custom. Any infraction, no matter how slight, was dealt with severely. The rule was to instill military discipline so soldiers would learn to follow orders without hesitation in a combat situation. Yet, here in a combat zone, I find considerable laxity. What a perplexing dichotomy. I wonder if this will be a continuing trend at my assigned unit?*

Upon the departure of LTC Wright, Sergeant First Class Pope introduced himself as their principal instructor on booby traps for the remainder of the afternoon. Directly in front of the bleachers was an area about the size of two football fields. The area had been subdivided into dozens of display sites, which Dunn, to his surprise and chagrin, had failed to notice.

"Concealed devices," emphasized Pope, "are proving to be effective weapons against the U.S. soldier. Booby traps are also effective against the equipment used for waging war. Thus, concealed devices are effective weapons against the strategists who plan the campaigns on how the U.S. soldier uses the equipment to wage war.

"We are not just fighting in Charlie's country; we're fighting in his war, in his way, and on his terrain. Remember, this is *his* war, not ours! If it were *our* war, then we would have already *won* the damn thing! If this were truly *our* war, then we would have declared war and our whole country would have been behind us to support it! As the mightiest country in the world, we would have used all our might to win, even if that meant bombing and nuking 'Nam and turning it into an asphalt parking lot! If this were our declared war, then you all would be here for the duration and not for just a one-year tour. A one-year contract with a mercenary is no way to win a war!

"You are all FNG's... Fucking New Guys, Cherries or Newbies for the first three months! A cherry is just a liability looking to set off a booby trap. When you get to your new unit and nobody wants to be around you, it's not because of your BO, body odor, it's simply 'cause you're a cherry.

"In order to become acclimated to the heat and learn how to do your job in the jungle without setting off a booby trap takes more than three months. Then, sometime in the middle of your tour, you depart for two, free weeks of Rest and Recreation, or R & R. The last three months of your tour, you're worthless because all you think about is your DEROS date... getting your orders for home, and you're too scared or too smart or just too superstitious to do anything because you don't want to become a senseless booby trap fatality at the end of your tour. So, basically, Uncle Sam will be lucky to get four to six months' good production out of you.

"It's my job to introduce you cherries to the various booby traps employed by Charlie. A cherry sent home in a body bag robs Uncle Sam of the measly six months of productive time you owe for your free, one-year tour to the Far East. Anybody caught not paying attention will receive a personal letter of recommendation from me to serve as 'point,' or the 'lead man,' on patrols for your new unit of assignment."

After he directed the group's attention to a series of constructed displays he continued, "How serious are booby traps? Booby traps are beaucoup serious. Nearly fifteen percent of fatalities and twenty percent of the wounds among U.S. Army troops are caused by Charlie's booby traps. His little ingeniously made devices have delayed and disrupted full-scale division-size maneuvers. Not only do these divert resources to clearance operations, the psychological impact is incalculable. Their devices are being used on a scale never before encountered by US military forces.

"Never, in our glorious history, have we had to face anything quite like them. That is why we go to great lengths to show them to you here. With the expert help of some recently repatriated North Vietnamese officers, we have built display sites of many booby traps employed by Charlie. Where applicable, the sites are split to show them hidden as they would be deployed and then fully exposed for inspection.

"Also, notice, except for indigenous resources such as bamboo, mud, coconuts, scorpions and venomous snakes, nearly all the materials used in making the devices are of US origin. That's right, the U.S. soldier supplies Charlie! Our garbage is his goldmine. Keep that in mind wherever you break camp or ever throw anything away. Never forget that your 'discards' could end up embedded in your buddy. Therefore, any trash left by a unit should be completely destroyed or at least booby-trapped to give Charlie a taste of his own medicine.

"Furthermore, since it is nearly impossible to distinguish combatants from the civilian population, abstain from collecting 'souvenirs,' and don't go accepting flowers from some cute little Vietnamese girl." He tossed a booby-trapped bouquet into the group for it to be passed around.

"Now, let's talk about the booby traps you're going to see in the displays along the marked trail. And by the way, do *not* stray from the marked trail. Although none of the munitions are live, the traps can nevertheless mess up you cherries, and I don't want to have to rebuild any of my displays.

"Most of you have heard of punji stakes-sharpened lengths of bamboo with needle-like tips that have been fire-hardened. Charlie also coats them with his own excrement to cause infection. You will see how we have dug them into shallow camouflaged holes and rice paddies and mounted them on bent saplings. Charlie's snipers employ them in killing zones, because when troops dive for cover into the ditches, more casualties are caused by the punji stakes than by actual sniper fire. Another similar device is a punji-spiked mud ball suspended by vines in the jungle canopy with a trip-wire release. It functions as a pendulum and impales its intended victim.

"Other non-explosive, antipersonnel devices on display include bear traps, crossbow traps, double-spike caltrops, and venomous snake or scorpion-filled boxes. Some of the explosive, anti-personnel devices include the powder-filled coconut, mud ball mine, grenade-in-tin-can mine, bounding fragmentation mine, cartridge trap, and bicycle booby trap.

"The mud ball mine is a clay-encrusted grenade with the safety pin removed. When stepped upon, the mud ball releases the safety lever and the result is the mine is detonated.

"A rifle round, buried straight up and resting on a nail or firing pin is what is known as the cartridge trap. Downward pressure applied to the cartridge fires it into the foot of the intended victim.

"The anti-vehicle devices' include: the B-40 antitank booby trap, concrete fragmentation mine, mortar shell mine, and the oil-drum or the #10 can charge.

"The B-40 is a rocket-propelled antitank grenade, which might be placed in a length of innocent-looking bamboo at the side of a road and command-fired at a vehicle crossing in front.

"The mortar mine is simply the warhead of a mortar that has been separated from its container and retrofitted with an electric blasting cap.

"The oil-drum or tin can charge is based on a standard US 5-gallon oil drum or a #10 can that is filled with explosives and triggered by a simple wristwatch-firing device.

"As you walk through the display site, don't hesitate to ask questions. Keep in mind that there are no *dumb* questions. Also, there are no limits to Charlie's imagination just as there seem to be no limits to the amount of discarded equipment we supply him. So, the types of booby traps are not limited to the ones on display here. Remember what I told you about this being Charlie's war, *not* our war. When you are in a line unit in Viet Nam, you must remain alert at all times or you will become a casualty to his war."

Good advice. Scary advice, thought Dunn. *Hank was right about this being a great class with realistic displays. As a pilot, Hank is lucky that he can avoid most of the threat of booby traps. Although, I have heard that booby traps are often concentrated in helicopter landing zones. They have nearly invisible tripwires that are adeptly positioned to entangle in the rotary blades. Well, I hope for his sake that Hank gets to be a fixed wing pilot as he wishes. As for myself... perhaps I should heed that old adage concerning my desire to be a line platoon leader: "Be careful what you wish for or it might just come true." I certainly don't relish the thought of going to a line unit and witness my men falling casualties to a sniper or a booby trap.*

After the class was over, and until the following morning, was free time. When Dunn returned to the barracks, Hank was not by his cot, and many of the other cherries were engaged in animated discussions about where they were from, past unit assignments or mutual acquaintances. Others had headed off to supper or to do personal chores.

Sitting on his cot, in a hut filled with other soldiers, Joe suddenly felt strangely alone and incomplete. It was then that he first realized the one thing he would most dread for the rest of his entire year in Viet Nam was "free time." As long as he was busy, facing a challenge or involved in any type of mission, his mind would be occupied. Sure, he missed Marie all the time-even when he wasn't actively thinking of her. It was strange how the least little thing could also remind him of her... the long, dark hair of a Vietnamese girl, a pretty flower, a song playing on the Armed Forces Radio Station, an elephant or a snake, or even a cloud in the sky.

It is amazing the crazy things that remind me of her, he realized. She was never further away from his heart than his own blood that coursed through it with every beat. But free time meant his mind would focus *only* on her. He loved thinking about her as it reminded him how much he loved her and how much he was loved, and such thoughts made him feel good and powerful. Also, these thoughts refreshed and energized him in whatever he was doing. However, he loathed thinking *only* of her. He knew whenever he had free time and was alone, he would think only of her. Focusing his thinking solely on Marie would torment not only his mind but also his body. His body would literally ache just as surely as a sore muscle aches without the possibility of relief except for the passing of time.

So, as he reached for writing material, he swore whenever he had free time, he would write to Marie. But, he reminded himself he had to be careful what he wrote, as he didn't want to share any of the ugliness of the war. He didn't want her to worry more than she already would. He didn't want her to be tormented the way he was by missing and thinking only of her.

"Another letter today to the little woman back home? Did you get your orders with your new mailing address?" asked Hank as he came back to his cot.

"No, I haven't received my orders yet," replied Joe.

"Well, how did you like Sergeant Pope and his boobies?"

"Hank, you were right about the class... it was really well done. It made me wonder how all the troops can seem so casual and relaxed when the hidden dangers are so real and so deadly. Anyway, what say we head over to the mess and try to beat the long lines?" Joe invited.

"Not tonight, lieutenant. I plan on celebrating my last night here by feasting at the Bien Hoa Officers' Club, and I'm taking you with me. My treat," said Hank with a big, smile.

Dunn was totally unprepared for the evening that followed. They took a shuttle bus, a service generally known only to the instructors and personnel stationed at the camp, to another large military air base. In addition to being one of the busiest airports in the world during the war, the facility was home to all manner of support units. The largest PX ever constructed anywhere in the world was there in Bien Hoa. *Unbelievable*, he thought, *there aren't many shopping malls back home as well stocked as the Bien Hoa PX.*

When they walked into the impressive two-story wooden building that housed the Officers' Club, Joe felt as if they had been transported into a Polynesian resort. On one side was a formal dining room attended by a local civilian maitre 'd, who seated patrons at large tables and chairs made of expensive teak. Since it was the first of the month and also a Saturday evening, the place was crowded with officers from all branches of the service.

Most seemed to be heading downstairs from where emanated the reverberating sound waves of a touring band from the Philippines. The music wafted throughout the entire building and made one feel in good spirits as the band played an excellent rendition of "Proud Mary." On the side opposite the formal dining area, was an equally well-adorned room with smaller teak tables and a fifteen-foot long ornately carved teak bar.

Upon sitting at one of the smaller tables, the two men were instantly waited upon by a charming, beautiful, young girl in her white silk ao dai who spoke pigeon English.

Joe enjoyed dining on steak and beer with the company of a cocky and irreverent flyboy. Hank was not only intelligent and entertaining, he was picking up the tab with "scrip," the play money issued by the military for use everywhere in 'Nam. Even better was the fact that they were dining where there was central air conditioning. But best of all, he was not left alone with only thoughts of Marie.

It was nearly 2:00 a.m. by the time the two of them literally crawled back into their respective cots. Hank had drunk nearly twice as much but was only half as wasted as Dunn, who passed out simultaneously with his head hitting his makeshift pillow.

Training on a Sunday was the same as any other day, except classes started two hours later at 1000 hours. The late start allowed those who wished to practice their religion to do so, and if a chaplain or rabbi were not available for a more formal service, then a group would convene to share and discuss various topics.

Fortunately, another cherry noticed Dunn was still sleeping and woke him at about 0945 hours, in time for a class on enemy dispositions. He regretted Hank had already departed and was sorry he had not risen earlier to personally wish him farewell. Then he was reminded of the advice of an NCO, who had told him, "Make many great friends in 'Nam but don't let yourself get too close to any one person in particular."

Later that evening after chow, Dunn returned to his barracks and found his orders on his cot. They said he was being assigned to the 173rd Airborne Brigade, or to "The Herd," as was their nickname. Normally, he would have been elated with this assignment since this particular unit enjoyed a strac reputation and consisted stateside of all airborne-quali-fied soldiers. However, since nobody was jumping out of airplanes as a method of deployment in Vietnam, The Herd was just another "leg" outfit of soldiers who had not earned jump wings. *Oh, well*, he thought, *at least I now know where I am going.*

The classes and the week seemed to linger forever, and Dunn thought he would never get used to the awful heat and humidity. On Friday, all the cherries collected their pay in scrip, and a few of them actually received some mail. When Saturday finally arrived, a group of six caught the shuttle to the club.

3
AWOL

A T THE END OF THE ORNATELY CARVED, FIFTEEN-foot long teak bar, was where the group of cherries took up residence. They shared drinks, laughter and an appetite for any war stories from veteran officers. During the evening, some "butterbars," young second lieutenants, were the target of ridicule from the older and more experienced officers.

At some point late in the evening, Dunn noticed another officer, a major, at the near end of the bar holding court and beguiling a group of officers with war stories and statistics. Major Woodrow H. Wayne was five feet six inches, short and stocky with a square, jutting jaw. He had a raspy voice that was the result of a pipe that he nearly always puffed, and his accent was punctuated with a hint of a southern drawl. Dunn noticed that Major Wayne generally stood in a defiant pose with his feet shoulder width apart and his hands on his waist with his thumbs pointing back. Frequently, he rocked or swayed onto the balls of his feet as if to appear taller. When he spoke, he either talked out of the side of his mouth or drew the pipe out of his mouth with a clenched fist that he waved for additional effect.

"Hey, Duke," shouted another Major seated at one of the tables behind Dunn. "What kind of real damage can one of your six-man ambush teams actually inflict on Charlie? Isn't your real value simply Snoop-N-Poop?"

"Real damage?" Major Wayne fired back as he waved his pipe-clenched fist in the direction of the officer behind Dunn. "My goddamn company alone has inflicted more damage than your entire brigade of companies. During the past twelve months, my company has been responsible for more Arclite strikes than any other unit in any year of this goddamn war. How many B-52 bombing strikes have The Herd ever been authorized? My company has the highest kill ratio with the fewest casualties of any unit presently in 'Nam. Hell, I'm on my way now to meet with the commander of First Field Force because your goddamned 173rd has requested operational jurisdiction of my company to help improve its numbers."

"Well, all right," shouted the Major, sporting a shoulder patch from The Herd. He jumped up from his chair and signaled to everyone in the bar with his glass of beer raised high. "Let's give a Ranger salute to 'The Duke,' commander of Charlie Rangers. Here's to Major Wayne!"

"Hooahh! Hooahh! Ahhooga!" everyone cheered as each person raised his glass, bottle or can in tribute towards Major Wayne before chugging down the full contents. As quickly as everyone had galvanized to pay homage, just as quickly everyone returned to his or her private party and conversations around the bar.

Dunn found himself next to Major Wayne, who was beaming in satisfaction from the ovation he had just received. "Sir, can you tell me more about your unit? Do you need any First Lieutenants? How does one get assigned to your company?" asked Dunn.

"As a matter of fact, I have immediate need of three lieutenants, and the goddamn replacement process is too goddamn slow. The unit designation is Company C, Ranger, 75th Infantry, Airborne, and is presently based at Ahn Khe. I have approximately 256 U.S. soldiers and a dozen or more Kit Carson Scouts, who are defectors from the North Vietnamese Army and have volunteered to work for us. All members of my unit are strictly volunteers. There are no goddamn Legs in my unit as all the soldiers are Airborne qualified. All my officers and all my senior NCO's are Ranger School qualified with tab. But, every person is a volunteer. You've got to want to be a Charlie Ranger to get in, and you've got to love it to stay a Charlie Ranger. Goddamn malingerers don't last, and anyone who doesn't want to stay gets a free pass out.

"I see you earned the Ranger tab on your shoulder, Dunn. So, interested in joining my company?"

"Yes, sir, I am interested. Tell me about the mission and how your company operates, sir."

"We dump a six-man ambush team into known enemy territory. My guys use Charlie's tactics against him. They don't get maimed by goddamn booby traps or picked off by snipers. But, my guys see more combat than any Leg unit. I am sick and tired of REMF's, Rear-Echelon-Mutha-Fuckas, claiming all the glory! You understand what I'm saying?"

"Yes, sir!" he quickly replied. When Wayne had said, "sick and tired," it sounded to Dunn as if he'd said, "sic-n-tarred."

"My unit has outstanding operational support. I have dedicated to me, in Direct Support, two gunships and two Huey troop transport slicks plus two 0-1 Birddog planes. 'Direct Support' means when I'm not using those assets, they are sitting on the ground, as they are available only to me. I also get plenty of general support assets, such as Cobras, artillery and air strikes." He paused and drew in a puff from his pipe for additional effect.

A "slick" is a UH-1 helicopter used for transporting troops in tactical air assault operations. The helicopter didn't have protruding armaments and was, therefore, "slick."

"I need a lieutenant who is good with commo gear to head up the Commo & Support Platoon, and I need two, line platoon leaders. My platoon leaders not only take teams into the field; they also have to fly C & C in a Birddog. I see you are a goddamn Ring Knocker. What class are you? And why should I consider you to be a Charlie Ranger? I only take the best."

"I'm Class of '69, sir, and I'd like an opportunity to prove to you that I am exactly what you want and need. If the good major will accept the challenge of canceling my orders to The Herd, he will own the best for himself."

"Well, then I accept your goddamn challenge provided you meet the challenge I am now giving you." Major Wayne puffed a ring of smoke and proceeded to blow a stream of smoke through the center of the ring directly into Dunn's face. "I challenge you to *ignore* your goddamn orders. Get yourself to our training facility at Ahn Khe. I'm on my way to report to my boss, Lieutenant General Coran, the commander of First Field Force. If you can check in with Captain John Roberts, my Executive Officer, before I return, goddamn it, then I promise you I will get your present orders vacated and have you reassigned to my company."

Dunn replied, "I accept and I'll be there waiting for you. When can I expect to see you on your return?" He wanted an idea of how much time he would have to make his way to this place called Ahn Khe.

"Forty-eight hours, Lieutenant, and if you're not there, then I know you don't goddamn have what it takes." With another chomp on his pipe and with a rolling wave of his pipe-clenched fist, Wayne heralded his departure.

Dunn had wanted to question the major as to how it was that Charlie Rangers were immune to snipers and booby traps. However, he dared not appear to challenge or question the man. He hoped in time to learn the answer first hand by serving in the unit. Besides, his all-consuming desire had been to serve under and learn from a charismatic and consummate professional. Now, he had a role model; he wanted to be just like Major Wayne. His ultimate goal and focus in life, ever since he had become a cadet, was to be a commander of a unit such as Charlie Rangers, just like Major Wayne now commanded.

Immediately after the major left, one of Dunn's fellow cherries turned towards him and said with some incredulity, "Forty-eight hours! Is he crazy? You're the one who must be nuts. I bet you don't even know where this Ahn Khe place is or how you're supposed to get there. Hell, I don't even know where I am right now. If it weren't for the war, I would have gone through life never knowing that this country, Viet Nam, even existed. And he expects you to go AWOL? What are you going to do?"

"I plan on reporting to Captain Roberts tomorrow. Come on. I've got to go pack my stuff and get back here to hitch a ride," Joe said as he was already heading for the exit. He figured his experience in flying "space available" was going to help him land a new assignment with Charlie Rangers.

"But, tomorrow is Sunday. Hell, it's already tomorrow!" His fellow student pleaded with him to see reason as he followed Dunn out the door of the officer's club and headed towards the shuttle bus.

"Last time I looked, I noticed they don't call off the war on Sundays, " Dunn commented.

His mind was racing, and he wasn't in the least bit worried about not finding a way to Ahn Khe. Going AWOL didn't bother him either. In a way, it was a great joke to play on the army. *How many times do young lieutenants, new In Country, end up missing and fail to report to their assigned units? For a while, some pencil-pushing REMF is going to have a tough time explaining my absence. Well, now I have a mission to perform and forty-eight hours in which to complete it. Furthermore, as far as I'm concerned, I have all the assets of the Army and the Air Force at my disposal.*

Now, in the lectures of this past week, I heard mention of Ahn Khe. What was it? he thought. *Oh, yeah, the Ivy Division, the 4th Infantry Division, operated a camp and some LZ's, Landing Zones, in and around the area of Ahn Khe. Since the 4th operated in the Central Highlands, then Ahn Khe must be in the vicinity of the Central Highlands. I have got to check out the map of Viet Nam that I noticed in the Orderly Room.*

The half hour they had to wait for the shuttle bus passed quickly as they were completely engrossed in their animated discussion about the opportunity Dunn had found. By the time they got back to the Indoctrination Facility, the other cherries no longer openly challenged the wisdom or the feasibility of his decision.

"I think you're nuts, but I can see how you would like the idea of being part of an elite, professional, volunteer unit. If it's true that Charlie Rangers avoid casualties from damn booby traps and snipers, which constantly plague The Herd, then we wish you good luck. So, what's next? How are you going to do this? You're not scheduled to sign out until Monday."

"I'll simply be gone tomorrow, and you guys can cover for me by just not volunteering any information about me."

"Agreed."

The next morning went off exactly as Joe anticipated. The orderly merely handed him the register when he announced he had to sign out. Dunn had figured, correctly, that he could get away with it by acting with authority and confidence. He studied the map of South Viet Nam, paying particular attention to the names of all villages surrounding Ahn Khe. When he climbed aboard the shuttle, the enlisted driver asked him what religious service or what destination he wanted. Since he was the only passenger, the driver readily agreed to drive him past the various hangars until they spotted an active tarmac.

The activity was hectic everywhere, so Dunn disembarked by a Quonset hut that bore the markings of the 334th Assault Helicopter Company "Sabers." The blades of two Hueys were churning with their jet engines revved up so Dunn approached the crew chief of one of the birds and explained that he needed a ride to the Central Highlands.

"You might just be in luck," responded the Warrant Officer. "An Air Force element that was formerly the 18thAviation Company out of Vung Tao is scheduled to have a Caribou CV-2 airplane in about an hour or so on its way to Pleiku. They should be able to accommodate you. In the meantime, you're welcome to stow your gear and have a cup of coffee in our 'Playboy Mansion.' I'm sending some mail with the 'Bou, so you can ferry over with my clerk to catch your ride."

The familiar "Playboy Bunny" was stenciled on some Hueys, and a sign over the door of the nearest Quonset indicated that it was the "Playboy Mansion."

Two hours passed before the flight actually arrived and nearly another hour before it was ready to depart again. There were four crew members and six other troop passengers already on board. Since the airplane could easily carry thirty passengers, he was added to the manifest without any fanfare. When his gear was on board and he was strapped into a harness seat, an Air Force sergeant squatted in front of him.

"Don't be alarmed," he yelled over the roar of the propeller engines, "before we land we'll make a sudden, very steep descent into the valley, and we'll use an extremely short landing strip. We have found these tactics to be a lot safer from Charlie's mortar attacks. Since we'll be on the ground only a few minutes, you must be ready to deplane quickly. Somebody will meet us to exchange mail. You are the only one deplaning as the other passengers are going with us to Camh Ranh Bay."

The flight was uneventful, except for the descent, which felt like a drop on a giant roller coaster ride. The Caribou did taxi for only twenty feet before coming to a complete halt. A happy-go-lucky enlisted jeep driver met him when the door opened. Before they had finished loading the mail, his gear and driven away, the Caribou was already winging its way straight up into the sky. "Welcome to Camp Holloway. Where can I drop you?" asked the friendly driver.

When he explained his situation, the driver readily suggested taking him to the outpost of the 633rd Security Police Squadron. "Those guys check out all the convoys and can probably hook you up with one going to Ahn Khe. You have a bit of a ride ahead of you, and that Ahn Khe

Pass is treacherous. No matter what, Charlie seems able to destroy at least one vehicle in nearly every convoy."

Camp Holloway consisted of an asphalt landing strip that was neither long nor wide and had no control tower. However, there were impressive rows of Cobras and other aircraft parked between protective embankments.

To Dunn, the heat seemed unbelievably more oppressive here than it was at Tan Son Nhut. But fortune, or good luck, was with Dunn because in the marshalling areas near the outpost were three separate convoys, one of which was heading through "Ambush Alley" to Ahn Khe. The graveled section of Route 19, between Ahn Khe and the base of the Mang Giang Pass with its many hairpin turns, had become the site of so many attacks that the truckers had nicknamed the area "Ambush Alley." There were usually between forty and a hundred vehicles in each "Maverick" convoy. A "Maverick" convoy is made up of trucks from different companies.

Escorting the convoys were dozens of the Military Police's V-100, an amphibious-looking mini-tank that rode high on four huge tires, and even more ATAV gun trucks. A typical gun truck was a converted 5-ton cargo truck modified with double armor plating on the front, rear and sides.

Some of the gun trucks were outfitted with the hull of stripped, armored personnel carriers mounted on the bed. These rolling fortresses were topped off with .50-caliber machine guns, either alone or in multiple mounts. Another innovation was the "Quad-fifty." This weapon consisted of four electronically synchronized .50-caliber machine guns mounted in the bed of a truck. A few escort vehicles were equipped with 7.28-millimeter "mini-cannons," a modern version of the Gatling gun. This "smoker" was capable of delivering 6,000 rounds per minute.

The crews were ingenious in creating modifications that afforded protection while providing additional firepower. The men also painted colorful names on their vehicles, such as, "The Assassin," "Satan's Chariot," "Pandemonium," "Snoopy," "The Red Baron" and "Eve of Destruction."

Despite the loud and impressive force exhibited by the gun trucks when they tested their weapons at a makeshift firing range before they departed, Dunn felt like a sitting duck in the back of the deuce and a half truck. The trip was slightly more than one hundred miles and when they drove through Pleiku, he thought it was an interesting village-a strange mixture of beautiful French-styled villas and impoverished tin-roofed shanties. Then the slow convoy headed out of the valley and up towards the mountains.

No wonder trucks are such easy targets, he griped to himself. *They are forced to a crawl on the steep grades, in gravel, through the hairpin turns. Thank God I'm not in the Transportation Corps.*

BLAMM!

Sure enough, one of the trucks behind Dunn's had either detonated a mine or was hit with a B-40 rocket. Gun trucks responded with a full, three minutes of hellacious retaliatory gunfire as the convoy simply continued.

Well, I have just received my unceremonious baptism by fire, and all I could do was sit here with my thumb up my ass, thought Joe.

❧

It was nearly 1700 hours when the final jeep ride he'd hitched pulled up in front of a wooden shack. The shack was emblazoned with a black scroll sign, outlined in red and bearing white letters: "C Co. Airborne Ranger 75 Inf."

Dunn paused to observe the surrounding area. Across the dirt road were a hand-to-hand combat pit and a rappelling stand that was a platform supported at least thirty 30 feet off the ground with three sets of ropes the length of the tower hanging over the side. In front of a second building marked, "C/75 Supply," was parked an Air Force jeep that had obviously been "requisitioned," Ranger style, as evidenced by the words, "Charlie Ranger" crudely hand painted on the bumper.

When Dunn hesitantly entered the base camp shack, he introduced himself and explained his meeting with Major Wayne. The only man in there, First Sergeant Thayne, listened politely but otherwise showed no particular interest in Dunn or his story and made no verbal response until Captain Roberts entered.

"New platoon leader to be outfitted and sent forward, sir," Thayne announced as he carried a ledger book from his desk drawer and handed it to Roberts. "You can have him sign in, but you'll have to discuss his orders with the Old Man since he showed up without paperwork."

"Thanks, Top," said Captain Roberts. "What time do you want him at the supply shack to sign for gear?"

"Anytime after 1800. Beaver will take good care of him. In the meantime, you can take him for chow and brief him about the company," said Thayer.

As the two men were having a nice conversation regarding him, as though he wasn't there, it gave Joe time to observe the two soldiers.

Thayer was a massive man with Popeye-like forearms and a huge barrel chest. His large, dark brown eyes perfectly complimented his ebony skin, which stretched wrinkle-free over his bald head. This wily veteran contrasted sharply with Roberts, who looked more like a proper English gentleman than a Ranger.

Joe decided he liked them and after finally entering into the tail end of the conversation and discussion with the two men, Dunn rode with Roberts in the requisitioned jeep over to a general mess hall operated by The Herd.

"For the entire month of May our unit was opconned to the 4th Infantry Division," briefed Roberts while they ate. "'Opconned' means, 'under the operational control of.' We were part of Operation Binh Tay I, the invasion of Cambodia's Ratanaktri Province and had the deepest penetration into Cambodia of any American unit. Our teams were highly successful in that we amassed thirty contacts with five confirmed NVA kills and fifteen captured weapons. When we were pulled out of Cambodia, we were released from the 4th Infantry Division control and rushed to DaLat. However, we remained there less than a month before being sent to join Task Force South at Phan Thiet. Man, I tell you...if I were ever to come back here as a civilian after the war, I would love to stay in DaLat. That place is truly gorgeous...a real resort that was built by the French."

"Is that where the unit is now, in Phan Thiet?" Joe asked.

"No, on orders from the Old Man, I transported the unit by cargo aircraft today to Landing Zone English, outside Bong Son. I have to fly there tomorrow to meet with Major Wayne, so you will go with me," informed Roberts

"So, what's the next mission? Who is the unit going to be working for now, or 'opconned,' as you say?" asked Dunn.

"I haven't the slightest idea and, quite frankly, don't care. My job is Admin Support. It's an almost impossible task for me to arrange all the administrative support for the company and would be a lot easier if we simply had a clear-cut chain of command and would just stay put in one place for a while. We probably move around more and are opconned to different commands more than any other unit over here. Then, on top of all that, I have to deal with guys like you, who just show up with no orders. I tell you, nobody seems to appreciate the amount of paperwork required to properly run this company." Roberts good naturedly complained.

"I imagine," commented Dunn, "that we'll get a mission briefing when we join the unit at LZ English."

"Absolutely. Captain Tommy Phillips is in charge of the Tactical Operations Center, the TOC. Tommy is really good. Before he extended and was promoted to the TOC, he was one of our platoon leaders like you. His assistant, SFC Richard Staples, was an Operations Sergeant in the Korean War and is top notch."

After eating, the two men returned to the base camp and went to the supply shack where SGT Willy "Beaver" Beave was busy working. Dunn was issued two more pair of camouflage fatigues, jungle boots, a pistol belt, a rucksack on a frame that was supposed to help distribute the 60 pounds of weight carried on a typical mission, a nylon camouflaged poncho liner blanket, a gas mask, two plastic canteens, a K-bar knife, a first aid kit (gauzes, sulphur, morphine, syringe, water purification iodine tablets), and an emergency escape and evade kit (compass, strobe light, penguin flare, aerial communication detector mirror, flash flag and beacon, malaria tablets, salt tablets, 3 camouflage sticks, matches, mosquito repellent and foot powder). He was also given a holster for a sidearm pistol, but no weapon.

"All the weapons are kept and maintained with the unit," explained Beaver.

Dunn accepted two olive drab colored undershirts but turned down the offer of underwear shorts. "It's simply too damn hot and humid," he explained. "I haven't worn any underwear since the day I arrived in this country and I swear I won't till I leave. But, I will accept a few extra pairs of heavily cushioned socks. Keeping my feet dry and protected is a high priority. Also, socks are good packing material for muffling items that might make a clanging sound on missions."

The next morning, Roberts claimed he had some work to finish up and that the chopper pilots did not appreciate early departures, so Beaver happily chauffeured Joe to the mess hall where he enjoyed a leisurely breakfast.

It was well after 0900 hours before Dunn, Roberts and the others headed off for the flight line. Once there, Joe struck up a conversation with the three crew members and discovered that they had actually been ready for the last two hours and were rather anxious to leave.

The Huey rose effortlessly and taxied only a few feet above the ground down the length of the runway before climbing hundreds of feet into the clear sky. "I wonder why they don't just simply climb straight upwards," yelled Dunn in Roberts' ear, barely audible above the sound of the craft.

"Probably some Leg regulation. I do know that rotary pilots like to fly as high as possible. The main reason is not just to avoid small arms fire, either. I understand that even if all the engines malfunction and completely stop, a helicopter that is high enough can auto-rotate safely to a relatively soft landing in any nearby clearing. High flying is definitely the way to go!" Roberts yelled back to him. The crew gunner, who must have been lip reading, flashed him a thumbs up in agreement.

The flight to LZ English was uneventful. The pilots indicated to Roberts they had radioed ahead for transportation to take the two of them to their company. Specialist E-4 (SP/4) Bobby Ramos, the commander's driver when he wasn't performing his primary duty of assisting Staples in the TOC, gave them a warm Ranger welcome and sped them off in a 1/4-ton truck to their new temporary home.

4
Charlie Company

THE COMPANY WAS LOCATED ON A HILL LESS THAN two miles from the runway. Standing on the side of the road in front of a structure that was clearly the TOC, was Wayne, dressed in new cammies and wearing a Black Beret. He was drinking coffee from a Styrofoam cup and speaking with an E-7, SFC William "Pappy" Butler, who was platoon sergeant of 3rd Platoon.

Joe noticed men in tee shirts or bare-chested, sweating profusely and obviously not enjoying their task in the high humidity. They were climbing all over a structure he figured must be the TOC, and covering it with layers of sandbags. He decided it was clearly the TOC because three RC-292 antennae were mounted on its roof.

"Well, it's about goddamn time. Hey, Tommy, come here. I want to introduce you to the new platoon leader I promised," Wayne said as he signaled to one of the bare-chested men filling sandbags.

"Captain Phillips, this is First Lieutenant Joseph Dunn. It's your job to get him squared away, determine his assignment and put him to work. I expect him to turn out just as good as Pappy's lieutenant." He nodded toward Pappy while Phillips approached.

"Too bad I'm already spoken for, but the platoon sergeants of the other platoons can do just as good a job on this cherry lieutenant," said "Pappy" Butler who clearly enjoyed a close relationship with Wayne. They both considered themselves, "good ole' boys" from the south. Butler was tall, thin and wiry with lines of experience etched deeply in his furrowed hands, face and neck, which made him look much older than he probably was.

Captain Phillips was a well-sculpted man with broad shoulders and a broad grin. When he spoke, it was with an authority that emanated from self-confidence. There was not the slightest trace of any dialect in his speech, and his body language expressed genuine likeability. His dark tan evidenced the depth of his experience In Country.

"You have no idea how glad I am to welcome you," Phillips told Dunn. "As you have probably already figured out, you have joined a great unit, and we can really use you. Leave your gear at the TOC till we figure out your sleeping arrangements. For now, I'll introduce you to the other platoon leaders and your platoon sergeant.

"Up there on top the TOC is Lieutenant Lee. He's got First Platoon and has been with us only a few days. SFC Randall Carreuthers is his platoon sergeant. Dunn, you will lead Second Platoon with the help of your platoon sergeant, SFC Donny Wilson."

Dunn was just leaving his gear at the side of the entrance to the TOC when Phillips exclaimed, "Here comes Scott Baylor now. Baylor was 2nd Platoon Leader but was promoted to Captain the day before yesterday. The Major intends to keep him as an additional Executive Officer. God knows we could use his skills at the rear offices." Baylor approached carrying a folder and an infectious smile.

"Hey, Scotty, come meet your successor, Lieutenant Joseph Dunn," Phillips jovially greeted the new captain. "Maybe in the next hour you can brief him on everything you know about Ranger operations in 2nd Platoon."

"Give me an extra half hour, and I'll teach him all we both know. I'll be happy to entertain him as soon as I drop off some stuff with Staples, the real brains behind our Ranger operations. Be right back for you, Dunn," promised Captain Baylor.

Phillips assured Dunn, "You are in good hands with Scotty, so I am going to get back to my work. Our daily Operations Briefing is at 1800 hours in the TOC. See you then."

Lieutenant Lee jumped down from the TOC, where he was helping hoist sandbags. "How y'all doin'?" he welcomed Dunn with a firm handshake and a wide grin over a square jaw. He had natural blonde hair, shorn close on the sides but wavy and long on top and looked more like a rugged rugby player. Since he, too, was shirtless, his pinkish, sunburned skin betrayed the fact that he also was a cherry. It also revealed a well-nurtured beer belly.

"The Old Man told us you were a West Pointer. I'm V.M.I., class of '69. What class were you?" asked Lee.

Smiling, Dunn replied, "Same as you."

"Great! Let's get together and chew the fat later. I was hogtied into helping them here, but I've got my own stuff to do now. Anyway, I'll catch up with y'all later so we can talk. Good to have ya with us, Dunn," waved Lee as he walked away.

Baylor reappeared from the TOC and asked Dunn, "Where's your gear? Grab it and we'll throw it in my hooch. I have an extra cot in my tent and that way we'll have time to get to know each other better."

Even though Baylor was the same height as Dunn, he had a much more slender build with blond hair, blue eyes and a tanned complexion that gave him an, All-American look. His hooch consisted of a two-man circular tent with the outer walls rolled up to the top of the polls holding up the tent and a mesh encircled the tent to keep out bugs. Inside were two cots, a single folding chair, a field desk and some hanging fatigues. The tent was situated on a flat section of the hill halfway to the summit. There were distances of at least fifty feet that separated each of the structures in the company area.

They paused at the tent long enough for Dunn to pitch his gear inside before they went back down the hill, stopping at a conex on the side of a long wooden structure with a tin roof. A conex is a steel storage/shipping container about 512 cubic feet (8'x8'x8') with a door that made up one side of the container.

Baylor explained, "This is 2nd Platoon's building. Every platoon has a conex in which all their gear is shipped when the unit is moved. It then serves as an office for the platoon sergeant. Pappy operates a nightly cash bar from his conex over in 3rd Platoon. Since this one's locked, your platoon sergeant, SFC Wilson, must be at chow or off arranging something. Let's head over for lunch, and I'll introduce you to more of the guys."

There were a number of 2nd Platoon members eating lunch, cleaning weapons or simply hanging out around the long building. Some of the guys were playing catch with what appeared to be a hollow baseball grenade. Dunn could sense they were all studying his every movement for some indication of who and what he was. The mess hall, where they were headed was a large tent at the opposite end of the parking area from the TOC. Joe found the aromas and the presentation of the food surprisingly enticing.

"Pancho does a superb job as mess sergeant. I have never figured out his secret, but he always manages to serve us more than what is allotted to our unit. Hell, he gives us steaks at least every other weekend. I think we probably eat better than the REMFs in the rear," said a laughing Baylor to Dunn.

SGT Manny "Pancho" Cisco could generally be found greeting everybody that lined up to help themselves to his hot meals. He was not the typical mess sergeant in that he was not overweight. In fact, he was slim and the only person in the unit Dunn ever noticed that always wore a white tee shirt and a black stocking cap that he pulled down tight over his head. Pancho sported a mustache and was as proud of his cooking skills as he was of being from Puerto Rico.

After they got their food, they spotted Lee who was just sitting down next to another officer, 1LT Jack Kent and went over to join them. "Jack, this is Joe Dunn," said Lee, "the guy I was telling you about that came in today. Jack was just getting ready to tell me what it's like being platoon leader of 3rd Platoon," he explained to both Baylor and Dunn.

"Well, I've only been here a little over a month," explained Kent a little embarrassed. "You really should listen to Captain Baylor, who was 2nd Platoon Leader for over eight months."

"No, go ahead," interrupted Scotty Baylor, "you have a closer perspective on the problems of being a new platoon leader here."

"The most important thing is supporting your platoon and your platoon sergeant; getting everything your guys need for the field; checking the supplies; checking the operational status of the equipment; maintaining the rosters; keeping abreast of R&Rs; constant training; and briefing and debriefing the teams on missions," Kent shared.

"What about leading teams in the field? And how about flying C & C?" asked Dunn who felt Kent hadn't revealed anything he didn't already know or could have figured out. What he was most anxious to hear about was C & C, something entirely new and exciting. And leading teams into the field had to be the biggest adrenaline rush ever.

"We're platoon leaders, not team leaders. Even Major Wayne frowns on lieutenants taking teams into the field," answered Kent. "I'd certainly be willing to fly C & C in the 0-1, but I haven't been called on for that duty other than one time. Ask Captain Baylor. He's flown quite a few C & C missions."

"Flying Command and Control from the back seat of a Birddog plane is demanding, gentlemen." Suddenly somber, Baylor spoke deliberately. "You and Lee both will have the opportunity to prove your competency at reading a map, adjusting artillery and directing teams from the air."

"I am also anxious to get my feet wet in a team mission on the ground," said Dunn.

"Airborne," Lee exclaimed in agreement. "Taking teams into the field is the main reason I volunteered for this unit. I feel this is what I was born to do. Damn, I love the guts and the glory! This is where I will earn the CMH!"

"Someone out to get the Medal of Honor usually just gets himself and others killed," Kent remarked with a shake of his head.

"Most of the recipients are just regular guys who do extraordinary things when they happen to be thrust in the middle of a lot of shit," added Baylor.

"Hey, I'm just a regular guy," Lee exclaimed. "Our teams always seem to be dumped into the middle of a lot of shit. Right? Y'all are gonna see, I'm gonna do some great things. It's my destiny... you'll see."

"Remember one thing," warned Dunn.

"What's that?" asked Lee.

"Most of the time the Congressional Medal of Honor is awarded posthumously."

"If that's my fate, so be it. I just know this is my mission; this is what I am here for. I eat this shit up." Lee insisted.

What a contrast, thought Dunn. *Kent is quiet, reserved and unassuming, while Lee is loud and larger than life. There is no doubt that the men like Lee. You just couldn't help but love the guy.*

When they finished the meal, Baylor noticed the 2ndPlatoon conex was open, so he suggested that he and Dunn go back over there. They found Wilson issuing munitions from the conex and he appeared genuinely delighted when introduced to Dunn.

"Come on up to the tent when you finish meeting everybody in your platoon. We should continue our talk," Baylor said as he excused himself and headed up towards his tent.

Donny Wilson was a large-boned man, towering well over six feet with a jutting jaw that was flanked by two obtruding ears. He had longer hair on his massive forearms than on his head, which he kept closely shaven underneath a Marine olive drab baseball cap he always wore. His appearance did not betray his lighthearted, almost jovial nature. Wilson had been with the unit less than one month.

"Hey sir, I hear you're a West Pointer. Is that true? 'Cause I don't see no ring, and you Ring-Knockers are supposedly never without that protection society two-way radio to the Department of Army," Wilson asked Dunn.

"I stashed my ring and all my jewelry, except my watch, with my permanent personal gear. Yeah, it's true. Is that a good thing or a bad thing?" Dunn asked.

"Around here, any non-Leg has an equal chance before being judged as a Ranger, even a fuckin' Pointer, sir."

"From what I understand, your job is to make sure I don't step on my dick," Dunn said as he challenged his platoon sergeant. They both smiled as Wilson then summoned the team leaders of the platoon to meet their new lieutenant and Dunn shook hands with each man as they were introduced.

"This is Staff Sergeant Reginald Parvis, patrol leader of Patrol 21," Wilson introduced first.

"Welcome to Second Platoon, sir. It's a pleasure," Parvis greeted Dunn.

SSG Parvis was one of four black soldiers in the platoon. His nickname was "Peace." He was tall and thin, serious by nature, intelligent and very well spoken. Comfortable with himself, he was content to be solitary; interesting and gregarious, he was equally comfortable in a crowd. His team was always well prepared.

"Next, this is SSG Robert "Buck" Forest, patrol leader of Patrol 22," Wilson continued.

"How ya doin', sir? Where ya from?" Buck asked Dunn.

"New York is my home of record, Buck," Dunn responded with a firm handshake and smile.

"Oh, yeah? We got a new man in Double Deuce from the Bronx. He's a big New York Yankees fan. Do you like baseball?" continued Buck.

Laughing, Dunn answered, "Of course, but actually I'm a Mets fan, and I'm also big on the New York Giants football team."

Buck had been with the unit for only a month but had already endeared himself to his team. A veteran of only two missions, he acquitted himself as a natural in the field. On his very first mission, he calmly accounted for four kills of NVA in an excellently planned and executed ambush. He worked exceptionally well with his assistant patrol leader, SGT Johnny Eagle, or "Chief," as he was affectionately referred to.

Eagle was a Native American from Wisconsin. At a later time, when Dunn got to spend a couple hours with Chief, he learned this was an exceptional young man. There had been an article in Life Magazine about him, as he was the World Champion Indian Dancer and the U.S. Indian-of-the-Year recipient. Prior to volunteering for Viet Nam, Chief completed a global tour of lecturing and dancing.

"Patrol 23 Leader is SSG David Halloway," Wilson said, announcing the next team member.

"Sir." He nodded his head ever so slightly as he grasped and firmly shook Dunn's hand.

SSG Halloway would be one of the finest and bravest soldiers Dunn would ever know. Though humble and quiet, he was fiercely proud. He was absolutely meticulous about even the slightest detail, regardless of whether it was about his fastidious appearance or about his team's preparedness for its missions. For some reason Dunn never discovered, Halloway's nickname was "Professor." Halloway had been to the field on Ranger missions only a few times but had not yet been in a contact. Halloway had been in a few firefights with The Herd, a unit he was with for three months prior to learning about and transferring to Charlie Rangers.

"This is 'The Mad Swede,' SSG Lars Swenson, patrol leader of Patrol 24," Wilson next introduced.

"Welcome to the best damn platoon in the fucking best unit in 'Nam, sir. I know 'cause I've been here two years, and my ATL has been with Charlie Rangers even longer than me," announced Swenson to Dunn as he gave him an almost bone-crunching shake.

"Thanks, Sergeant Swenson, I am damn glad to be here," said Dunn.

Swenson was a towering, burly man with a barrel chest. He had a well-earned reputation of being both fierce and fearless. His assistant patrol leader was SGT Gregor "Rusky" Gregorov, who was the finest tracker and the best interpreter of intelligence data in the field among the Americans.

Wilson continued, "Next is SSG Louis Nate. 'Lucky' is leader of Patrol 26."

Nate assured Dunn, "The Mad Swede is right. Charlie Rangers is home to the best of the best. You've got a lot of guys with experience to help you, Lieutenant. I'm on my third goddamn tour in 'Nam, myself."

Nate had spent one tour with the Special Forces, and the other two had been with Charlie Rangers. He seemed to have an inherent hatred for anything civilian and especially hated the "gooks," which is what he called all Vietnamese and refused to take a repatriated scout with his team into the field. Claiming, "I don't trust nobody already proven to be a traitor." Needless to mention, Nate was an excellent soldier, happy to do his job with no fanfare or recognition.

At a later time, Dunn was shocked when he discovered Nate had been wounded on the first of his consecutive tours with Charlie Rangers, and he had not yet been awarded the Purple Heart. In fact, he hadn't even received the Combat Infantryman Badge, which was automatically awarded to any soldier in combat with a Military Occupation Specialty of Infantryman. He had mused, *The operational support given Charlie Rangers might be outstanding, but the administrative support is clearly inadequate, if not downright non-existent.*

"Finally, let me introduce you, sir, to Staff Sergeant Peter Dobkowski. 'Ski' is patrol leader of Patrol 27. There is no Patrol 25 because the platoon is short some men right now."

"Sir, it's a real pleasure. If there's anything at all we can do for you or help you with, just holler," Dobkowski promised Dunn.

Ski was the most outwardly friendly of all the team leaders and could always be counted on for some type of cheerfulness and a joke and was genuinely liked throughout the entire company. Whenever he spoke with a heavy European accent, it seemed to make his jokes even funnier.

"These guys all have their shit together," claimed Wilson. "They are real pros in the bush but don't ever go into their hooch...it's a real pigsty. But, they sure can put a big hurt on fucking Charlie."

"I bet you didn't realize since you now belong to 2nd Platoon, sir, you have a bounty on your head," announced one of the men.

"Yeah, Charlie's willing to pay a thousand U.S. bucks for one of us, dead or alive. He also knows and fears us, because we always leave a calling card on the dead gooks we ambush," chuckled Ski. "Hell, they'd probably pay five thousand for our lieutenant."

Most of the men had informally assembled around him as Wilson introduced him to the team leaders. Sensing the men had plenty of tasks to complete, especially since they had recently been airlifted to this site, Dunn politely said, "I appreciate meeting you and look forward to knowing and leaning more from you and the rest of the men. But, I don't want to keep you from your duties. I'll get myself settled in and see you later." He knew there would be time enough to personally meet the rest of the men in the platoon later.

As he walked away, Joe observed two Vietnamese Kit Carson Scouts, standing quietly apart but paying close attention to him. *I wonder if I'll ever really get to know the two scouts assigned to 2nd Platoon. For that matter, I doubt any of the Americans will ever truly know the scouts. Their lives have to be most tragic. They have deserted their own country, are now fighting against comrades and friends, apart from any family and living with the former enemy that did not always express trust or welcome feelings.*

Because Joe was genuinely interested, he eventually found out a little information about the two scouts assigned to 2nd Platoon: Nguyen Trang had been a former Captain in the North Vietnamese Army and had traveled over 100 miles, alone, from the north to defect. Trung Dai Lon had been a former NVA First Lieutenant who, after he had been captured, requested the opportunity to serve as a Kit Carson Scout.

❧

Dunn found he genuinely liked his platoon. He had good feelings about the men and steadfastly believed they were indeed a rare lot. The first thing that really impressed him was their hardcore, rough meanness and professionalism, which they displayed. Then, much to his utter amazement, he discovered his men were actually highly educated and extremely intelligent. All were at least high school graduates and many of them had been to college for a few years. In fact, two of his men were presently enrolled in college correspondence courses.

As Joe glanced down at the image of the grim reaper on the platoon calling card given to him by Ski, he read the motto of the 2nd Platoon: "A Beer and A Body count, Sir!" *Simply amazing,* he thought. *It will certainly prove to be both a rare privilege and a memorable delight to work with and for these men.*

As Dunn made his way up to his tent, he was looking forward to renewing his conversation with Baylor. As it turned out, Baylor was resting on his cot and was just as eager to continue the briefing.

"First off, I want you to know that I don't necessarily agree with Jack Kent," Baylor said. "He's lucky his shit is together and owes that to "Pappy" Butler's many talents. You're going to soon discover Pappy is the real leader of 3rdPlatoon. As far as flying C & C... there is a bona fide reason Kent doesn't pull that duty. You see, the first time he went up in a 0-1, he immediately barfed all over the inside of the cockpit... including the pilot and himself. After that, the Birddog pilots told the Old Man they refused to fly with him as their backseat."

"Did the pilot intentionally cause him to lose his lunch?" asked Joe.

"No... and that's the real kicker," responded Baylor. "I personally spoke with the pilot, and understandably he was pissed. He told me he had just cautioned Kent to stick his head out the window if he felt nauseous. The pilot had just taken off and was *gradually* rising was when

Kent lost it, and that was *before* the pilot could perform even the slightest maneuver. Also, according to the pilot, Kent totally freaked out. So you see why the Old Man won't ask Kent to fly C & C again. Even if he did, I doubt Kent would agree to fly."

"What can I expect?" asked Joe.

"Hey, the Old Man has to have somebody in C & C, and he has no intention of ever doing it himself. Lieutenant Lee and you and whoever else he hires as platoon leader are 'it.' Have you ever flown in a fixed wing aircraft like the 0-1 before?"

"No."

"Well, expect a baptism on your first flight. There is some 'macho' thing going with the pilots. They deliberately, and with smirking malice and forethought try to make their backseat barf on his cherry flight. It's nothing to be ashamed of, Joe; I also got pea green sick on my first flight. Just remember to stick your head out the window and you *will* survive... even if you don't believe it at the time."

"Would you mind telling me what's actually involved in flying C & C?" asked Joe.

"Good question. The first thing you have to do is direct the insertion of the ambush team into the correct Landing Zone. So, number one, The Cardinal Rule is: Know how to pinpoint on a map any location on the ground from the air. Absolutely do *not* rely on your pilot, as in general they can't read a map to save their asses. Actually, they try to navigate by using automatic pilot or by major landmarks they can see, such as, on which side of the airplane is the South China Sea or by following some four-lane highway, which, by the way, doesn't exist in Nam.

"The most difficult and the most critical job you *have* to master is reading a map from the air. Think about it. How are you going to protect your team, if you can't drop artillery in the right spot? You can end up killing your own men if you are off by as little as twenty meters. So, before you go up, *thoroughly* study the map. Try to figure out the topography in your mind so when you view it from the air, you will be able to relate it to the grids on the map. Another important thing: Never pass on an opportunity to recon with your team leaders, and *constantly* try to get them to improve their map-reading skills."

Splat! Scotty momentarily interrupted his discourse while he slapped and squashed an ugly bug that had been determined to extract some Ranger blood from his forearm.

"Next," Scotty continued as if nothing untoward happened, "when you have figured out the exact location for inserting the team, you will have to vector in the Huey to the Landing Zone. You must remember the choppers carrying the patrols are flying just above the treetops at about 70 to 90 miles per hour. At that level and at that speed, the rotary pilots are basically flying blind and haven't a real clue as to where they are headed or how far they have to go without your guidance. You have to constantly provide a direction vector so the pilot can head towards the Landing Zone; then, you have to continuously provide distance to target so the pilot knows when to decelerate into the LZ or he will over or under shoot it."

"Why are they flying at treetop level? Isn't that more dangerous?" asked Dunn.

"No, on the contrary, it is much safer for the teams. Remember, it is a clandestine insertion into enemy territory of only six men. If Charlie knows their whereabouts, they could easily be wiped out. High flying choppers can be observed and watched. On the other hand, if the enemy is in triple canopy jungle and hears a low-flying chopper, he can't tell where it is unless it happens to fly directly over his fucking head. Then, it is going by too fast for him to respond. It really is weird, but it is really impossible to detect even what direction noise is coming from in a triple canopy jungle. So, maybe the pilots do or maybe they don't like to skim the trees, but that's the way they have to insert our patrols."

Thoroughly fascinated and interested in all this new logical and practical information, Joe wanted to know, "What else can be done to help protect the teams?"

"If our intelligence suggests Charlie is especially active in an AO, then we shrewdly vector the ships into several Landing Zones. Of course, the team will jump out at the predetermined one, but in that way, if fucking Charlie happens to be around, he won't know which LZ was actually used."

"Earlier, you mentioned the word 'artillery.' I assume C & C is also responsible for calling in Fire Missions?" Dunn wanted to know.

"Right you are. At the daily Operations Briefing in the TOC, Sergeant Staples briefs on any firebases within supporting range of the AO. He'll also give the locations, call signs, radio frequency and gun types of the Red Leg outfits, which are our artillery. But frequently, like when we were in Cambodia, our teams have had to operate beyond the range of any available artillery support. Now, that is really being out there fucking alone. However, in this AO, there should be no problem because we are fortunate to have multiple firebases available to support us. That reminds me Joe, have you ever adjusted Red Leg fire?" Scotty inquired.

"Yeah, I received a fair amount of training as a forward observer one summer while at Fort Sill, Oklahoma. One thing I learned was that adjusting artillery is one thing that has to be easier from the air than from the ground. You definitely need to have a good view of the impact," Joe commented.

"Sure, but the secret key is to be able to call in the rounds close enough to support the team without risking injury from friendly fire. The vulnerable teams on the ground see you as their fucking lifeline. If they happen to be operating in a deep valley, the Birddog may be the only one they will be able to contact by radio. That is when the teams really feel isolated, alone and scared...especially at night."

As Scotty was talking, he noticed Wilson, "Looks like you are wanted by your platoon sergeant, Joe. We'll continue this discussion after the Operations Briefing," Baylor said as he pointed in the direction of Wilson, who was coming up the path from the platoon area toward their tent.

Dunn was almost sorry for the interruption and looked forward to the continuation of his crash course on a Ranger platoon leader's duties. He was glad he was bunking with him and wanted to learn as much as he could over the next few weeks. Since Scotty had been recently promoted to Captain, Joe wasn't sure how much longer Scotty would be available.

As Wilson came up to the two men, he said, "I'm sorry to interrupt you men, but I have secured a .45 caliber pistol and I need for you, Dunn, to accompany me back down to the platoon conex. Your signature is needed on the register for you to accept responsibility."

As the two men headed down to the conex, Wilson asked him, "Do you prefer the standard issue 5.56mm (.223 caliber) M-16A1 assault rifle or the Car-15, a compact version of the M-16?"

"Despite the reputation of the Car-15 easily and frequently jamming, I definitely prefer the retractable periscope feature of its stock and its compactness. Also, I believe the Car-15 would be easier to carry than the M-16 in the cramped back seat of a Birddog," said Joe. Since Joe didn't want to rely on carrying only a sidearm pistol, he chose the Car-15 as he figured he could regularly work on the spring mechanism and keep it cleaned, oiled, and functioning as good as possible...just in case. Wilson also gave him ammunition and a magazine for each of the weapons.

Baylor was no longer in the tent when Joe returned to stash his newly acquired weapons and ammo with the rest of his gear. One of the things he had been a little surprised at, was the seemingly casualness with which weapons and munitions appeared to be kept. However, he was personally glad to have them.

After all, he reminded himself, *no matter where we happen to be now, we are still in a combat zone and danger could possibly erupt at any unsuspecting moment and from any given direction. Nevertheless, it is most disconcerting to see all the claymores, boxes of grenades, smoke bombs, other sundry weapons and all that ammunition so casually stored in the platoon areas.*

His wayward thoughts were interrupted by Lee, who cheerfully called out, "Hey, Dunn, y'all get your Ranger ass down here and join Kent and me before the mess line gets too long!"

"Hold your bloomin' horses. I'll be right there in a jiffy." Dunn was surprised to see from his watch, how late it really was. *Boy, this day has practically disappeared without my even realizing it.*

"So, what's the very most daring thing you've ever done?" Lee asked as he turned toward Kent after they got their meals and sat down. "I mean, everybody who ends up in this unit must be a little bit fucking crazy, don't you think? I figure we've all done something daring. So, what's the most daring thing you've ever done?" Lee insisted.

"Well, I once went water rafting on the Colorado River in the Grand Canyon. If you knew me better, you would know, for me, that was pretty daring. How about you, Dunn?" Kent asked as he deftly turned the attention towards Joe.

Smiling broadly at his recent memory, he shared, "On my honeymoon in Mexico, I got to go into a bullring as a matador with a cape to face a bull."

"Whoa, that's pretty damn daring!" exclaimed an impressed Kent. "I don't think I could ever do that... not me!"

Lee added his two cents, "No way! That sounds like y'all are literally bullshitting us."

Still smiling and laughing Joe proceeded to affirm his statement. "No, guys, really. I've even got pictures to prove it. It was at a training facility, which was also a restaurant for impressionable tourists and honeymooners. The bull was a small guy, only about three hundred pounds, but it did have pretty impressive horns that were almost four inches long. So, Lee, your turn," Dunn said with a grin.

"No way I can top that. Anyway, y'all are gonna have to wait for my daring. It's gonna come on one of my missions in the bush with an ambush team," Lee promised his compatriots.

At about that same moment, Dunn registered something somewhat peculiar. A tiny, hairy arm darted out of the cammie shirt of a Ranger seated at a table across from them. Its tiny hand grabbed some peas and withdrew back into the shirt. In response to Dunn's quizzical gaze, both Lee and Kent turned around to look just as the tiny arm reappeared, grabbed mashed potatoes and again retreated.

"Oh, that's 'Monkey Man.' He's in my platoon," said Kent. "He's a short timer. His DEROS home is in a couple days."

"What ya got there?" Joe curiously asked the Ranger.

"Say 'hello' to the officers, Bo. This is Bo." The tiny hand drew back the shirt just for an instant and just enough for a tiny, elfin face to peek out. "Bo is well trained. I plan on sneaking him back to The World with me just like this," the Ranger said as he gently patted the small bulge at his stomach.

After supper, all of the officers and some of the senior NCOs gathered at the TOC for the nightly Ops Briefing. Wayne started off the briefing, for the benefit of the newcomers, by introducing all attendees.

A Signal Officer, 1LT Kelvin Appier, had just arrived on orders directly from First Field Force. He was to be the platoon leader of the Commo & Support Platoon. Kelvin stood 5'8", had a perfectly round, baby face, dark hair, was soft-spoken, and generally quiet. It seemed he was always nervous and in a hurry.

However, he was a consummate professional, had a thorough knowledge of all the military radio equipment and could make miraculous repairs seem commonplace. He protected the men assigned to his platoon with a vengeance and thereby quickly earned their respect and confidence. Despite his reticence for spending time in the jungle, he garnered Dunn's immediate respect when he announced his intention of being inserted with the next X-ray Team.

The plan was to insert a reinforced team of ten support troops on one of the highest mountain peaks of the AO to act as a radio relay station with the ambush teams. Ideally, the X-ray team would be inaccessible, except by helicopter. The X-ray team would be expected to remain for ten, long days at a time.

Dunn really admired the X-ray teams. Although not infantry trained, they were signalmen, cooks, drivers and others who employed Ranger tactics for relatively long stints. He could only imagine the pressure it would be to maintain a high state of readiness in a static site on the top of an enemy mountain. The ambush teams loved the X-ray team, as it would be extremely comforting at 2:00 a.m. for the ambush patrol member on watch to hear a friendly, responsive voice from someone who was also awake and on guard.

Following the introductions, Wayne turned the meeting over to Phillips, who began the briefing in earnest. "Our move by cargo aircraft from Phan Thiet here to Landing Zone English outside Bong Son was accomplished without incident or loss. I commend each of the platoons and the headquarters element. It was a job well done, men.

"Now that we have moved in, the Old Man wants all the structures and tents covered and protected by sandbags as this camp is periodically harassed by sappers and mortar attacks, and we don't think much of the Legs responsible for our perimeter defense. Therefore, make sandbagging a priority.

"Next, operational control of Charlie Rangers has been returned to the 173rd Airborne Brigade. We have been directed to support Operation Washington Green in the coastal Binh Dinh province with small unit ambushes, limited raids and pathfinder assistance for heliborne operations. Since we previously worked with The Herd and specifically with Company N, their designated Ranger Company, we can be most grateful that The Herd is also familiar with Ranger employment.

"Important: We weren't just assigned...we were requested. The amount of support which you will hear about from Staples shows how much we are also very greatly appreciated." Gesturing to Staples, Phillips then turned over the remainder of the briefing presentation to him.

SFC Richard Staples was a large-framed man. Nothing ever seemed to rattle his composure, except when he showed his ire to anybody who challenged his control of the TOC. He was a seasoned veteran of the Korean War and not even the Old Man ever openly challenged him. It was abundantly clear that he was the real authority and experience that kept the Tactical Operations Center running efficiently, smoothly, and always with up-to-date and accurate intelligence data. He and Phillips made an extraordinarily competent team and treated each other with considerable mutual admiration and humor.

Before beginning the intelligence portion of the briefing, Staples handed out acetate-protected maps of the new area of operation. He then briefed on the supporting friendly assets, including aircraft, artillery and reaction forces. Next, he detailed the unit designations, locations, radio frequencies and call signs. After that, he proceeded to share all relevant information on enemy dispositions and followed by the latest weather forecasts. Finally, he stipulated the schedule, sectors, and the general locations, for insertion of the X-ray and ambush patrols. This is what he did nightly at each Ops Briefing.

"Captain Phillips will be flying C & C," emphasized Staples. "Tomorrow at noon, he will direct the insertion of X-ray plus Team 14 and Team 42. On the following day, Team Double Deuce and Team 35 will be inserted. Two Demon slicks will lift off at the south end of the runway at precisely 0700 hours to take team leaders on a visual reconnaissance of their target areas. Two Devil gunships will accompany the slicks. As I indicated earlier, the Demons and Devils are in Direct Support from the 134th Assault Helicopter Company. Gentlemen, what are your questions?"

Since there were no immediate questions, Wayne asked the newly assigned officers if they had any comments or observations. Appier indicated, "The Commo Platoon Sergeant has already anticipated the X-ray assignment and has constituted a team, which includes the new platoon leader."

Lee followed, stating, "Sir, I will be going with Team 14 into the field tomorrow. One thing I have noticed is I am short an entire patrol. Can we expect replacements any time soon to fill out the men I am short?"

"Sorry, Lieutenant, your platoon is actually in better shape than the others. We have a goddamn tough time getting good Airborne volunteers, but our rear support knows this is an ongoing priority. How about you, Dunn, any observations?"

"Yes, sir, two items. I have noticed that the cammies most of my men are wearing are faded and pretty raunchy. Some of the guys like the grungy cammies for missions in the bush. However, they have all complained that they really need new ones before these disintegrate off their bodies. When I was issued my gear in the rear, I saw that Supply Sergeant Beave had a large amount of new cammies on hand.

"Second, in meeting and speaking with some of the men, I was surprised to learn that there are men who have earned but not been issued the C.I.B. or even The Purple Heart. Sir, what is the policy or procedure for this basic administrative support?"

"Goddamn great point, Lieutenant!" Wayne exploded. "Let me make this point perfectly clear for all the officers right here and right now. I am sic-n-tarrred of our troops not getting their due. It is the responsibility of you officers to see to it that your men are put in for the decorations they earn. Furthermore, it is the *enlisted man* who does the goddamn fighting and it is the *enlisted man* who is in harm's way. Therefore, *only enlisted men* will be entitled to a valor award. No officers in this unit will be put in for a goddamn valor medal. Maybe this policy will help free you officers to start putting in your men for the recognition they truly deserve." On that note the meeting broke up.

Evidently the issue of the cammies will have to be revisited at another time, Joe figured.

After leaving the TOC, Dunn sought out Lee. "You're going to beat me by one day to the field when I go out with Team 22. Guess the Old Man's policy is going to make it a little tougher for you to get the Medal of Honor," he kidded Lee, who simply shrugged and headed off towards his platoon area.

Dunn stopped by the 2nd Platoon hooch to pass on the information from the briefing to Wilson and the team leaders. He also gave each of them maps of the new area of operation and advised "Buck" Forest of the 7:00 a.m. recon. Further, he advised him that he would be going into the field with his team as the RTO, Radio Telephone Operator.

Then pulling Wilson aside, Joe said, "Tomorrow, I want you to make sandbagging all of the 2nd Platoon's structures a priority. I would like a roster of all the men in the platoon with their rank, social security number, date of rank, date of birth, DEROS, R&R status, religion, blood type, and finally the name, relationship and address of their hometown contact. Also, would you please put together a list of all the men who need a new set of cammies, include their sizes and give it to me?

"Tomorrow morning, I am going on the recon with Buck and will be going into the field with Team 22 the following day. So, we should try to spend some time together tomorrow afternoon. Please be prepared to lay on me any advice, suggestions or information. Also, let me know what you want of me to help run this platoon."

Wilson responded, "Well...sandbagging is a cruddy job and shouldn't getting the teams ready for the field be the priority, not sandbagging?"

"You are absolutely right, Sergeant Wilson. So, make them *both* a priority. I will be at my tent for the rest of the night if you need me."

As Dunn turned and left he thought to himself, *Here I am, asking for advice. Hell, I'm crying out for it, as I really want to have a good working relationship with Wilson. As a Second Lieutenant, I feel I have learned more about the real army from listening to sergeants than all of the training classes and the four years at the Point combined. But, for some reason, Wilson doesn't seem to want to work closely with me. Yet, I couldn't help but notice that Wilson doesn't seem particularly close to any of the men, including the team leaders. Oh, well, I'll just have to try harder,* he concluded.

Night had literally fallen. At least that is the way it seemed to Dunn who observed that it had not crept up as one usually expects, but had, in one swift move, like a closet door suddenly slamming shut, erased any evidence of daylight.

The Commo Platoon had fortunately wired the TOC, the platoon hooch and a few tents, including his and Scotty's so that a few generators provided each with a single light bulb. The noise made by the gas motor-powered generators was a strangely comforting sound. As Dunn carefully and slowly *felt* his way in the dark up the path to his tent, he heard shouting and laughter coming from the direction of 3rd Platoon's hooch.

Pappy's cash bar must be open for business, he thought. *Only, the teams not going to the field within the next two days are over there, as the guys don't drink, or tolerate anybody who does drink, for two days before being inserted on a mission. It's nice how they police themselves, as it sure makes being a platoon leader here easier than in any Leg outfit.*

Baylor was sitting on his cot writing a letter home when Dunn crawled in underneath the tent's bug netting. "I am finished with this letter," he said. "Do you need the light? If not, I'd like to turn it off. Even with the netting, the light attracts so many damn bugs, and if you're not careful, they can eat you alive."

"That is fine with me," agreed Joe. The light was turned off, and then the two men undressed, hung their fatigues on hangars from the top of the tent, and slipped nude into their respective cots under a nylon blanket. The slight chill of the night was a welcome treat after the daylong oppressive heat.

After a few minutes of silence Dunn, whose pumping adrenaline prevented his body from recognizing its fatigue, said to his tent mate, "If you're not too tired, I'd like to hear more about your experiences flying C & C."

"Absolutely," Baylor said. "I'd be more than glad to brief you on what I have learned. The Old Man briefly mentioned he wants to talk to me sometime tomorrow about my running the operation in the rear. So, while I am still here, you're smart to get all, or at least most of your questions answered.

"Okay, as I mentioned to you earlier, map reading is the most critical task for you to master. One thing I try to do is to find the highest mountain in the area and locate it on the map. Then, I count ridgelines and create reference points I mentally tag. Sometimes there are easily identifiable natural features like a saddle at the top of a mountain or a series of forked ridges that can help with navigation. But sometimes, quite frankly, you just have to fucking do the best you can."

"How about the radio procedure? How does that work?" Joe asked.

"You wear a flight helmet with built-in ear phones and a voice-activated microphone at your mouth. There is a line protruding from the back of the helmet with a jack that plugs into your radio. Built into the armrest is a bank of five radio sets that you can program with a frequency that allows you to monitor all frequencies simultaneously. Obviously, you can speak on only one radio at a time, but you can preprogram the frequencies and switch between them, as you deem necessary.

"There is another switch, the intercom, which lets you speak privately to the front pilot. Remember, when you are in the air, you are the one in control. That means even the damn pilot works for you and all goddamn communication goes through you or is approved by you. The TOC, the team on the ground, the slicks, gunships and the artillery base-all of them have to communicate through the C & C.

"Another thing you need to keep in mind is aircraft are equipped with UHF radios. Our teams on the ground carry FM very high frequency (VHF) radios. The C & C is often the only one who is equipped to talk to everybody. However, a lot of times the choppers carry a VHF radio with them, in addition to their ultra high frequency (UHF) radios, so they too can talk to the guys on the ground."

"What about leading a patrol in the field? How do you feel about that?" Joe asked.

"Actually, I went into the boonies only one time with a team. Then, we made contact on the first day out, so we were extracted. As it turned out, I never had to spend overnight in the bush. However, that one fucking experience taught me what I needed to know. I have first-hand appreciation of what our guys go through.

"You know, I always intended to go back into the bush. But...there was so much more to do. I got caught up in everything else, and before I realized it, eight months flew by without another ground mission. I understand Lee is going out tomorrow, and you are going out with Team 22 the following day. That's good."

Dunn paused reflectively, thinking about everything Baylor mentioned. Just as he was about to ask another question, the sound of the generators was accompanied by light snoring from the opposite side of the tent, which indicated Baylor was fast asleep.

❦

In the morning, Dunn awoke and looked at his watch. Although it was not even 5:00 a.m., the camp was already active. Rising noiselessly, so as not to disturb Baylor, he dressed quickly, but before he could leave, Baylor stretched, sat up, and threw on his trousers. Not in the habit of wearing socks, Baylor reached for his jungle boots under his cot and thrust his right foot in his boot.

"Oowww! Fuck! Oh, my God!" Baylor shrieked in pain and clutched his bare right foot while falling back on his cot. "Yeow!"

Slithering out of Baylor's boot was a green snake with a flat, diamond-shaped head and pinkish eyes. With adrenaline rushing, Dunn quickly grabbed the other boot and like a crazed man proceeded to pound the snake repeatedly and well after it was obviously dead.

Baylor's agonizing screams caught the instantaneous attention of the entire company and especially all who were remotely close by, who responded immediately. Phillips yelled down to the TOC personnel to call for an immediate medivac helicopter and then called for the Major's driver to get the jeep. Two soldiers quickly lifted Baylor on his cot as if it were a stretcher.

Pappy Butler calmly picked up the dead snake and handed it to Phillips as he said, "Wait. Take this with him. The doctors are going to need this as proof that he was bit by 'Mr. Two Step,' a damn Bamboo Viper." Turning to Baylor, who had stopped screaming and appeared to be going into shock, Pappy continued. "Hey, sir, can I have your watch? You were bitten by a fucking Bamboo Viper, which means that you're gonna die. So, you don't need your goddamn watch no more."

The Bamboo Viper (*Trimerserus Popeiorum*) is one of three species of green vipers in Vietnam. While venomous, its bite is not lethal.

However, it was abundantly clear from the tears in his eyes and the level of his shrieks that Baylor was in considerable pain. Although Dunn would not again have a chance to speak with him, he later heard that Baylor fully recovered. Word was that he described the pain as having the sensation of "submerging your foot in boiling water for a week." Thanks to another lesson he learned from Baylor, Dunn never left his jungle boots on the ground. Plus, he double-checked them each time before he put them on.

After breakfast, Dunn planned to spend some time in the 2nd Platoon area getting to know the men. When he approached, he noticed that Wilson had them busy policing the area, cleaning and performing maintenance. So, he continued to the TOC, where he helped himself to a cup of coffee and studied the map of the AO.

Staples, who was busy at the time on the radio, welcomed him with a pat on the back. A short while later, Wayne entered with Phillips and Roberts. Phillips mentioned Scott Baylor would most likely not return to the unit. Roberts said he would take Baylor's belongings to the rear at Ahn Khe later that afternoon.

"Captain Roberts, sir," said Dunn, seizing the opportunity, "if I give you a list of men in my platoon who need new camouflage fatigues and their sizes, can you see to it they are shipped forward to us?"

"Sure, Lieutenant, just don't let your men throw out the old ones, though, as we can turn them in for replacements to keep us in stock with new ones," Roberts responded.

"Absolutely, sir," Dunn said with a smile. "Please let me know what time you have to leave so that I can have Sergeant Wilson give you the list before you depart."

Since there was nearly an hour before they had to go to the runway for the reconnaissance flight, Dunn headed back to the platoon area. He wanted to get to know the men and expected them to be interesting but was amazed at how diverse they were. He found they were from nearly every state, including Hawaii, and from Toronto and Ontario, Canada, and even one from Guatemala. They were Roman Catholic, Greek Orthodox, Baptist, Jewish, Mormon, American Indian, Muslim, Agnostic and Atheistic. But, in spite of the differences in their cultural heritage, background and upbringing, they all got along like brothers in a large family. Each man was fiercely protective of his particular team, identified closely with his platoon, and finally, he was inordinately proud of being a Charlie Ranger, a member of Company "C" Ranger, 75th Infantry, Airborne.

Above all, the men were bound together by love: love of country, love of duty, love for one another and love of self. They needed one another. They had to rely on each other; their lives literally depended on each other. They would be six men, dropped alone into a harsh country in an area controlled by a fierce enemy that was intent on killing them.

It has been said that blood is thicker than water, and water is the sustenance of life. Well, the spilled blood of the first wounded Ranger became the baptismal water that forever bound the entire Ranger family.

Just like in any family, there would be the occasional squabbles over some minor item that would escalate unnecessarily. The seasoned and wise platoon sergeant, the mother hen of the platoon, instinctively knew when to step in and when not to interfere. The platoon sergeant interacted daily with every member of the platoon, cajoling, nurturing, directing, ignoring, training, scolding, checking, correcting, praising and playing as was needed.

The role of the platoon leader and ultimately of the company commander, the Old Man, was to fulfill the mission while preserving the interest of the men. The best leaders knew instinctively when to tip the scale slightly at times in favor of one task over the other. The most charismatic leaders were able to get their men to want to do what their leader wanted them to do. However, the most charismatic leaders were not always the best leaders; and, in war, what men were required to do was rarely in their best interest.

The men of 2nd Platoon were as anxious to know their new platoon leader, as he was to know them. By virtue only of his rank, he could command their obedience, but he would have to earn their respect and loyalty. They saw Dunn as a cherry, wet behind the ears and fresh out of school, while some of them had already served two or three previous combat tours. Therefore, he would be given a chance to prove himself, the same as was given to all new recruits. Somebody was always arriving or ready to DEROS home. Many of the men were new arrivals themselves. So, everybody was given an opportunity to prove what kind of Ranger he would be, either a good in-law or a bad outlaw of the Ranger family.

Word quickly spread that their new lieutenant was going to the boonies with Double Deuce. "That's good," voiced many of the men. When the lieutenant announced he was going to carry the radio and act as RTO for Buck, they said, "That's even better. He's not challenging the team leader. Maybe he's willing to learn from us. But we will wait and see," the men agreed.

Wilson, their new platoon sergeant, had screwed up in Phan Thiet, as far as they were concerned. Ski had been shocked when Wilson created an argument over something silly on a mission in the field. Then, when the team initiated an ambush upon two enemy personnel, Wilson, in complete disregard for the team's safety, deliberately stood up to seek better personal cover. His action could have compromised the ambush or, worse, resulted in friendly casualties. Ski also confided in the other team leaders, but not the men or anyone else, he suspected Wilson had been drinking prior to their insertion. So, they would definitely debrief Buck and the entire Double Deuce on how well their first Looey performed in the field.

"Hey, sir," called out Lucky, "you don't have to do that. You're gonna get all fucking dirty."

"A little hard work never hurt anybody," Dunn replied. "I've got a free hour or so. Besides, helping you guys sandbagging is a lot better than helping the poor guy on crapper duty."

"You got that fucking right, sir," agreed Hilltopper. "Burning shit in a fifty-five gallon drum in this heat has got to be the worst fucking job in the whole goddamn army."

Afterwards, and before heading back to the TOC with Forest, Dunn sought out Wilson. "Would you please make an extra copy of the list and sizes of all the men who need new cammies for me? Also, make sure you get that list to Captain Roberts before he heads back to Ahn Khe today."

"Yes, sir, I'll do that," responded a less than enthusiastic Wilson.

Dunn and Forest got to the TOC just as the three-quarter ton truck arrived that would take the party to the airfield for the visual reconnaissance. In addition to the two of them, the recon party consisted of 1LT Appier and SFC Bullock of the X-ray Team, 1LT Lee and SSG Moody of Team 14, SSG Osborne of Team 35, SSG Purdy of Team 42 and Phillips, who would be serving as Command & Control in the Birddog for the remainder of the week. This would be their first actual look at the company's new area of operation.

※

The men excitedly talked about locating heavily trafficked footpaths or any other signs of activity in their respective designated team sectors, while the team leaders challenged each other as to who would gain the first contact. The team leader's reconnaissance determined his requested insertion into a particular suitable landing zone within his sector. Each team's sector could vary in size from one to sixty square kilometers.

Ideally, the landing zone was big enough to permit the simultaneous landing of two Huey helicopters. The TOC rarely overrode a team leader's request for a particular LZ. Generally, when a patrol was inserted into an LZ other than the one selected, it was because the team leader fouled up on mapreading. Of course, it could just as easily result from the C & C misreading the map. More often than not, though, they both were guilty of error in pinpointing a spot on the map to represent a specific LZ on the ground.

The aerial reconnaissance flights were important as the visual reconnaissance (VR) gave the team leaders a better sense of familiarity with the terrain and the type of vegetation. It erased some of the normal tension associated with entering into unknown territory. Too, this greatly reassured the entire team whenever the team leader could calmly express first-hand knowledge of the team's sector. His authority was further enhanced when the team actually encountered the exact conditions he described.

The X-ray Team usually had little choice or say in its deployment as it was understood that it needed to be located on the highest defensible mountain peak in the area. It was imperative that the TOC maintain line-of-sight, continuous communication with X-ray through the enhanced gear it carried. Hopefully, the ancillary teams operating in the surrounding area would likewise communicate with X-ray and thereby pass and receive information to and from the TOC. Of course, when daylight and weather permitted the Birddog to be aloft, the C & C managed and controlled communications.

※

Two and half-hours later when the recon party returned to the TOC, Phillips asked Appier and Billings, of the X-ray Team, to remain inside and for Lee and Moody, of Team 14, to stand-by outside. Then he asked Purdy, of Team 42, to return in about a half hour.

Forest indicated he would not convene Team 22 until after he sat with Phillips and they addressed the issue of his LZ. So, Dunn decided to remain and observe how the missions were methodically developed.

The Herd aptly nicknamed this mountain range The Tiger Mountains. Their initial team sectors were located about a hundred kilometers east of Monster Mountain, an area well-known for its elusive enemy traffic, almost undetectable booby traps on paths and the hazardous, wait-a-minute vines that snared men and their equipment, making foot passage slow and painful. Every one of the teams had said the Tigers were an extremely "dirty area" in which to work. Its hills were nearly vertical, extremely hot and dry, vine covered and infested with just about every kind of insect known to man or beast.

"It seemed pretty clear to me," said Billings, as he pointed to a spot on the map board, "that this one high peak is centrally located. It has a fairly accessible plateau that looks large enough for a helicopter to get into, yet looks remote and extremely hard to climb or access from below. It offers my team natural protection and serves as a good location for X-ray. What do you think, sir?"

"I had the same thoughts, Sergeant Billings." Phillips motioned for Staples to annotate the location on the map. "Gentleman, please note, we have the coordinates of our X-ray."

Staples used a grease pencil to mark the agreed upon location of X-ray on the TOC map. Then he recorded the map coordinates in a logbook. Finished with the legalities of his task, he rose from the desk and with a broad smile and a nod towards Appier said, "I suggest we designate this as 'Kelvin's Peak.'"

"Kelvin's Peak it is," Phillips said smiling as he patted Appier on the back. "I bet you never thought you'd have a mountain top in Vietnam named after you..."

Then changing subjects Phillips continued in a more businesslike manner, "I understand your team is already constituted and ready for deployment. The mess has been officially notified you will be drawing rations for ten men, for ten days. You and your men may not be on site for that long, but I don't want to take any unnecessary chances and want you prepared to stay if it becomes necessary." Then, he walked over and once again tapped his finger on the designated spot on the map now called Kelvin's Peak. "Since we have all unanimously agreed that this particular X-ray location is ideal, have your team ready to leave for the tarmac at 1200 hours. Any other questions or comments? If so, now is the time ...not after you are on your mission."

"No, sir," Appier and Billings said in unison. As they hurried out, Lee and Moody entered with map in hand.

Without any preamble, Lee announced, "Team 14 has a hot sector and plans on a quick hit and being back before chow. There's a large clearing next to a wide path that is a perfect place for us to be put in and set up. Let me show y'all where I think it is on the map."

"Hold on a minute, Lieutenant Lee," said Phillips. "Think a moment. Wouldn't it be a better tactic for your team of only six men to infiltrate into a smaller LZ, and then quickly and safely vacate that immediate area? Then you could head to the particular trail you spotted and set up the ambush."

"Sergeant Moody," Staples chimed in, "did you check out any other LZ that you also liked?"

"Sir, as a matter of fact, Lieutenant Lee and I *were* talking outside about a particular clearing we both spotted that probably would make a good infil site," he deftly answered, turning towards Lee.

"That's right," said Lee quickly trying to cover his enthusiastic but flawed statement, "and it's only about one klick southeast of that trail."

"Can you show me where it is on the map?" asked Staples as he picked up his *brown* grease pencil. He had various colored grease pencils, and each color indicated a different type unit or asset.

Lee and Moody simultaneously pointed out the general area of the LZ on the map board. Without any prompting, Moody gave Phillips a complete, detailed description, including the surrounding area of the desired LZ, so he would not have any trouble recognizing it from the air. As Moody, in qualified detail, described the LZ, Phillips made notations in his green, pocket-sized memo book he always kept in the breast pocket of his shirt.

Still silently observing, Dunn made a mental note to get a couple of those handy memo books for himself. Then, as if he had read his mind, Staples reached into one of the desk drawers and handed him a new one in a moisture-proof, self-locking plastic bag. "I noticed you using a large notebook at my briefing earlier, but I think this will better serve you. Be sure and keep it in the plastic bag with whatever you use for writing. That way they will be kept dry, especially as the heavy rains are coming, and when they come, it is a deluge."

"Thanks," said an appreciative Dunn.

I'm looking forward to knowing Staples better, Joe thought. *It's obvious, from my short and cursory observation, that his organization of the TOC and his easy, skillful manner with the men has well-earned Staples his excellent reputation.*

"No problem, Lieutenant," Staples again smiled. "When you get back from the field, it might be a good idea for you to spend some time here, in the TOC, with us. This is the nerve center of the company and as you observe, you will learn the most here; you will learn the fastest here;

and you will learn the right things in here. If you are observant, and I definitely think you are, you will see and hear a great deal."

※

Richard Staples genuinely liked this new lieutenant right from his first impression. He admired the way he handled himself during the unfortunate snake-biting incident and how he maintained his focus. *If this cherry lieutenant is trained properly, he thought, he's going to be a good one. No doubt about it. He is intelligent but seems unusually mature for his age and experience, while at the same time he is inquisitive and entirely willing to listen and learn from those around him... no matter their rank, creed, race, or age.*

Phillips dismissed Lee and Moody, telling them to be on the tarmac before 1315 hours to await the return of the choppers from inserting X-ray. He talked with SSG Purdy, who arrived with SSG Buck Forest. Once again, Dunn listened attentively.

The conversations with Purdy and Forest centered on the location and description of their respective insertion Zones. Purdy's team was ordered to be ready at 1430 hours, and Buck's team was scheduled for 1100 hours the next day. A small clearing covered with elephant grass at the base of a ridge was selected as the best LZ for Team 22.

"Say, Dunn, why don't you join the Team 22 briefing at the platoon conex at 1230 hours following lunch," Buck invited.

"Be glad to," Joe responded immediately as this would give him an added dimension to his understanding of how things were handled.

As he left the TOC, he met SSG Osborne of Team 35 as he entered to conclude his own pre-insertion briefings.

※

At lunch Dunn was somewhat taken aback by the large amount of communications equipment and the stacks of C-ration boxes lined up along the inside of the mess. *It's a good thing it's a static site and they don't have to hump that gear around,* he thought.

Dunn quickly ate and hurried over to the 2nd Platoon area, where he found Buck supervising Team 22 by the conex. Looking around, he studied the men of the X-ray Team and mentally noted that all the men looked mean, fit, and ready for combat. Their faces and hands were completely painted with the camouflage sticks. Prominent features, such as their forehead and cheekbones, were colored dark green while everything else was covered in pale green.

In spite of the damned heat, the sleeves of their camouflage shirts he noted were rolled *down*. Some of the men wore floppy booney hats, while others tied an olive drab bandana around their head. Each rucksack was fully loaded, inspected and prepared for departure. Each Ranger also carried a couple of fully loaded magazines.

To a man, they all seemed jovial, laughing and generally in a good mood, which surprised him. "Hey, guys!" Dunn called out as he approached. "Got to hand it to you. You sure seem happy to be going out on this mission."

"That's a roger, sir," replied one of the troops. "No KP, sandbagging or other shitty details...almost as good as a vacation. And, we get to teach Lieutenant Appier how to run a first-class X-ray!" they all either laughed or chuckled at the comment.

Another man, nicknamed "D.J." added, "This is why we came here. Now we get to do what we were trained for. We'll be talkin' at ya when you're out there with Double Deuce. You'll be glad to get a time-check from me when it's 3:00 a.m. and you're the only one awake on your team in the middle of the fuckin' jungle. You'll see!"

Joe, laughed and said, "I believe you already."

Buck interjected into the repartee between Dunn and the men, "Go get your weapon, sir. When you get back you can join us when we test our weapons at the firing range. I already got clearance from the TOC for a live-fire. Each man will get to fire two magazines...except that I have three filled for you."

"Great, I'll be back in just a few," promised a thrilled Joe as he headed for his tent.

When they were in ready position at the firing range, the TOC alerted the entire camp over a loudspeaker system that had been rigged up by the Commo Platoon earlier that day. Then he gave the eager men the "all clear" signal. A deafening roar followed as all the men, except Dunn, quickly emptied both their magazines as though they were up against a deadline and what ammo wasn't used would be forfeit.

Since the CAR-15 was new to him, Joe methodically squeezed off a few single shots and periodically adjusted the sighting. By the time he started his second magazine, the rest of the team was finished and gathered behind him.

He was an expert marksman and after making the few necessary adjustments, he was confident in the accuracy of his new weapon. So, turning to the surrounding men he offered, "Choose any target on the range and see what I can do to it."

Instead, in unison they all demanded he "rock 'n' roll" on full automatic. Smiling at them Joe turned, got into position and fired. Cheers from the team rang in his ears after the few seconds it took. Then they let the TOC know to signal a cease-fire completion.

Dunn thought, *Thank God, my weapon didn't jam. That wouldn't have been a very impressive display for them to see.*

When they returned to the platoon area, everyone broke out cleaning equipment: LSA lubricating oil, brushes and steel rods that looked like four foot sewing needles with a square white patch of cloth in lieu of thread to thrust down the rifle barrel.

Cleaning his own rifle gave Dunn a chance to informally visit with each member of the team.

Assistant Patrol Leader, SGT Johnny "Chief" Eagle, was in Dunn's humble opinion, not only one of the largest men in the platoon but maybe of any he had ever seen. Chief was extremely proud of his American Indian heritage; he also professed it as his religion. But in spite of his size, he was a quiet, reserved and self-confident man.

Dunn later found out Chief always volunteered to carry the heavy M-60 machine gun with the extra belts of ammunition. The reason he always volunteered was not because he was so big and strong, and it would be expected of him to carry more than the average Ranger. No, the bottom line as to why he volunteered was he basically trusted only himself with the superior firepower it provided. Bottom line-he plainly did not have equal faith in anyone else.

Although clearly against army regulations, Dunn observed Chief had evidently used a heavy-duty hacksaw to cut off a goodly portion of the barrel. Again, Chief's reason for shortening it was not to make it lighter and easier to carry, but for the dramatic effect it produced. Joe found out the roar of that weapon was absolutely deafening, even frightening. When the flash suppressor was cut off, the resulting blaze around the barrel looked like a mini explosion, especially at night. Since most contact was at close proximity, Chief figured the psychological impact was more important than pinpoint accuracy. Much to the chagrin of the unit supply sergeant, most of the teams in the company followed Chief's lead.

SGT Richard "Slant" Garbo was another newcomer to the unit, and this would be his first mission. Slant got his ethnic nickname from the men because of the slanted look of his big brown eyes. They often kidded him by saying, "We're gonna make you walk point, so if we come across any enemy, they will be confused and mistake you for one of their own."

Everybody loved Slant. He was a street-wise kid from the Bronx, stood about five feet eight inches tall and had wavy brown hair. Everywhere he went around base, he could be seen with his pet monkey that he kept on a thin, chain leash. When the little booger was not causing mischief, the rambunctious monkey sat on Slant's shoulder and clutched at his wavy hair while he chattered and furtively glanced around. Garbo was an excellent, proud soldier who proved as dependable in the field as he was playful in camp.

Next there was SP/4 Peter "Blue" McCormack, from Texarkana, Arkansas. Blue was on his second tour. In an abbreviated first tour with the 173rd Airborne Brigade, he had been brutally wounded at the start of his second month In Country. When seen with his shirt off, it was unnerving, because the scars of his wounds made his skin look like Swiss cheese. Mounted on a tall, thin frame, he had blond hair and a wry smile. He would go around reminding everybody, "Charlie Rangers is the best damn unit because it has the best opportunity of killing those sneaky Charlie's." He never evidenced any fear and was the most comfortable soldier in a field-mission environment.

In addition to his regulatory M-16 rifle, Blue carried the "Blooper," a M-79 Grenade Launcher. This weapon first appeared during the Vietnam War and closely resembled a large-bore, single barrel, sawed-off shotgun. The M-79 was a single shot, shoulder fired, break-barrel, loading weapon, which fired a spherical 40mm diameter H E grenade, smoke grenade, CS gas or a flare. It was a terrific weapon, both in close range and at distances far greater than what a person could throw by hand.

Since Blue had distinguished himself with uncanny accuracy against even moving targets, Garbo volunteered to carry extra grenades for Blue's M-79 as well as extra rounds of ammo for the M-60. Blue strapped the M-79 to the outside of his rucksack, where it was instantly accessible.

Completing the team was another cherry, Private First Class Michael Martinez from Santa Clara, California. Martinez joined the unit after completing basic Ranger training at Ahn Khe two days before the company relocated from Phan Thiet to LZ English.

Forest took Martinez under his wing and gave him extra time to insure he would be adequately prepared by the time the unit went out on a mission. Martinez talked bravely, and, at times, even appeared to be defiant. As Dunn observed him, he couldn't decide whether Martinez was nervous or simply did not like being told what to do. He decided he and Forest would have to keep a watchful eye on this defiant eighteen-year-old.

Just then the quiet camaraderie was broken by a loud curse from Blue. "Goddamn it, Slant! I swear I'm gonna kill that hairy, fat little gook! Nosy bastard, isn't he?" The little monkey had decided to inspect the parts of Blue's disassembled weapons. "Shit! Now look! He's spilled the fucking cleaning fluid!"

"Ya better keep that fucking thing away from me for real," sneered Martinez as he chimed in his two cents worth. "I swear I'll kill it with my bare hands. I really don't like living things."

"What do you call the cute little fellow?" Dunn asked, ignoring Martinez' unfriendly comment.

"I call him Deros, sir. He is cute, ain't he? I nevah had no pet before," explained Slant.

"You're not gonna have the fucker much longer, either, if you don't pull him away from me." But Blue smiled as he harmlessly flicked a cleaning towel at the monkey and ended up playfully engaged in a game of tug of war.

"You guys all like him. Youz just won' admit it. Look at that cute little belly on his skinny little body," Slant insisted.

Blue disagreed with a laugh and a smile, "He's a fat little fucker 'cause he's always scrounging food from everybody. You shoulda called him, 'Scrounge.'"

☙

While Dunn was cleaning his rifle and speaking with the different members of the team, Forest went to the Commo Platoon and checked out an AN/PRC-25 FM radio set with an extra battery. Upon returning, Buck said to him, "Here you go, sir. I am putting this radio and battery with the stack of gear I assembled for you. As the RTO, it's your responsibility to perform a commo check with TOC tomorrow before we leave to make sure it works. After humping it in the boonies for a few days, you'll understand why the men call it, 'the Prick-25.' You sure you're up for this?"

The AN/PRC-25 radio weighed 10.5 lbs even without its battery. It had a range of ten miles in ideal operating conditions with the whip antennae. In the Tiger's the conditions would definitely not even be close to ideal.

"Absolutely, Sergeant Forest," replied Dunn. Maybe I can pick up some rock-n-roll stations with it. By the way, anyone know where Wilson is now?"

"I saw him getting some chow at the Mess Hall about two hours ago," said Chief. "He's probably working with some of the new men or the other teams."

"Well, since all of you are packed and ready for tomorrow, I should head for my tent and get my rucksack ready." As Dunn rose to leave he turned and asked, "But tell me, how is it that you guys can manage to get 65 lbs into a 10 lb bag? Oh, if you happen to spot Sergeant Wilson, let him know that I want to talk with him."

In addition to the radio and extra battery, a box had been filled by Buck for Dunn with the following items: 100 loose rounds of ammunition and 12 loaded magazines for his CAR-15, 3 Claymore mines with accessories, 1 White Phosphorous grenade, 9 baseball grenades, 2 concussion grenades, 3 smoke grenades, 1 teargas grenade, 1 parachute flare, and 9 LRRPs of freeze-dried rations. The dehydrated rations needed a lot of water to reconstitute. Probably the only good thing one could say about LRRP rations was they provided the body with necessary nutrients.

When Dunn reached his tent, he found it eerily empty. All of Scotty's personal effects had been removed which left only his own meager items. *Everything in life is relative,* he thought. *By this time tomorrow, I'll probably think of this one-light-bulb-tent as my palatial home.*

It didn't take him as long as he expected to pack everything except the nylon blanket, which he would use that night and pack tomorrow. He was taking only six of the nine rations, figuring he wouldn't be that hungry in the field anyway. When he finished securing everything in the rucksack or on his harness, at times even using tape, he put it all on and adjusted it. Then, jumping up and down to make certain nothing rattled or fell off, he felt confident he was ready. Then he removed his pack and decided to use the available time to write a loving letter to Marie while it was still daylight.

Just as he was taking out some paper the loudspeaker above the TOC blared, "Team in contact! Gunships are on station and now in action!"

"Holy shit!" blurted Dunn as he dropped the blank sheet of paper that was to have been a letter. "Lee's prediction of being back in time for supper just might come true." He hurried down to the TOC, where he spotted the Old Man, rocking and standing with his hands on his waist and puffing like mad on his pipe. Staples was monitoring the radio and occasionally relaying information on the developing incident.

"Goddamn! That Purdy is a hellava team leader," muttered Wayne. "These goddamn mountains are filled with enemy base camps. I know it. I can feel it."

Team 42 had initiated a successful ambush, was exfiltrated and already heading back with the enemy gear removed from the kill zone. Dunn could feel his adrenaline level rising and found he was looking forward to the Ops Briefing where he hoped to hear the details. As he walked back to his platoon's area, he sensed the heightened enthusiasm and excitement that permeated the entire camp personnel. Just then he spotted Wilson locking the platoon conex.

"How are you, Sergeant Wilson?" Dunn called as he approached with a warm smile.

"Great, sir. I assume you were over at the TOC. Did Staples indicate which team made contact or any other details that I can tell our guys?"

"Just that it was Purdy of Team 42. The team is on its way back. I should find out more at the Ops Briefing and will gladly pass on any information I am given. Is it a good time for us to get together? I would sure like the benefit of your input, plus, I'd like to get those lists that I requested yesterday. By the way, were you able to get the cammie request to Captain Roberts before he returned to Ahn Khe?"

"He had to leave earlier than planned, before I could get to him, sir. So, I figured it'd be better for me to take some time to put together a complete list. Some guys are away on R&R. When I finish it, I'll make a copy for you as you requested, and I will send it to the rear. Everything will be taken care of, you'll see. As far as us getting together, I'd really like that, sir. But, now is not a good time. I have arranged to interview some dink hooch maids, and I'm already late."

As he headed off in the direction of 3rdPlatoon, Wilson turned around and called back, "We will get together, Dunn, soon, I promise. Things will slow down once we're settled. In the meantime, I'll get you a good-looking local to keep your fatigues clean and our platoon leader looking sharp."

Dunn was a little miffed since this meant it would take even longer before his men received new cammies. *Oh, well, Wilson probably has his own ideas about the highest and best priorities for the men,* he figured.

Before heading back to his tent to compose a letter to Marie, Dunn paused at the platoon barracks to chat with a few of the men. Walking in he picked up right away on the barely suppressed excitement that the reported contact generated. He felt it was a good sign that it happened almost immediately after being inserted into this new area.The men were anxious to tell their own war stories and experiences in the field and spoke proudly, almost reverently, about the heroic deeds of past Rangers, former members of the unit. Also, they decided to see how far they could push their new lieutenant with some gruesome tales.

"A year ago," said "Lucky" Nate, "there was a platoon bar that had dozens of gook ears in bottles on display. I saw them personally. The fucking guys then were real hard-core. Rumor has it that one particular pipe-smoking team leader used a goddamn female gook breast as a tobacco pouch."

"Hey, Lieutenant," said Sergeant Stanley Morgan, from Huntsville, Alabama, "what would you say about a guy in our platoon that wears an ear from a fuckin' dead Charlie on his dog-tag chain as a good-luck piece? I'm not saying who it is or that I have even fuckin' seen it. Word is though, that the guy won't go to the damn field without it He supposedly puts it in his mouth and bites down on it for luck whenever he's in a fuckin' firefight."

"I am glad you asked me, Sergeant Morgan." All lips were sealed and all eyes were riveted on Dunn as he spoke. "I want everybody to listen to my answer and to understand me. The best advice I could give this guy is to immediately get rid of the thing...permanently. This is not the type of souvenir you take home to mom or to your wife and kids. This is just the kind of thing that could blow up in your face.

"You guys are all aware of what's going on back home with the demonstrations, students rioting against the war and the newspaper and television reporters calling us 'baby killers.' Just picture some REMF getting hold of this story and turning it into some vicious war crime and blowing it all out of proportion. I am not going to allow this sort of thing to potentially discredit the sacred Ranger tradition. If I see it, I will confiscate it, and I will destroy it. So you tell this guy what I have said and not to wear it. That gruesome thing around his neck does not define who he is, what he does, or the ideals he serves. He is a greater person than that thing. I mean it. I will not allow it. That thing could hurt the Ranger reputation, our unit and that guy. Please, just tell him to get rid of it."

With that note, he felt it was time to end this period of fraternization, as he could not tell whether his message was well received. *No doubt they will have to discuss it among themselves. In the event the guy were to challenge me by wearing it, at least there is no question about my position. I certainly hope it doesn't come to that, though,* he thought.

〣

Joe returned to his tent and planned to spend some special time with his girl. As he wrote a letter full of his boundless love and adoring feelings for her, he mentioned very little of the reality of 'Nam. When finished, he allowed his mind some freedom to wander as his thoughts dwelt on memories of her luscious lips that he loved to kiss. *I could spend hours just making out with her and be totally satisfied...I'm not greedy...I'd be ecstatic if I could just kiss her. Oh, how I miss her sweet kisses. On the other hand...I definitely think I'd be greedy.*

〣

When it came time for supper, Joe reluctantly pulled himself away from his fantasies of Marie and headed for the mess. He enjoyed the hearty beef stew as it fully hit him: *It could be another four days before I savor another hot supper like this one.*

Afterwards, Dunn proceeded to the TOC, anxious for the Ops Briefing to begin. He didn't understand why the Leg outfits were so willing to trade valuable stuff for LRRP rations. *It must be because Legs are not authorized LRRPs and can only get canned C-rations. What can possibly be the fascination with freeze-dried stew?* he idly wondered.

When the Ops Briefing finally began, Phillips detailed the unit's strength and disposition, giving the names, rank and assignments of the new replacements that arrived. "We will be provided two fixed-wing Birddogs, call sign "Seahorse," from Phan Rang Airbase in Direct Support. I enjoyed flying with the Warrant Officer pilot earlier today in my role of C & C."

Staples then briefed on the expected weather, which would be the monotonous 100+ degrees with 100+ humidity during the day with a possible sprinkling of delightfully cooling rain at night. Wayne concluded the briefing by praising Purdy and Team 42, who produced two confirmed kills on a trail on the side of a ridge. The team brought back a pith helmet and an Avtomat Kalashnikova, Model 1947 (AK-47), a Russian made semi-automatic assault rifle, and a pouch full of North Vietnamese currency.

From the recovered documents, Army Intelligence gleaned the team had killed a paymaster and his armed courier. It appeared some enemy soldiers were not going to get paid this month. Intelligence promised to extrapolate additional information from the documents about types of enemy units and strengths of those units. Charlie Rangers had made a favorable debut.

After the briefing, Dunn decided to retire early so as to be well rested for his cherry mission. But before heading once again to his tent, he passed the information from the Operations Briefing on to Wilson and the team leaders. Even before the generators were fired up, the sound of revelry coming from the 3rd Platoon bar indicated that Team 42 contact was in full celebration. *If this is a nightly pastime*, he mused, *any veterans we create will turn out to be lifetime members of Alcoholics Anonymous.*

This particular night he did not want to block out any thoughts of Marie because thinking about her might help relieve the anxiety that was unwontedly creeping up on him concerning his upcoming cherry mission into the bush. He knew his men would consider his conduct in the field a test and understood he had to earn their acceptance of him as their leader. Missing her terribly, anyway, he allowed his mind to wander...

Immediately after graduation, he had driven non-stop down to Hollywood, Florida. The newly commissioned officers had been granted sixty wonderful fun filled days leave before starting their military careers. These two months of freedom were a token to make up for the past four years of gray and seemingly endless confinement.

Those four years did not count for pay purposes or towards any seniority for time in service. Some hotshots might wind up with a full ROTC scholarship at a coed college of his choice with his books paid in full and a $200 monthly stipend to spend on beer. When the hot-shot graduated, he would collect 2LT pay with credit for over four years service and have four years seniority over any West Pointer who would be drawing straight 2LT pay with no time served. Somehow, the sixty, free days off were supposed to level the playing field.

Joe had been planning on relaxing on the Florida beaches for a week before heading to Charleston AFB. After that, he hoped to catch a "space available" flight to a South American destination where he planned on spending four to six weeks touring around South America. On his prior trips to South America he had enjoyed such great times.

Marie had agreed he could spend his last week of leave with her before he had to report to Airborne School at Fort Benning, Georgia.

During the June week before graduation, he and Marie had been inseparable. Even though he had known Marie for less than two months, he felt as if he knew and understood her better than anyone else he had ever met.

Marie swore that everywhere one walked at West Point was only uphill and she was exhausted and had actually stated she was glad to be going home where she planned to lounge in her bathrobe for two full days without getting dressed or putting on any make-up.

He would have gladly changed his plans if she had invited him to go directly home with her. But she wanted him to go and have a good time...but not too good a time. Marie had also remarked that she could not believe how fast the week had gone by and that every moment had been packed.

What a week that had been, Joe remembered. *The beach party at Camp Buckner, the picnic at the redoubt, the parades, the flying hats at the graduation, the swearing-in ceremony and the formal graduation dance. Boy, that white beaded gown her girlfriend, Debbie, had let her borrow was exquisite and sure had fit her like a glove.*

Debbie's uncle was a powerful and successful Italian businessman with a walled mansion in Westbury and was also very generous to her. She had a closet full of formal gowns and had allowed Marie to pick any gown she wanted from it.

Later, Joe had confided to Marie that she had been chosen, "the best looking date," at the dance by an informal poll of Cadets. Another Cadet had collected a bag full of money for dating the least attractive girl. Dunn's reward was respectful applause by the cadet judges when they were escorted to the site for photographs of the couples.

He knew that Marie had wanted to please him and she must have known she had succeeded from the look on his face the moment she descended the stairs at the Thayer Hotel to greet him before the dance. With his dark, olive drab tanned face split in a grin from ear to ear and in his all white cadet uniform, he probably looked silly. She later admitted she dared not let him really know how impressed she had been with him, especially since he was so well traveled and interesting.

Joe chuckled to himself as he remembered how surprised and pleased he had been on their first date when she ate all of her meal plus part of his. She was not some prissy girl who pretended not to eat when out with a guy. He smiled as he acknowledged that in their relationship, she obviously was not going to let him make all the surprises.

With a lullaby of distant cursing, shouting and laughing, accompanied by the hum of the gas-powered generators, he fell asleep, praying he would dream of Marie.

5
Cherry Mission

WHEN HE AROSE EARLY THE NEXT MORNING, HE noticed the camp repeated its same activities. *Strange*, he pondered, *how we humans are such creatures of habit that we need to create routines in order to feel comfortable. Well, my activities today are going to take me out of my comfort zone...but I am definitely ready for this.*

He tried to analyze his own feelings and emotions about going into the field on his first mission. That's when he realized he just wanted to get through it so he was no longer a newbie. He wanted it to be a part of his routine job. The morning passed more quickly than he expected.

"Sir, I am impressed," Buck remarked after thoroughly checking the gear attached to the lieutenant's web, harness and rucksack. "You look as if you've been doing this all your life. Now we just need to get your face painted like the rest of us."

While Buck covered Dunn's face with camouflage stick paint, Chief offered, "How 'bout I tie a bandana on your head. It will be best to keep everything covered for protection against bugs. The heat might be uncomfortable, but the damn bugs are downright nasty."

When Buck was satisfied with the preparedness of the team, he called them together and specified the order of "march" for the entire mission. Buck would be in point, followed by Dunn as RTO, then Assistant Patrol Leader Chief with the M-60 machine gun, followed by PFC Martinez, SP/4 McCormack and SGT Garbo in the slack position as rear security.

Dunn had previously dialed in the unit frequency on the radio set. Now turning it on, he pressed the send button on the handset field phone to call the TOC.

"Fastball Three, this is Fastball Two Two. Radio check. Over." The unit call sign for that operation was "Fastball," and the Three meant the TOC, while Two Two indicated Team 22.

"Fastball Two Eight, this is Fastball Three. I read you loud and clear. How me? Over."

Dunn recognized the voice of Staples, who had obviously recognized him as well. Staples had responded using his personal call sign as 2nd Platoon Leader instead of the call sign for Team 22, which he used for the commo check. "Six" is always used for the unit commander; and "Two Eight" means the leader of 2nd Platoon, probably because there were never more than seven teams.

"Fastball Three, this is Fastball Two Eight. I read you same. Out."

Standing outside the TOC, Phillips waited for the team next to the three-quarter-ton truck that would soon take them all to the airfield. When they arrived at the tarmac, the Birddog pilot stood outside his plane with an extra flight helmet in his hand. Two helicopters were poised with their main rotors already churning. Phillips bid the team good luck and sprinted over to the Cessna airplane. A door gunner on the nearest helicopter motioned with his arms for the team to climb aboard the chopper. With his flight helmet on and the black visor pulled down, the door gunner's chin was the only visible feature of his face. All six climbed aboard the one chopper, leaving the other chopper empty, except for its crew of four. Chief and Blue sat on the floor of the center troop-carrying compartment with their legs dangling outside, toes barely touching the skids. Martinez and Slant sat, half reclining, in the middle while Buck and Dunn sat with their legs hanging outside the opposite side.

Sensing that everyone was safely aboard, the door gunner gave the team a thumbs-up sign, and then evidently relayed that fact over his intercom to the pilots. Despite the burden of weight carried by the team, the helicopter lifted effortlessly, hovered and turned. Over the loud wop, wop sound of the main blades, Dunn could hear Chief and Blue yelling, "Airborne!" and "Ranger!" and "Hooahh!" The tail of the chopper lifted upwards, the front dipped slightly, and the chopper lunged forward, quickly accelerating and climbing.

Soon afterwards they were speeding along just above the tops of the trees. The chopper would rise or dip as the pilot guided and conformed to the contours of the surfaces he was skimming. Dunn felt the wind whistling past his ears when he leaned forward out of the open doorway. He had no fear whatsoever of falling out, despite the turns and maneuvers of the aircraft because the 65 pound rucksack on his back weighted and fixed him to the sun-heated metal flooring.

Suddenly, their craft slowed and came to a hover as the empty chopper descended into a fake LZ. Just as suddenly, they were off again, now heading to the designated LZ where they would jump out. At this point is when anticipation was usually at its peak on any given mission and the adrenalin higher as each man automatically readied himself for a quick exit. This was when both the Rangers and the helicopter crew were most vulnerable. The most dangerous situation was landing in a "hot LZ," a landing zone with an unknown number of enemy soldiers waiting to fire them up. A Ranger team's best weapon was the element of surprise.

Before the skids touched ground, the six men jumped from the descending helicopter, which immediately took off again. The green elephant grass was so thick and so tall that when they jumped they really could not tell how far they had to fall before hitting the ground. It was a wonder more Rangers were not injured just exiting the choppers.

Instinctively, they had all executed a PLF, a Parachute Landing Fall. Twisting, they contorted their bodies to absorb the shock of the fall on the fleshy parts of their bodies, the balls of the feet, the calf, the buttocks and the side. As they fell and rolled through the tall grass, they received minor cuts from the sharp, jagged edges of the grass-it never failed. Elephant grass leaves always inflicted cuts on just about any exposed flesh-nothing serious, but was just enough to cause a nagging sting, rather like paper cuts.

The team quickly assembled, crouching below the concealment of the six-foot elephant grass and faced outward in all directions. There was putrid smelling smoke everywhere and the crackling sound of burning fire. The LZ was literally hot, but not from the enemy, it was because it was on fire. The temperature must have been close to 120 degrees with the fire plus the usual heat of the day. Dunn swore that it was the hottest day of his entire life.

The first thing done when the men assembled was to perform a commo check. Because of the unexpected burning LZ, Phillips kept the two gunships and one slick on station. They would be nearby if Team 22 encountered trouble. The other slick was sent back to LZ English to prepare for insertion of the next team.

Looking to distance themselves from the LZ as well as from the flames, the team started to climb, single file, up the steep hill as planned. The climb was exhausting, not just the actual uphill climb, but adding insult to injury was the almost intolerable, humid heat, which sapped their strength with each step they took. Joe really sympathized with Chief, who was carrying the heavy M-60, and with Slant, who not only was carrying extra ammo but was also assigned rear security. Slant had to reposition all that trampled elephant grass while they "Charlie Miked," which meant, "to continue the mission," up the hill.

Not even fifteen minutes later and less than half way up the hill, word was quietly and quickly passed up that Martinez was, "having difficulties." Martinez had already drunk both of his canteens of water, was sweating profusely and was crying and begging to rest.

Upon inspection, Dunn suspected that Martinez might be suffering from heat exhaustion. In addition to drenching sweat and pale, clammy skin, Martinez felt cold, as well as acting disoriented.

Dunn took Martinez' rucksack and gave his weapon to Blue to carry. He told Martinez, "Just climb to the top of this hill, and I promise you will be evacuated back to LZ English."

Then Dunn contacted Phillips in the 0-1 Birddog and arranged for a chopper to meet them. Buck signaled their exact location to the Birddog with a detector mirror.

Feeling the team could be compromised, Phillips wanted to extract them, but there was no way Dunn wanted to return from his "cherry mission" after only a half hour in the field. After a family council, the rest of the team agreed to Charlie Mike without Martinez.

Since the top of the hill was a narrow ridgeline, there was only enough room for the evacuating chopper to hover with one skid near or touching the ground. The skid on the other side of the helicopter was left in mid air. The pilot was excellent, and the procedure was over in slightly more than an instant.

"You can tell the Birddog Double Deuce is A-OK," said Buck to Dunn. "If Charlie had been nearby, he would have fired up our ass while we were exposed on the ridgeline. So, we are not compromised."

The team made its way down the far side of the hill and then slowly, carefully, and painfully through bramble bushes. It was about 1400 hours when they suddenly came upon a narrow, defined path. While the rest of the team maintained vigilance, Buck put out nine, separate Claymore mines that he set up in a daisy chain with a single triggering cord. The Claymores were positioned to concentrate shrapnel in a killing zone at a sharp turn in the path.

The team members were then strategically placed to permit viewing down both approaches to the turn in the path. The trees, fallen logs and earthen mounds provided both excellent cover and concealment. They were ready.

Over the next four hours, Dunn studied his surroundings and discovered the jungle was teeming with life. Thousands of species crawled, hopped, or flew around him. As strange as it may seem, the jungle with all of its wildlife, was eerily quiet and, at times, it was absolutely, unnervingly silent.

During this wait, Dunn found he could detect every shift, every movement, every slight cough made by any member of the team. Moving through the jungle without making a sound, moving without stepping on a crackling branch, moving without allowing a bending branch to slap the Ranger behind you, moving without becoming entangled in vines was terribly taxing. But lying motionless in an ambush site for hours was far more tedious and even more difficult. *This experience brings new meaning to the phrase, "They serve, who only sit and wait,"* he irreverently thought.

Before it turned dark, Buck collected the Claymore mines and gave them back to the men who had brought them. Then, after insuring they left no evidence of their presence, the team stealthily and slowly moved a couple hundred meters away from the path where they found a good, defensible spot.

They huddled in a wagon-wheel formation for the night and slept with their heads all together, nearly touching. In the center was Dunn's rucksack with the radio. Starting at midnight, each man was required to stay awake for one hour on watch while the others slept.

The first thing each person did on watch was to perform a radio check with X-ray. Prior to midnight, anyone who wanted to could advise the others that he wanted to sleep and do so. However, that was a rare event. The men also took turns at eating-only one person ate at a time. The freeze-dried meals were eaten with cold water from their canteens. When a Ranger finished eating, he buried anything left over, including the wrapper.

Although some of the teams permitted it, Team 22 did not allow anyone to smoke while on a mission. The reasoning was if they could detect the smell of Charlie, then Charlie could also recognize the smell of Americans. It was true, a Ranger could definitely smell Charlie because the food he ate had a smell that was very pungent and unmistakable. The aroma of "nuoc mam," a fermented, spicy fish-head sauce, which the Rangers called "armpit sauce," was enjoyed by the Vietnamese, but it also permeated their bodies and was not easily removed or forgotten.

Slant volunteered for first watch as each man tried to settle in for the night. Blue volunteered to take second watch, followed by Dunn, Chief, and then Buck. It was not long before weary bodies turned limp and cat-like on the ground.

After a while, Dunn woke because the jungle air had turned cooler. He was glad to have his camouflage nylon blanket to wrap around him. Almost instantly he fell back to sleep once he was snuggled and warm. A breeze, which had been non-existent all day long, began to pick up. Shortly after midnight Dunn came to the surface just long enough to realize he was drenched from a hard pounding rain. Stoically, he mentally commanded his body to ignore the cold, the wet and the jabbing ground, thus Dunn was able to permit sleep to dull his senses.

It felt to Joe as if he had just barely fallen asleep when Slant gently shook his shoulder. He quietly explained in his ear that Blue had fallen back asleep shortly after he was supposed to have started the second watch, so Slant had let him sleep and stayed on watch for the additional hour.

The first thing Dunn did when he shook the sleep from his mind and could think straight was perform a commo check with X-ray, who gleefully responded and spent some extra time on small talk.

"The huge raindrops are noisy," whispered Slant, wide-eyed, nervous, and not in the least bit sleepy. "It fucking sounds like they are sneaking up on us. Listen, doesn't that sound just like fucking somebody stepping on twigs? It makes you imagine that we are completely surrounded by Charlie, doesn't it sir?"

"We just might be," Dunn agreed, "and that's just what we want, because they don't know we are here. Don't worry Slant, nobody in their right mind would be out here in this mess, not even Charlie. Get some sleep, I'll be on guard and wide awake."

Instead of sleeping, during the next hour, Slant entertained Joe with stories of growing up in the Bronx, his favorite foods: pizza, pasta and bagels, his favorite baseball teams, the New York Yankees and the hated New York "Miracle" Mets, and other small talk about everything and nothing.

"Man, I hope the guys back at base are taking good care of my little buddy, Deros. I sure have become attached to the little fucker," Slant worried in a whisper.

At the end of the hour, they woke Sergeant Eagle. Before Chief could complete the hourly radio check with X-ray, Dunn had curled back into his wet, nylon camouflage blanket and fallen back asleep. In the morning, Buck and Slant, who had not slept a single wink during their first night in the field, quietly roused the team.

Even though the rain had stopped, large drops of water continued to occasionally drip from the triple canopy above. The men took turns eating a portion of their LRRP rations and repacking soggy gear into their rucksacks. Before heading off, they again made certain to cover any signs that they had even been there. Although the sun was hardly visible, the air was quickly warming which caused an eerie evaporation mist to rise from their bodies as they walked. Long before they would see the sun, they and the earth would again be parched, and they would be cursing the heat.

Since they all needed to refill their canteens, they slowly and as quietly as possible made their way downhill. Due to the thick bushes and thorny vines, the climb down was every bit as difficult as the climb up the ridge through the elephant grass the day before. When the team first spied the stream playing peek-a-boo with them through the thick brush, they saw that it was swollen from the rain that night. They were more than ready for some water.

But first Buck carefully and thoroughly investigated the surrounding area and placed each member in a defensive position while Blue collected everyone's canteens, stringing them on a stretch of rope. While the rest of the team maintained watch from their defensive positions, Blue filled and returned their canteens. In order to make the water potable, each member of the team had to first drop in a water purification tablet plus an iodine pill.

The next time I write to Marie, thought Dunn, *I have got to remember to ask her to send me Kool-Aid or some Fizzies. The little brown iodine pills might kill the germs in a quart of dirty stream water, but they sure don't improve the taste any. Yuk!* The taste made his whole body give an involuntary and violent quiver. There was no point in commenting or complaining about something for which everyone was already aware and for which there was no immediate cure.

Before they continued, Chief quietly whispered to the man next to him, "I strongly suggest everyone check themselves for blood-sucking leeches as I just removed two from my own body."

The word quickly spread and Dunn was surprised to find a small one on his left forearm, as he had not felt it attach itself. Poor Blue found four of them on his body. Probably since he was already soaked from the rain, he had thought nothing of wading into the stream to fill the canteens. That was probably where he picked up the four disgusting bloodsuckers.

The rest of that day was uneventful, as were the following two days. Not finding any other trails in their designated sector, they followed the trail they had discovered on their first day. Although they came across numerous signs of activity, such as tracks and even spent AK47 cartridges, they never saw or heard anything more promising. The only difference in their routine was that Slant, probably out of sheer exhaustion, had finally allowed himself to sleep when not on watch.

Late, on the morning of the fourth day, the disappointed, filthy and tired five men were steered by the Birddog to an LZ, where a beautiful OD "egg-beater" with a red devil face painted on its front picked them up. The ride back in the chopper was the first time in four days that any of them allowed themselves to actually relax.

When the team got back to the platoon area, Buck indicated for Dunn to leave the radio and his unspent munitions and that he would turn them back in.

Joe didn't argue and was delighted since the 65-pound rucksack now seemed heavier carrying it from the truck to the conex than at any time in the field. Also, he looked forward to grabbing his towel from his tent and heading off to the shower to cleanse his body. It was only then that he realized he couldn't stand the stench of his own body.

Afterwards, feeling refreshed and like a new man, he dressed and got ready to leave his tent for the platoon area. Just then, Forest, still looking as he did when he arrived from the field, and SP/4 Peter "Blue" McCormack in clean fatigues, approached and asked to speak with him.

"Sir, I think we need to send Blue on immediate sick call," stated a serious-faced Forest.

"Blue, tell me, what's the problem?" Dunn asked as he turned to face McCormack.

"Sir, I didn't say anything but the last two days in the field I couldn't go to the bathroom. I never shit in the field as I always wait till I get back to take a shit. But I couldn't even piss. I didn't think much about it while we were in the field and just figured it was my body waiting till we were back. But, sir, I still can't take a leak and my bladder is fucking killing me now."

"You're telling me that you need to piss, but you can't?" asked Dunn.

"Yes, sir. I have to go real fucking bad but I just can't... and there's no reason for it. I don't fucking understand it."

"Okay, Blue, but first there is something I want you to do. It is entirely possible that you picked up another leech and it is blocking your urinary tract. Go over to the side of my tent and thoroughly check yourself out."

While Buck and Dunn waited, Blue went over to the side of the tent and did as instructed. "Holy shit!" exclaimed Blue in amazement. "How did this goddamn, blood-sucking mutha-fucka crawl up inside my dick? What the hell? Fuck!"

Dunn assured, "Don't worry, Blue, they won't have to amputate! Come on. I'll go with you to TOC to authorize you for immediate sick call. Most likely, that leech is ready to fall off anyway after drinking its full of your blood.

"Sergeant Forest, you go ahead and clean up. I'll take care of Blue."

6
New Recruits

AFTER HE SENT BLUE TO GET MEDICAL ATTENTION for his penis, which had been invaded by an unlucky leach, Dunn went looking for his platoon sergeant. He found Wilson at the platoon conex speaking with SSG Lars "The Mad Swede" Swenson, patrol leader of Patrol 24, and with SSG David "Professor" Halloway, team leader of Team 23. The Professor had just returned from a beneficial reconnaissance flight that day and was working on the preparations to take his team into the field in the morning. The Mad Swede's team was scheduled for insertion the day following.

"Hey, sir," Wilson greeted him, "we heard the only Double Deuce blood spilled was by a horny leech!" They all laughed.

Before Dunn arrived, the three sergeants were engaged in a mildly heated discussion about the assignments for two new recruits brought in that morning to 2nd Platoon. These two new recruits were both 18-year-old privates who arrived together from Ahn Khe. Wilson allowed The Mad Swede first choice in selecting one for his team and Swenson chose PFC Daniel Smith, a muscular looking young man from Phoenix, Arizona. The Mad Swede indicated that Smith looked like he would be a perfect fit for his Popeye-like muscular team.

The real problem stemmed from the other young recruit, PFC William Armstrong, from Topeka, Kansas, because he showed up wearing love beads on his uniform. Around his neck, and on his dog-chain, Armstrong sported a metal, round emblem that said, "Make Love, Not War."

The Professor angrily ordered Armstrong to remove them and never wear them again. Because of this, Halloway demanded that he be allowed to have Smith instead of Armstrong. He pointed out his assistant patrol leader was away in Thailand on R&R.

Going into the field the next day, he didn't want his team made up mostly of newbies. Including himself, the only Ranger with prior contact experience was SP/4 Roger Goldstein, a 20-year-old from Long Beach, Mississippi, who was on a second, consecutive tour with the unit.

"Sorry, Sergeant Halloway," Dunn intervened, "I will not interfere with Sergeant Wilson's assignments. Every Ranger, even one who indorses love over war, is entitled to a chance to prove himself. Remember, he did volunteer to come to this unit, and you might be able to develop him into a good warrior as well as a lover. In any event, I would like to personally hear how he performs in the bush. So, sometime after you get back from the field, let me know how he did."

After the two other sergeants left, Dunn asked Wilson, "Would you please brief me on all platoon developments that went on during the four days I was in the field? I don't want to be caught at the Ops Briefing with a situation on which I'm unaware."

"Sir, the Old Man wants to talk to you about Martinez, the guy you medivaced from the bush. I am also happy to report 2nd Platoon has hired four local women to do laundry and cleaning: Tran Thi Chinh (George Ann), Le Thi Bang (Lanna), Nghiem Thi Huong (Candy) and Nguyen Thi Tinh (Fran). All have been approved and issued identification picture cards."

When Dunn was convinced there were no other issues of any substance, he asked Wilson, "I hate to keep bugging you, but what is the status of the lists I previously requested and what about the matter of the security sandbags?"

"Sorry, sir, I have been so busy I have not yet started on the lists nor has much been done with regard to the sandbags. Everything will get done in due time," Wilson said trying to placate Dunn.

"The TOC is completely covered with sandbags and the other platoons, notably 3rd Platoon, are likewise," Dunn calmly said. "I must insist on a sandbag effort starting immediately."

"Very well, sir, but I must point out that Pappy hires locals with money from his cash bar to do all the shitty sandbag work for 3rd Platoon."

"Sergeant Wilson, you can cause our own men to do it; hire local help to do it; or any other thing you can figure out. I don't care...just do it, and get it started now." Dunn felt too tired to argue or even get into a lengthy discussion on the subject.

He strolled over to the platoon hooch. Out front were two rows of six rucksacks neatly aligned. Evidently, even though their teams were going out a day apart, the team leaders had set aside their differences and were drawing rations and collecting munitions together. When it came to combat operations, these men were consummate and meticulous professionals, and a petty squabble wouldn't stand in their way.

Dunn momentarily stood on the top of the rickety wooden steps the men had hastily built outside the hooch. Silently he peeked inside the hooch. He saw assorted gear, clothing, strange trophies and a collection of who-knows-what, strewn all around the floor and walls. The men of double Deuce were fully dressed but sound asleep and, unlike while in the bush, snoring loudly on their respective cots. Dunn could also hear the playful shrill chirping of Deros from somewhere inside.

As he turned around to go down the rather unstable steps, he noticed the men of Teams 23 and 24 had returned and were packing the necessary supplies they obtained. Then he saw Rusky waiting for him at the bottom of the wobbly wooden stairs. Instead of walking, Dunn jumped down.

"How ya doing, boss? I've got to get something in the hooch for the Mad Swede. Be right back," explained Rusky as he swiftly climbed the stairs and entered the hooch. Dunn then heard him yelling.

"Hey! You, monkey. Hey! Scat. Get away from there! Oh, no, monkey! That does it."

BAM!

"What the fuck?" said a Ranger.

"Who fired a shot? Why was a shot fired?" Dunn called as he hurried back up the steps and into the hooch.

"Rusky, you fuckhead! You shot Deros! You killed my pet monkey! Why the fuck did you do that?" asked an enraged Slant, who had been shocked awake from a deep sleep.

"Hey, man, it got into that box of grenades over there under the cot," Rusky explained.

"You didn't have to fucking kill it!" shouted Garbo.

"It was either you or the monkey. It was pulling the grenades out of the box by the pins and that damn monkey could have killed us all!" Rusky turned towards Dunn and pointed at Garbo. "Hey, boss, tell this cherry here there's a war going on, and this is no place for pets."

"I've been on a mission. I'm no fucking cherry!" insisted a most poignant and distressed Garbo.

"Double Deuce was not in a contact. Until you've been in a contact, you're still a cherry in my book," replied the unrepentant Rusky.

"Alright, guys, it's fucking over. Let's get this cleaned up. I'll take care of this, sir," The Mad Swede took control.

※

Having been rudely awakened by Rusky and the monkey incident, the men of Team 22 left the hooch and joined the rest of the men outside.

They found another distraction as they listened to the Professor's team grilling its newest member because it wanted to make sure its new cherry would pull his own weight.

"I'm no coward," said Billy Armstrong. "Just because I don't believe in this damn war doesn't mean I'm a coward or that I cannot be a good Ranger."

"Oh, yeah?" said Eagle, as he muscled his way past Shortround to stand directly in the cherry's face, except that Armstrong's head was at the level of the Indian's chest. "How is it you can wear love beads and then expect to wear our Black Beret? Man, that makes no sense. I mean, why are you even here? We all know why we are here."

"Oh, yeah? Then why are you here, Chief?" challenged Armstrong.

"That's easy. Before I can unify all the tribes and be the leader of my people, I must distinguish myself in combat. Our last great leader was a tribal chief who won a valor medal in World War Two. When he died, there was nobody worthy to take his place. I am the head of my village and I need this damn war to earn the right to unify my people. So, I ask you again, cherry, why are you here?"

"That's easy, too," answered Armstrong. "I am here because I love my country, and I want to prove to everybody that I am not a damn coward, but a true warrior who belongs among the best."

"Those are easy words to say, but they don't explain your fuckin' love beads," insisted Chief.

"Okay, I'll explain it to you. In Kansas, where I come from, it is mostly farmland. People there are very patriotic, like my folks. That's how I was reared. Well, when I was a junior in high school, there was this guy, Brad, who was a big shot... senior class president, captain of the football team... you know the type. Anyway, Brad started this anti-war club, and I joined. That is where I learned this damn war is political and being run by money-grubbing, dirty politicians. We didn't have rallies or anything. But, I learned this war is simply wrong.

"Well, Brad ends up skipping off to Canada to avoid the draft. After that, everybody labeled him a coward... even his own folks disowned him. Hey, I still believe this damn war is wrong, but I am no friggin' coward. Hell, do you think a coward would dare show up in this unit wearing love beads?"

"Ha, ha, ha! You're right about that. Billy Armstrong, you're okay in my book," endorsed the now appeased Chief.

"Well, I'm not afraid to stand up for what I believe. I also believe I'll be a damn good Ranger... that is, if you guys will just give me a friggin' chance to prove myself. I am no coward," Armstrong vowed and promised at the same time to his team.

"So, since you're from Kansas... then, that's it. Your nickname is now, 'Billy Kansas.'" And so Chief christened him.

Dunn walked away from the discussion, delighted that the matter had been handled in such a peaceful, yet logical manner. The aroma coming from the mess reminded him that it was suppertime, and the thought of a hot meal made him realize he was absolutely ravenous. He decided to check out the TOC and see if he could find someone with which to share a good meal.

On his way, SFC Charles Varnes, platoon sergeant of 4th Platoon, intercepted him. He first met Varnes when he was a student in Ranger School at Fort Benning, Georgia. Varnes, who then was the Non-Commissioned Officer in charge of the first phase of Ranger training, had mightily impressed Joe. This was now the beginning of Varnes' third tour in Viet Nam. Between each tour, he always returned to serve as an instructor in Ranger School.

Varnes said, "Lieutenant Dunn, let me introduce you to my new platoon leader, First Lieutenant Rodham Winthrop. He joined the unit and took over 4th Platoon while you were out with Double Deuce. Perhaps you can entertain him at supper while I get some work done."

Since Dunn believed that Varnes was an excellent soldier, he felt Rod was fortunate to have him as his platoon sergeant. He responded to Varnes in the affirmative, shook Rod's hand and said, "That's great! I was just looking for someone to join me."

Rod was a big man. He was an All American High School Fullback from Charleston, South Carolina, and a four-year starter as a linebacker at his alma mater, The Citadel. He kidded Dunn about attending a "second-rate military school in New York," claiming that West Point was "The Citadel on the Hudson."

As he was hungry for information, Rod peppered Dunn with a myriad of questions. While eating, Dunn managed to tell him all he had learned from Baylor, what he heard from Kent and what little he had seen so far while in the field.

On the way back to the TOC to attend the daily Ops Briefing, Dunn spotted Wayne talking to Phillips and Kent. "Major Wayne," he said, when the group had stopped talking and looked in his direction. "Sir, you wanted to talk to me about Private Michael Martinez. Is this a good time?"

"Yes, Dunn. Did Martinez tell you or his team leader he was not feeling well and he never wanted to go on a field mission?"

"No, sir. I was with the team the entire day before the mission and the full morning before insertion. There was never any indication to me that he was either sick or unwilling to go into the field," Dunn briefly explained.

"Well, that's not what he said to me. When you asked to join this unit, I specifically told you every man was a volunteer. You had to goddamn *want* to get in and goddamn *want* to stay. Somebody who is sick has no business being *forced* to go into the field. Right after the team was put in, you had to send for a goddamn medivac! In addition to wasting aircraft assets, it probably compromised the team and spooked away any targets.

"Anyway, I have taken care of *your* problem and have reassigned Martinez to the supply section with Sergeant Beave in Ahn Khe. Martinez will be given a fresh start as the unit armorer."

"I understand, sir," was Dunn's steely response as the group, led by Major Wayne turned and entered the TOC for the Ops Briefing.

Inwardly seething at the unfairness of the verbal censure, he thought, *How could the Old Man take the word of a cherry private over the team leader's and mine? It was clear by the way the Major waived his arm at me that he considered the discussion terminated. At least Buck will be happy to be rid of the man and now Martinez will no longer be a concern.*

❧

In tribute to the preparedness of Staples, the briefing was presented in its usual excellent manner. Basically, it boiled down to his telling everyone what their next assignment or mission would be. In spite of his inner turmoil over the Martinez situation, Joe listened attentively as Staples outlined the next two day's missions.

"First, Team 23 will be one of two teams inserted tomorrow. Second, Team 24 will perform a reconnaissance tomorrow and then be inserted the following day. As Lee flew his first C & C today, he will fly again tomorrow and will direct the insertion of Team 23. Dunn will fly C & C the following two days."

After Staples concluded with a few more remarks, the operations portion was over and Phillips rose to speak. "I am happy to report we have received badly needed new recruits from Ahn Khe. For the first time in six months, this unit has its full complement of officers.

"Our commander has also assigned Private Martinez to assist Sergeant Beave in Ahn Khe. Martinez is now the unit armorer. Accordingly, effective immediately, there is a new policy covering captured weapons. All captured weapons, including souvenirs, shall be sent to Ahn Khe, where Martinez will be responsible for their maintenance and safekeeping.

"This policy benefits our men since most of the captured weapons are banned as souvenirs because they are automatic fire or otherwise illegal Stateside. If requested, Martinez will modify such weapons, thereby permitting retention as a souvenir. A primary reason for this policy is to provide a secure place for these war trophies until the soldier is ready to DEROS home.

"On another note, gentlemen, the unit is pretty well settled, having been here almost a week now. The mess section is doing a fantastic job. All the pilots are begging for invitations to join in the feasts that we take for granted. Commo Platoon has been great in getting the unit wired for sound and electricity. 3rd Platoon deserves recognition for getting its area completely secured with sandbags and taking care of TOC and the headquarters elements. 4th Platoon has also done a good job. So, there is no excuse for the poor condition of 1stPlatoon and especially 2nd Platoon. You two have not given priority to sandbags as directed."

"Goddamn right!" Wayne exclaimed as he rose angrily to his feet with his hands on his hips and faced the seated group. "I won't stop platoon leaders from going to the field and pretending they are team leaders. However, that does not absolve them from their platoon leader responsibilities. I am 'sic-n-tarred' of you not paying attention to my directives. I expect better. Dismissed!"

On the way out of the meeting, Lee sought out Dunn before they headed back to their respective platoon areas. "Hey, I guess Charlie heard we were in the field so he hid from both our teams."

Still upset at his previous unfair treatment, Dunn replied with a tinge of bitterness, "It's clear that the Old Man doesn't really want us going to the field with our teams. How do you feel about that, Robert?"

"Oh, screw the Old Man!" Lee exclaimed. He hasn't ordered us *not* to. So, until he orders me otherwise, I plan on going into the field as often as possible. How about you?"

"Well, I had already planned on taking out a different team each month as the team leader. I'm on my way now to tell my team leaders, and I don't expect them to like it. How was your day in the Birddog?" Dunn asked to change the subject.

"I'm only now beginning to feel better. God, I felt like shit the whole day. I hate feeling so puny, and I puked out the window twice. Forget about reading a map. Every time I looked down, I had to stick my head out the window for fresh air. Thank God nothing happened. I just pray that tomorrow I don't put the teams into the wrong LZ. Hope I get the same pilot as I had today as he was really helpful and told me it usually gets easier with each time."

"Boy, I'm full of both trepidation and excitement whenever I think of my first time up. I hope I have an understanding and compassionate pilot like you. I heard some of those guys love to see how green they can make us get... especially on our first time up. I truly have no idea how I'll do," Joe confessed.

"You will probably do just great. Well, I'll see ya' later," said Lee as he turned to go back to his tent.

When Dunn got to his platoon hooch, he was somewhat surprised to discover there had been some, although it was little, progress made by the men on filling and stacking sandbags. Wilson and the team leaders were sitting on a stack of sandbags, and he realized they were waiting for him. He acknowledged them and suggested they go over to the entrance of the conex to take advantage of the light from its one, dull, bulb.

Halloway spoke first. "Sir, my team, including the cherry is fully outfitted and prepared for tomorrow's insertion."

"Good, Halloway, men," Dunn commended. Then he turned to Swenson and advised, "I will be going on the reconnaissance flight with you."

Then, he dropped the real bombshell on his proud team leaders. "I intend to go into the field once a month, each time with a different team. When I go, I am not going as an inspector or to give critiques. I will be going as the team leader," Dunn announced.

The men didn't disappoint him in their expected, explosive reactions to his announcement. The team leaders reacted with anger, cursing and yelling in unison. Even Wilson joined in, expressing his support for the team leaders who threatened to boycott going to the field. When they had substantially finished venting their anger and before he would allow any of them to leave, he continued.

"If any of you choose not to go into the field, that is your right. But remember you will be abandoning your team. They will go with me and without you. I promise I will treat you with respect. I will give you the respect that you have earned and deserve. Please consider this. As far as the army is concerned, it doesn't matter who is called the team leader. As the ranking officer, I will always be responsible for everything that happens when I am with a team. Don't abandon your teams. When I go with your team, I ask you to go as my assistant. Your actual status and position with the men is not challenged or threatened. However, this is the way it has to be. This is the way it *will* be."

"Sir," interrupted Parvis, the leader of Team 21, "what's your real agenda? I mean, you're a West Pointer, so you're probably looking to make general, just like Major Wayne. The very first time we met him and he spoke to us, he told us we were going to make him a fucking general."

Looking the men straight in their eyes, Dunn responded in his sincere, firm manner, "All I can do right now is reassure you with only my words. The truth is I have no agenda, other than what I believe to be your best welfare... the best welfare of all the men in 2nd Platoon and the performance of assigned missions. I'm not looking for any medals to pin on my chest or any stars to pin on my shoulders.

"I'm also not necessarily looking to make friends either up or down the chain of command. I am simply going to do what I think is best. Will I make mistakes? Sure, but I will learn from them. Will I listen to advice? Sure, although not always, but probably more than you are thinking right now.

"Now on another note. I understand through the grapevine I need to thank you for taking a united position against wearing enemy body parts. I appreciate your support. Believe me, I recognize I am only the nominal leader of Second Platoon. You men are the day-to-day leaders the men look up to and rely upon. I need your support, and I thank you for giving it to me," concluded Dunn.

Having looked each team leader straight in the eye, to insure his message was delivered, he left them after commenting to Wilson about making a good start on the sandbags.

Joe went back to his tent to give the men time to mull over what he said and to spend some time writing a letter to Marie. This was his "escape time" when he wrote and poured his feelings for her from his mind through his hand and onto the paper. He made this time as if it were a reoccurring visit, and was able to shut out the world for a while. After time spent concentrating on his girl, Joe would be refreshed and strengthened. At the end he did remember to ask her to send him some Kool-Aid and Fizzies in different flavors, and why.

After his finished "visit" with Marie, Joe let his thoughts drift to tomorrow. *After the scheduled reconnaissance flight with Swenson, I'll plan to spend some time in the TOC with Staples. Also, during daylight hours, tomorrow, I need to steal some time in order to clean my weapon.*

Then looking around his tent, he had to admit to himself, *It sure is nice to return to my tent to find it clean and my camouflage fatigues and nylon blanket laundered. Everything might be relative, but I'm not yet ready to start calling this tent, "home."* Leaning back on his cot, though, his last remembered thought before dozing off was, *This cot seems much more comfortable than I remembered...*

The routine of the following day flowed without substantial interruptions or without any announcements of team contacts. Early in the morning before any interruptions, Dunn thoroughly cleaned his CAR-15 and got that task out of the way first thing.

When the events of the day began to unfold, he found they tended to complicate his day. A suitable and agreed upon LZ for team 24 had been made during the day's reconnaissance flight, so he wanted to spend a few hours in the TOC. There he studied the map thoroughly as he envisioned and committed to memory the contours and certain outstanding features he would need to know for tomorrow's insertion when he flew C & C.

Even though he was concentrating on his own work, Joe couldn't help but hear and found it most interesting to listen to the various radio transmissions, but what was even more interesting was listening to Staples.

Richard Staples took a little time and explained to Joe how the unit received mission assignments. He further explained the procedures he used to secure B-52 bombing strikes; the steps he took to insure local firebases responding to Fire Mission requests; the considerable contacts he amassed to acquire the different aircraft support invariably required; the sources he developed for his weather forecasting reports; and the network he had built of intelligence gatherers upon which the company heavily relied.

"Let me speak to you frankly, sir," Staples said to Dunn. "I anticipate significant contributions from you as a competent C & C. I consider that one particular duty to be the paramount need of our unit. You should not allow collateral factors, no matter *who* or what, to interfere with its performance."

Staples had emphasized the word, "who." Dunn was not certain of the intended meaning and wondered if Staples was actually referring to the commander. In any event, it had been made abundantly clear from both Staples and Baylor that they felt C & C was a critical task he *had* to master.

It pleased Dunn to realize he could always expect straight answers and hard truths if ever he needed to ask a question of Staples. Better than being a friend, Staples was a professional whose sound advice was not based on any agenda, other than the best welfare of the men on a mission. Joe suspected he might also have a friend in the TOC.

That evening the four line platoon leaders gathered together to enjoy a scrumptious steak and potato dinner. The conversation was entertaining and light, consisting primarily of college-life episodes, sports and hobbies. Each man revealed a little of his personal make-up and private life while the others listened attentively and appreciatively.

Dunn shared about his travels in Europe as a teenage military brat while his father was stationed in Germany. He also told them a little about some of the great times he had in South America while still in college.

Afterwards, on the way to the TOC for the daily Ops Briefing, he was surprised and pleased to see the men of 2nd Platoon working diligently on filling and stacking, ever higher, the detested sandbags surrounding the hooch. They wisely chose to work in the cool of the evening, as during the majority of the day, the suffocating heat made the performance of any physical task an extremely taxing labor. Salt tablets were plentiful and made available at every meal in the mess, and all the men were encouraged to conscientiously take them to replenish the loss of salt from either regular or work related perspiration caused by the intense heat and unrelenting humidity.

Staples delivered a superb and short briefing that evening. The only item out of the ordinary was an announcement, "The monthly book box has arrived." The book box was a wooden crate filled with approximately sixty books on various subjects. The USO, United Service Organizations, a nonprofit organization providing a "home away from home" and celebrity entertainment to U.S. soldiers, delivered it to combat units as a recreational service.

Since Charlie Rangers never received an allotment of tickets to any of the celebrity shows or concerts, some of the men relished the arrival of the book box, delving through it like kids in a candy store. But, actually, most of the men could care less.

Joe later moseyed over and checked out the box. He found a series of paperbacks that caught his interest called, "Mack Bolan, The Executioner." The books were about a Viet Nam veteran sharpshooter who is returned to the States on emergency leave and proceeds to wreck havoc upon the Mafia. He figured the easy reading fiction would provide him another measure of fantasy escape from the stark reality that was quickly becoming routine.

Upon returning to the 2nd Platoon area, later, Joe found already gathered were Wilson and the team leaders, except The Professor, who was in the field. He was glad to find the men joking, laughing and generally in high spirits.

After Dunn gave his update briefing, Wilson said, "Sir, the team leaders have something for you."

"First Lieutenant Joseph Dunn," ceremoniously stated SSG Peter Dobkowski, "the team leaders of 2nd Platoon have deemed that you, sir, are not in the proper goddamn uniform; and, therefore, you do not reflect the high standard that befits your position as platoon leader of 2nd Platoon."

"Therefore," continued Forest, "in recognition of your successful completion of a field mission with Double Deuce..."

"And, furthermore," interrupted Parvis, "as a tribute of our support and commitment to you..."

"We present you this Ranger Black Beret!" shouted Ski, handing him a new Black Beret embroidered with a subdued Ranger tab and a subdued First Lieutenant bar.

"Hoooahhh, Hoooahhh! Ahhoogaa!" They all gave him a round of Ranger cheers.

Surprised, Joe at first didn't know what to say. He smiled, put on his new beret and began to stammer, "Thhank you..." Then he was cut short. All the men surrounded him and unceremoniously ushered him over to the 3rd Platoon conex bar, where he was forced to buy a round of drinks for everybody, except for Swenson. The Mad Swede's team was going to the field the next day, and a Ranger did *not* drink or take any kind of drugs for two days *before* going into the field.

Dunn hung around the bar for over an hour, nursing his one drink and truly had a great and enjoyable time. He was amazed at how much hard liquor these men could put away. But since he was going to be flying Command & Control the next day, he was careful not to even finish his one drink. He had promised himself that he would *not* allow himself to be sick in the Birddog, no matter what maneuvers the pilot performed. So, he knew he needed both a clear head and a good night's rest. A hangover was definitely out of the question.

When he decided to leave, the men kidded him for being the first, not scheduled for the field, to leave the party. He good-naturedly thanked them once again and headed for his tent, thinking, *I sure have a lot of good things to write home to Marie, tonight.*

Arriving at his tent, he was pleased to note that it, too, had been surrounded and fortified with sandbags by his men. After finding and turning on his light bulb, but before he could get out the writing paper, he heard Swenson calling to him. "Hey, Lieutenant Dunn, I thought you would want to know tonight, rather than tomorrow, that the new recruit, PFC Daniel Smith, is sick and cannot go to the boonies tomorrow morning."

"What do you mean he is sick? What is the matter with him? Take me to him."

"No, sir, that is not necessary. He is just not feeling well and should not go."

"Sergeant Swenson, I insist you take me to him. Are you going to tell me what is really going on? Is he actually sick? If he is, I want to see him. If it's something else, you might as well tell me now, because you know I am going to find out." Before Swenson could answer, Dunn passed him, going down the hill towards the platoon area.

"Hold on, sir," Swenson said, running after him. "Let me explain before you go. As you know, the team always gets together the night before an early morning insert to go over the fine details. You know what I mean, the positions in the route of the march, the responsibilities in an ambush site, the procedure for crossing an open trail, the hand signals we use and a dozen other things.

"Well, fucking Smith knew when and where we were getting together, but he was a 'no-show.' He was nowhere to be found, so the team split up to go looking for him. When we found him, the fucker was smoking marijuana and was stoned. We beat the living shit out of him as there is no way that fucking bastard's going with us! No cock-sucking pothead is going to freak out my team because he's still under the effects of a fucking weed! I'm afraid the whole team just went off on him. You know we have to be able to rely on one another. That selfish bastard could get us all killed. Sir, can't we just say that he is 'sick,' because he has to be fucking sick in the head for doping up before a mission?"

"Thanks for coming to me, Sergeant Swenson, replied Dunn. "Go settle your team down and get them ready to go into the field tomorrow without Smith. I will take care of PFC Smith."

By the time he walked down to the platoon area, he found a heavily bandaged Smith out front with Wilson, who had collected and packed all of the man's personal belongings.

"Sir, I was just coming to get you," Wilson began. Private Smith has requested a transfer out of the unit. He wants to be assigned to the 173rd Airborne Brigade."

"Roger that, Platoon Sergeant. I will see to it that this young man's request receives immediate command attention. There are some empty bunks with the headquarters element. Ask Staples if he will allow a boarder for one night as a favor to me. Then, see to it that PFC Smith reports to TOC first thing in the morning, and I do mean *first thing*. That means he is *not* to go to the mess for breakfast or any other place. He is to stand by the TOC prepared to depart the unit. He is *not* to move from the TOC unless given specific instructions by me," Dunn ordered before he headed for the TOC.

"Yes, sir," said Wilson, who then turned to Smith. "You heard the lieutenant. Grab your gear and follow me."

Dunn found Wayne enjoying a drink of his private stock and holding court outside the entrance to the TOC. He was entertaining a small group, including Rod Winthrop and two Warrant Officer pilots that had stopped by for a visit.

After a few minutes Joe drew the major aside and explained for his ears only, "Sir, PFC Smith, the new recruit, is wanting an *immediate* transfer to the 173rd." However, if he was not asked, he saw no reason to volunteer any information about motives. But he emphatically stated, "Sir, I am *strongly* endorsing his wishes and ask for a favorable and *speedy* acquiescence to the request for transfer."

"No problem, lieutenant," said the major in a loud voice, intentionally, so all could hear. "I do not want any goddamn soldier who does not want to be a Ranger. Have him report to the TOC tomorrow morning. I will personally send his sorry ass to join his Leg buddies with The Herd."

Decisive, thought Dunn, *a "take-charge" kind of commander who can get things done. That's the kind of support we line platoon leaders crave.*

When Joe got back to his tent, he lay on his cot and paused to reflect on this latest occurrence. *The members of Team 24 reacted purely out of a sense of self-preservation. They weren't making a statement against drugs... they would have reacted the same way if Smith had been drunk on whiskey when they found him. With their own lives in the balance, members of the team must be reliable, which means being both physically and mentally ready for an ambush mission. The informal code demands that no man use any substance, drug or alcohol, for two days prior to a field mission. Clearly, the men adequately enforced their own law.*

I wonder what value was served by the Old Man's policy of unannounced searches for illegal drugs. The searches never seem to uncover drugs; although I'm certain drugs are being used.

It is simply too easy to get any drug as they are all too plentiful and cheap. The enemy probably makes pure heroin available and cheap to American troops as a tactical measure. Then I'm sure they use the money from the sale of drugs to buy weapons...

For the short time Dunn had been with the unit, he thought the much bigger problem was alcohol. Even the senior officers and especially the senior NCO's imbibed rather heavily nearly every night. *Well, my preferred methods of escape would be reading fiction, sleep and sweet dreams of Marie. Speaking of Marie, I'm going to write a short note to my lovely wife before going to sleep... then I will be sure and dream of her.*

Joe wrote the short letter to Marie and shared with her the especially good things of the day and before signing, reminded her he could use some more Kool-Aid. When he turned off the light and reclined on his cot, he was still wide-awake but didn't want to dwell on thoughts of the past day nor did he want to torture himself with longing for Marie. The discussions at dinner with the other lieutenants about his travels to South America were a reminder of pleasant times during his days as a cadet. So, that is where he decided he would now allow his mind to wander; he would escape into his memories...

❦

After each school year, Cadets were granted 30 days leave in the summer. Instead of going home, he used his leave time to travel. After his Plebe year, he caught a, "space available flight" to Hawaii, where he celebrated turning the magical age of twenty-one. Somehow, he felt robbed of entitlement since the legal drinking age was only twenty on the islands.

While waiting for the flight to Hawaii, he was amazed at the announcements of available seats for numerous exotic destinations. The lone requirement to embark was to be in uniform with travel orders that enumerated the flight's destination.

When it came time to submit for leave the following year, his Yearling year, he listed every country in the world as "destination." The Academy lined out Cuba, Russia, Viet Nam and other prohibited locations before issuing him cadet leave papers.

Dunn's research led him to Charleston AFB, where he hoped to catch an early morning diplomatic shuttle to London, England. Unfortunately, the flight was transporting ammunition and would not take on any passengers. But, fortunately, the next flight was already being announced.

The destination of that following flight turned out to be Rio de Janeiro and had room for only one passenger. *I am going to Rio!* he had delightedly exclaimed to himself.

While in Rio, Joe learned some history of Brazil. Other interesting experiences were: The music, by Portuguese-speaking students from Sao Paulo; hitchhiking a ride from a German-speaking former nazi; stripping off his Levi jeans and selling them on the street for an exorbitant price near the Ipanema Beach. He thoroughly enjoyed the people and definitely planned on returning.

Finally, relaxed in his tent and on his cot, Dunn escaped into a much needed, deep sleep.

7
Cherry Flight

I N THE MORNING, DUNN PURPOSELY SKIPPED breakfast, as he wanted as little in his stomach as possible to help him from throwing up on his cherry flight in the Birddog plane. He was up earlier than usual but was not surprised to find the gear of Team 24 lined up outside the platoon hooch. The members of the team had gone to the mess to insure that they were the first in line. There were no special considerations given in line as it was always first come, first served. It was also tough luck on any item that might run out. However, to be fair about it, there was rarely any shortage, even of specially prepared or baked items.

After breakfast, the team members were in exceptionally good spirits and kidded him and each other about staying out in the field for a week just so they could get away from Wilson's sandbag details. They also voiced their pride and confidence and exclaimed they intended to prove they were the best team in the entire company.

"We'll give you a great bird's eye view of how to execute a fucking 'Hatchet' on Charlie," said SGT Jorge "Hilltopper" Torres. "Just follow the tracers from my M-60. It'll be like the 4th of July back home!"

"Great! I'll definitely be watching," Dunn said before leaving for the TOC.

When he arrived at the TOC, Staples informed him, "Smith's paperwork has already been sent to The Herd and the night crew reported no significant activities or changes. Since Seahorse is waiting at the airfield, I instructed the major's driver to take you there in the jeep."

"Thank you, Staples. You sure have everything under control. See you later," Joe said before heading for the waiting jeep.

The coolness of the morning had already begun to dissipate in the wake of the high humidity and heat. Even on the jeep ride he had to brush beads of sweat away from his eyes.

"Jim Wails is my name." The pilot reached out to shake Dunn's hand as he approached the parked Cessna Birddog. "Are you with the LRRP outfit?"

"I'm Joe Dunn and I've been looking forward to this. Have you flown for Charlie Rangers before?"

"No, but I have worked with other LRRP outfits, so I am familiar with how you guys operate. I understand this is your first time up in a Birddog, so let me give you a quick briefing on the aircraft. First of all, don't worry about Charlie shooting us down in this plane. This baby can take a hundred hits and keep flying. It would take a helluhva lucky shot to bring it down. The top speed is 115 mph, and our range is 530 miles. I was told to bring an extra helmet for you. You'll find it on your seat. Any questions before we go tour this beautiful country?"

"I'm ready when you are."

"One more thing," Wails cautioned, "if you feel nauseous at first, that's normal, and you should soon get past that feeling. However, if you do have to throw up, then stick your head out the window and let'er rip. Don't worry, the wind will blow it away and not leave a trace."

Dunn climbed up and into the cramped quarters of the back seat and was soon followed by Wails as he settled into the frontseat. While Wails started the single propeller and taxied in position for a take-off, Dunn did his first job, that of setting the various radio frequencies as previously directed. He dialed in the unit frequency on the closest switch, then the slicks, gunships and finally the artillery base, leaving the other two stations unprogrammed.

"We're up," Wails stated over the intercom as they lifted off. "Looks like this is going to be another beautiful day."

"Smooth as silk and great visibility; I think I am going to like this," Dunn said, rather surprised how much at ease he felt.

"We're heading north to northeast for approximately 40 kilometers to the area you specified. I have a general idea of the area you want, but let me know when you spot anything you recognize," informed Wails.

Dunn responded as he looked around, "Actually, I do recognize the features of the approach path we are on. Looks like we are right on course and in about twenty minutes should be joined by the Devil and Demon slicks for the first team insertion."

Other than an occasional air pocket that caused the plane to momentarily shift up or down, the ride was not in the least upsetting to Dunn. The view was breathtaking and from their high, distant vantage point, the man-made structures below looked clean and brightly spotlighted by the brilliant sun. The mountain peaks looked closer and inviting and the lush jungle looked like thick, green carpeting. From above, everything they saw appeared peaceful and unblemished. Joe was relieved he could readily identify the features on the ground and relate them to his map.

Joe notified the pilot, "Okay, we are approaching the site of our radio relay team. I see it dead ahead and to the right. We need to come to our right about ten degrees."

"Roger that." Wails put the plane into a relatively steep bank to the right as he said, "While we have time, let me show you a little of what this plane can do. If you're going to be flying C & C, you need to get a feel for the plane so you can learn how to keep your bearings."

All of a sudden, the horizon disappeared from Dunn's view and centrifugal force yanked his body but left his stomach behind. By the time his stomach caught up with his body, he felt as if he were floating weightless above his seat. Just as abruptly, the plane repeated the same pattern but in the opposite direction. Dunn now felt light-headed and couldn't tell which way was up.

Where is the ground? he wondered as he fought back the sick feeling that welled up from his bowels and reached into his stomach. Focusing on one point, the back of the pilot's head, Dunn stretched out his arms against both sides of the cockpit in order to help steady himself.

At about the same time he regained his bearings, he tasted bile that rose involuntarily into and filled his mouth-yucky and acidic. Tightly clenching his teeth and sealing his lips together, he forced himself to swallow it back down where it sloshed in his empty stomach. He needed fresh air, so he reached to prop open both side windows. When he cracked open the left window, Wails looked back at him with a smirk and gave a quizzical expression as if he expected to see Dunn's head out the window.

But Wails was doomed to disappointment that day. Instead, Dunn matter-of-factly commented, "I lost my bearings for a moment, but I think you gave me a pretty good feel for the plane. We have got to go back to the left to be in the area we are to work today... by the way, at any time were we upside down?" Dunn prayed his head would quickly clear. No way was he going to allow that wretched tasting bile to reach his mouth again.

"We were every which way for a little bit. You look a pale green, are you alright?" innocently asked the pilot.

"I feel like I'm dark OD. But now that I found the horizon again and have some fresh air, I'm fine. How are you feeling?"

Laughing, Wails replied, "Since you're asking, I'm just fine and looking forward to going to work. I promise the rest of the day will be calm and comfortable flying."

Switching on the closest radio setting, Dunn decided to contact the radio relay site below him. "X-ray, this is Forkball 28, commo check. Over."

"Forkball 28, this is X-ray, we hear you Lima Charlie. That was some show. Tell your frontseat we rate him a big One Zero, a real ace. Over."

"X-ray, this is Forkball 28. Roger. Out." Then, switching to the inter-com, he passed on the message to Wails. "The guys on the ground salute you for the aerial display. They obviously enjoyed it a lot more than I did." All Joe heard in response was a chuckle.

Following the second ridgeline east of the X-ray position, Dunn directed the pilot to the sector where Team 24 was to work. Once they were in sight of the sector, he was relieved he so easily located the pre-determined Landing Zone. He knew the slicks from the 134thAssault Helicopter Company would be arriving directly from the south so he switched on the frequency for the Devils and Demons, who would soon be approaching with the team.

Everywhere Joe looked, the vegetation in this sector was almost entirely triple canopy. *Now I know to what they have been referring all this time. Fortunately, the five-man team is all in one chopper, as that is about all that could fit into this particular diamond-shaped LZ.*

As if on cue, the slick carrying the team made a radio call. "This is Demon Niner Two calling Forkball in the Oscar One. Over," making a reference to the "0-1" aircraft in which Dunn was flying C & C.

"Demon Niner Two, this is Forkball 28, what is your status? Over."

"Forkball 28, this is Demon Niner Two, we should be five away from your location. When you spot us, we will go to canopy and use your eyes. Over."

"Demon Niner Two, roger, I have your party in sight." Tapping on Wails' right shoulder, Dunn pointed to the distant, approaching, four helicopters and signaled for the pilot to swing around so they would be over the descending helicopters and in the same direction of flight towards the LZ. "Maintain your current direction. You are eight hun-dred away. Over."

"Forkball 28, this is Demon Niner Two. Roger, eight hundred and closing. Over"

"Demon Niner Two, come right five degrees. You are six hundred away. Maintain current heading. You are four hundred away now. Good. You are two hundred away. Come right two degrees. Perfect. One hun-dred now...fifty...twenty-five...ten...this is Forkball 28. Over."

"Forkball 28, package delivered. Thanks for the heads up approach. We are now heading back. This is Demon Niner Two. Out."

The light was flashing on the closest radio switch. Dunn assumed it was Team 24, who had just been inserted and was following good proce-dure after insertion by making a radio check. He switched the flashing signal and suddenly heard, "Contact!" The RTO for Team 23 screamed. "This is Forkball 23! Contact! I say again, Contact! This is Forkball 23! Contact! Over!"

Even before first light of day, every member of Team 23 had been wide-awake. SP/4 Roger Goldstein convinced the Professor, his team leader, to allow him to determine the placement of the Claymore mines and to control their detonation with the wire clacker. This made Goldstein feel a great deal better. After the team spotted the heavily used trails the evening before, he had sensed the pressure of an impending anxiety attack. He thought, *I'm in this field with a bunch of newbies! Sure, the Professor is a kind-hearted, talented and wonderful NCO, but The Professor has only been to the field a few times...he seemed to do everything right. But, how would he react in a firefight?*

Goldstein reminded himself, *I have been In Country over 22 months straight and have been on countless missions and in six, separate contacts. When it counted most, I have seen big talkers freeze up and it cost the life of my good, beautiful friend, and I was there and saw the ugly, haunting face of death. That fatality was because a Ranger hesitated to kill...but not me! Now I live to kill!*

Once again he swore revenge and fought back the anxiety. *I think today might be a day of atonement for the damn Viet Cong!*

Soon the team came across a trail that showed signs of heavy use. It took the 6-man team nearly a full, half hour to slowly, carefully and yet without a trace, cross the path one at a time to reach some boulders on the far side. The boulders provided a secure and natural bunker from where they could oversee an ambush.

Once the team was in place, Goldstein crawled out to position twelve, Claymore mines, hiding each behind a clump of grass. Using detonation cord, he linked each mine together. During this entire time, he was fully exposed to any enemy and totally dependent on his cherry teammates for protection. Finally, he crawled back to the safety of the boulders with the wire that gave him control. Now he could fire all twelve mines with a single squeeze of the clacker.

After about two, long hours of waiting, the cherry, PFC William Armstrong, suddenly gave the hand signal to the team that he had heard something. He cupped his ear and pointed. The team intently listened and watched. Breathing slowly, every man readied himself. Sure enough, they soon picked up the sound of voices and even some laughter. Then, one by one, six uniformed North Vietnamese Army Regulars emerged from the trees and walked up the trail. There were three men and three women, and all were armed.

To Goldstein, they were not humans out for a stroll, but just vicious animals walking to their own slaughter. *No one on the team is to fire. They are to wait. Wait until the entire group is in the kill zone directly in front of me. I will be the one to cause their world to explode into a million pieces. Wait...his heart pounds. Wait...he held his breath. His grip tightened. Now!*

BALOOMM! BALOOMM! BALOOMM!

As all twelve mines exploded, down went two of the enemy, dead from the blasts. The bee-bees punched hundreds of holes into their fragile, tiny bodies.

Bam, Bam, Bam, Bam! Billy Armstrong was the first to fire his M-16 at the four who were shaken or wounded, but not killed by the blast. The rest of the team quickly followed suit, raking killing fire into the entire zone in front of them.

The Professor instructed the RTO to radio in the contact and then instructed the men to cease-fire. There was no retaliation... only a few audible death moans. No movement came from the bodies strewn along the path and blood quickly gathered in pools around the dead and dying.

Goldstein waved his arm with his palm down, motioning to the men to stay while he duck-walked his way to the kill zone. As he waddled, he kept his rifle poised and ready to fire. Then, still in a squat and holding his rifle with his elbows between his knees, he methodically fired a well-aimed shot into the head of each enemy soldier. When he reached the furthest soldier down the trail, she turned her face to him, and he put a bullet right between her eyes.

Then he rose into a huddled crouch, looked back and didn't want to believe his eyes. His teammates were nonchalantly walking up and down the trail just looking at the dead. *This was when the Rangers were sitting ducks; this was when most guys bought it. Who is watching the perimeter?* Then, and only then, did he realize there were only five bodies on the trail, not six!

Bam! Bam! Two shots rang out.

Billy Armstrong had also left the boulders with the rest of the team; however, he instinctively took up a security position to guard his assigned sector. His new position gave him a better view of the flank, up the tree-lined path where the enemy had first emerged. As he scanned the area, he detected movement and spotted one of the female soldiers rising to her feet against a tree. With her weapon in her hands, she raised it in preparation to fire on his team. Both of his shots found their mark, and she died instantly.

🕊

"Forkball 23, this is Forkball 28, Contact Sitrep. Over." Dunn asked for a "situation report" from Team 23 to relay to the TOC. When he switched over to the unit frequency, he expected to simply perform a commo check for Team 24. Instead, he was shocked to hear Team 23 was in contact. Team 24 would be monitoring with a great interest, but would be smart enough not to cut in for a mere commo check.

"Forkball 28, this is Forkball 23." He recognized the new voice as that of the Professor. "We request chariots to get us. We confirm six unfriendly, and we have six trophies. Contact is concluded. No friendly casualties. Request suppressing fire to cover extraction. Over."

"Forkball 23, this is Forkball 28, the chariots and spear-chuckers are already in the arena. Pop smoke when you are ready. Over."

Dunn switched over to the frequency of the slick, figuring it could not have flown too far. "Demon Niner Two, this is Forkball 28. Over."

"Forkball 28, this is Demon Niner Two, we have been monitoring. When we identify, Devils are ready to go hot. Then, we'll be happy to pick up hitchhikers. Over."

Aircraft were equipped with UHF radios but the Devils and Demons must have carried an VHF radio with them so as to listen in on the frequencies used by the teams. Therefore, they had turned around, and were ready to provide gunship support after they identified the color of the smoke marking the exact location of the team.

A constant concern frequently expressed by gunship pilots was inflicting casualties on a friendly. Therefore, he would not commence his gun run until he knew exactly where the team was located. Then, he would further make certain not to fire too close to them.

After collecting the enemy weapons and stripping the bodies of anything remotely valuable to the TOC, the Professor motioned for the team to saddle up and "di di mau." As they made their way across the trail and through the trees to the north, they heard the approaching choppers. Since heavy forests surrounded the large clearing ahead, they could not risk having the aircraft simply fly in and pull them out. That is why he had requested the 0-1 to direct the gunship to pepper the far tree line. When he popped the smoke as directed, the 0-1 properly identified sunflower yellow as the color. Almost immediately, two gunships went to work. What a beautiful sight to behold! The team excitedly watched. They didn't fire any rockets, just their mini-guns. The sound was like a very long, very amplified burp. Small trees were felled and after the devastating sweep by the gunships, the Huey made its approach. As soon as the skids touched ground, the team and their booty were on, and the slick was immediately airborne again.

The members of Team 23 sang and shouted at the tops of their lungs and high-fived each other all the way home as the Demon's door gunner watched their antics in stunned silence. Then they asked the pilot to fly over the Charlie Ranger hill before landing at the airstrip. When he complied, they popped and dropped a red smoker they had tied to the chopper skid with a length of string.

"These fuckers are crazy," said the door gunner over the intercom. "But, the fly-by with trailing red smoke attached is definitely cool!"

"Forkball 24, this is Forkball 28. Over." Now that the excitement had settled, Dunn checked in with the team that had been recently inserted.

"Forkball 28, this is Forkball 24. Tell 23 we send congratulations to our brothers! We were listening to the sitrep. Are you still in the air? Over."

"Forkball 24, this is Forkball 28. Wilco. I will be on station for another six zero, but will be back again later today. Did you find any Tangos? Over." Dunn would comply later with their request regarding Team 23, but he was now curious if they had found any trails.

"Forkball 28, this is Forkball 24. Roger that. Beau coup Tangos, so glad that you are up. Over."

"This is Forkball 28. Out."

Ending the transmission with the team, he flipped on the intercom. "Jim, let's head back over to the area above X-ray, over there to the left. It's a central location for the different teams working the sectors below. I appreciate the job you did for me this morning. You kept a good vantage point and allowed me to have a great view."

"Thanks, my job is a lot easier than yours. It's hard to believe this is your cherry flight. I have to tell you just based on your performance this morning, you are one of the better observers I have worked with. So, here's hoping your unit is saving us some food for a late lunch by the time we get back."

It was then Dunn realized, *I've lost that light-headed feeling and sense of nausea. Perhaps I'm not yet acclimated to the infernal heat, but I do know I am comfortable in the back seat of a Birddog.*

He spent the rest of the fast, disappearing hour marveling at the beauty of the dense jungle below. When he listened in to some transmissions between the teams and X-ray, he found he gained a respect for Jim, who clearly enjoyed flying this particular fixed-wing aircraft and was proud of his role in serving his country.

Joe found himself relaxing. For the very first time, he wished he were at the controls of the plane and that he could fly. *Maybe I could get my frontseats to teach me. I suspect there will be plenty of time as I figure I'll be doing a lot of flying C & C.*

When they did return for refueling, they had just enough time to eat a quick lunch that had been specifically set-aside, waiting for them. The next patrol, Team 31, was already at the airstrip waiting for instructions to load into the chopper. So, with no further fear of filling his starving belly, Dunn woofed down the delicious meal.

They were soon airborne again and back flying over now familiar terrain. The second insertion of the day was as uneventful and smooth as the first. Since no team reported anything out of the ordinary, the Devils and Demons returned to their base.

When Dunn learned Wails would be flying frontseat for him the next day, he was delighted and spoke the idea running around in his head. "Say, Jim, I've been thinking... How about giving me a flying lesson tomorrow, provided the teams cooperate with a quiet day?"

"Sounds like you have been bit by the bug," replied Wails. "Sure, I'd be glad to show you some of the ropes."

"Great!" exclaimed an excited Joe. *I've exacted a promise of a first lesson in flying,* and Joe hugged the new idea close.

With only half an hour of on-station time remaining, their peaceful flight was shattered by a frantic call. "Contact! This is Forkball 24, Contact! Forkball 28, this is Forkball 24, please come in! Contact! Over!"

"Forkball 24, this is Two Eight, contact. Roger. Sitrep. Over." Even though the TOC would not be able to hear the transmission from Team 24 directly, it should have been monitoring his transmissions, which is why he had repeated the word, "contact."

"This is Forkball 24, we need gunships now! We are under fire. We have one man wounded. I say again. We are receiving fire. Small arms fire only. At least eight unfriendly... maybe more. Send us gunships and get us the fuck out of here! Over!"

"Forkball 24, this is Forkball 28. Roger. Stand by. Over. Forkball 3, this is Forkball 28. Over."

"Forkball 28, this is Forkball 3, Devils and Demons are in the air, enroute to your location. Over."

Good old Staples! He was monitoring and has already scrambled the choppers. But...it will take them valuable minutes to get here and the team needs help now, Dunn thought.

Without being told, Wails had also been listening and had navigated the Birddog back to the area where Team 24 had originally been inserted.

"Forkball 24, this is Two Eight, guns and slicks are on the way. Do not pop smoke. Use the mirror. Over."

There was still a bright enough sun in the late day's sky to pick up the flash from the mirror below. Not knowing the situation, he did not want the team to expose their exact location to the enemy with smoke until the gunships were on station.

"Two Four, this is Two Eight, I have you. What direction and how far from you is the enemy? Over."

Then, switching to the intercom, Dunn asked, "Jim, did you see their signal mirror? How accurate are your rockets? I am going to call for artillery. In the meantime, can we do anything?"

"I've got them spotted, Joe. Soon as they answer, we can line up for a shot. We're not a gunship, but we can help them with a couple of rockets!"

"Two Eight, this is Two Four, the fuckers are south, southwest of us. They are on the other side of the trail. The bastards are in the goddamn trees across the clearing about sixty meters away. Where is that fucking gunship? Over."

"Got it. We're going in for a shot now!" Wails put the plane into a shallow dive.

"Two Four, this is Two Eight, rockets away. Where do you want the next ones? Over." Knowing that Wails was listening to the team, he would automatically make the necessary adjustments for the next pass and fire another set of rockets from under the wings of the 0-1. Dunn wanted to call in immediate artillery support, which he would adjust after he saw the splash of the round. So, he switched to the preset artillery frequency.

"Deadly Dealer 2, this is Forkball 28, Fire Mission! Over."

॰

It was late afternoon at Fire Support Base Mustang, a hilltop, miles away. Cannoneers were busy cleaning equipment or playing cards. Suddenly, the sound of a siren rang through the air. An FO, Forward Observer, had radioed for immediate artillery fire support. The men of the 7th Battalion, 15th Artillery, scrambled to action, living up to their motto, "You Yell, We Shell Like Hell!"

"Forkball 28, this is Deadly Dealer 2, roger transmission. Send coordinates. Over." The artillery Fire Direction Center would compute the correct trajectory from the transmitted coordinates. Then the computed information would be given directly to the gun crews, who could send eight-inch shells on their way in moments. Certain death rained upon anybody within 80 meters of impact.

"Deadly Dealer 2, this is Forkball 28, plot Bravo Oscar Five Five One, Four Seven Two; One Round, Hotel Echo. Over."

Despite the uncanny accuracy, Dunn had called for the High Explosive round to explode at least one hundred fifty meters distant from the team. The large killing zone and the devastation of the impact would still disrupt the enemy. He would then adjust by creeping the rounds closer to the team.

Forkball 28, this is Deadly Dealer 2. Shot. Over." The artillery let Dunn know that they had fired one round to hit the requested coordinates.

KA...BLAMM! KA...BLAMM! The two rockets from the 0-1 slammed into the forest directly behind from where the enemy was firing.

"Great shooting, but that's not much more firepower than our fucking Blooper," yelled The Mad Swede, upset and angry.

CARR...RRUMP! The earth shook.

"Holy Fuck! What was that? Where did that hit?" asked the Swede.

"Deadly Dealer 2, this is Forkball 28. Drop fifty, Foxtrot, Foxtrot, Echo. Over." Dunn was calling for the artillery to shift 50 meters closer to the team and to "Fire For Effect," to fire with the entire battery of guns.

"Forkball 24, this is Two Eight, keep your heads down for incoming Red Leg support! Do you copy? Over."

"Two Eight, this is Two Four. Roger that. Over."

CARR...RRUMP! CARR...RRUMP! CARR...RRUMP! CARR... RRUMP! CARR...RRUMP!

The team hugged the earth as it shook, swayed, splattered, spewed and spit at them with harmless pieces of itself. The ear-splitting sounds of the explosions were deafening. Then, as abruptly as it had begun, it stopped. Silence... eerie silence.

Then the team members cautiously and carefully looked at one another. SGT Ricky "BJ" Bevis called out with a plaintiff cry that was part moan and part scream. The wound in his groin was bleeding profusely. Swenson immediately went to BJ, ripped apart his trousers and applied bandages and wrapping to stop the flow of blood. Motioning to the rest of the men to carry his and BJ's gear, he helped the wounded Ranger move deeper into the trees.

Moving south, they fled as quickly as they could through the heavy brush and dense forest. There was a large opening forty meters away that Swenson knew would serve nicely as an extraction Landing Zone. The team had walked all the way around it earlier that morning.

What a goddamn, fucking, lousy place to get shot! Swenson thought about BJ. *He is either the bravest man in the world or suffering from shock. How can he not be screaming in agony? What fucking bad luck! Just a few more minutes and BJ would have been back behind the cover and concealment of the ambush site. We were getting ready to pack up to leave when those fuckers chanced upon us and hastily fired. Oh, shit! We left behind the Claymores that BJ was collecting. Fuck 'em! I hope the artillery destroyed them and all the gooks, too.*

Bevis clutched tightly to his team leader. "Hang on, BJ. We're almost there, Buddy." The Mad Swede spoke words of encouragement to Bevis, whom he was now practically carrying. By now the bandaging was completely blood-soaked. "I hear the choppers. You only have to walk a few more steps."

Finally reaching the clearing, The Mad Swede yelled to his RTO to pop smoke and call for the choppers to come in to get them. Once again, the Gunship raked the far side of the clearing and the area the team had just departed. The only thing this team noticed was the approaching slick coming to get them the hell out of there.

"Deadly Dealer 2, this is Forkball 28. Mission Complete. You saved the day. Thank you. I will provide details on the landline. Over."

"Forkball 28, that's a big roger. We'll be looking forward to your call. Glad to deliver our help. Deadly Dealer 2. Out."

Dunn next alerted X-ray the Birddog was returning to base and would check back with them the next day.

"Okay, Jim, take us home," Joe said, rather pleased with what they had been able to do.

After Wails dropped Dunn off, he flew on to his own camp at Dong Ba Tin Airbase. But Joe had a nearly forty minute wait at the airstrip before getting a ride back to camp.

By the time he got back to the unit, the Operations Briefing at the Tactical Operations Center was nearly concluded. He found out he would fly C & C again tomorrow, and that Lee would be flying C & C the following two days. Also that tomorrow, a new X-ray Team would perform a reconnaissance while the remaining two teams in the field were to be extracted. It was explained that the day after, the current X-ray would be extracted, and the new X-ray would be inserted at a location closer to new sectors to be worked. For Joe that meant he needed to spend time studying the maps again.

It was also announced that Sergeant Bevis would be all right but had lost one testicle and was medically evacuated to a hospital in the Philippines. Having served of his own accord with honor and dignity, his country would demand no further combat contribution from "BJ" Bevis.

Pancho, the Mess Sergeant, had saved a meal for Dunn and brought it over himself to the TOC. Dunn was truly amazed yet thankful at the level of service provided by Pancho to all the men of the company. That day he learned that if a man missed a meal because of pulling duty, Pancho invariably saved a bountiful helping for that man. It did not matter what was the rank of the man or what was the duty. He treated everybody as though they were five-star patrons.

While eating the scrumptious meal of fresh fish that had been fried to perfection, Dunn asked for and received from Staples copies of previous valor medals awarded to members of the unit. Dunn wanted samples of the various phrases and acceptable language successfully used in the past as he intended to make every possible effort to secure medals for the men who saw action. Coincidentally, they were all in his platoon, and he was a witness with a bird's eye view.

Staples further promised him, "Sir, the night crew on duty at the TOC will type the submissions for you."

"That would be wonderful, Staples. I want to personally submit the typed recommendations to the Old Man first thing in the morning."

When Joe left the TOC he headed over to the platoon hooch and was not at all surprised to find most of the men informally gathered. Even though they had probably already told their story a dozen times, the members of Team 23 recounted the details of their mission for Dunn's benefit. The men of the platoon listened attentively, as if hearing for the first time.

When each team member had recited his perspective on every single detail, the members of Team 24 took their turn. Dunn joined in on the teasing and kidding when each man finished, usually drawing some additional comments and laughter. However, he also made certain to praise each man with a sincerity they understood and appreciated.

Drawing Swenson aside for a private conversation, Dunn said, "I'm planning on putting Bevis in for a Bronze Star with "V" device, for valor, and for a Purple Heart. What do you think?"

"I concur but don't feel any other citations are warranted," Swenson said.

Then, Dunn asked The Professor to accompany him back to the TOC as he wanted a private and earnest conversation with Halloway concerning what valor medals should be requested and for which men. Following their short discussion, Dunn planned to stay in the TOC to write the narratives describing the valorous conducts. He requested a Bronze Star with "V," for valor, for Roger Goldstein and an Army Commendation with "V" device for Billy Armstrong.

Before The Professor left the TOC, he made a point to tell Dunn, "I'd love any other new recruit "Peaceniks" for my team." The Professor praised the performance of Billy Armstrong, calling him "A true Ranger with a red, white and blue heart."

While still in the TOC and before heading back to his tent, Dunn placed a landline telephone call to Fire Support Base Mustang. His call had been eagerly anticipated as the Cannoneers thrived on hearing firsthand reports on the results of their distant work. His every word was repeated to a waiting group, whose wild cheers were audible over the landline.

After the call, and even though it was dark, Joe was able to find his way back to his tent much easier than before. He wanted, more than anything, to crawl into his now, comfortable cot, but, since he was Duty Officer that night, instead, collected his nylon blanket and some toiletries and returned to the TOC.

An officer was on duty each night, which meant one of the platoon leaders pulled the duty every two to four nights. The Duty Officer periodically checked the perimeter guard towers and was available in the unlikely event a team got into trouble in the field. Most of the time, though, the Duty Officer was able to pull some quality sleeping time.

8
Letters from Home

URING THAT NIGHT, THERE WERE NO ADDITIONAL
situations or anything out of the ordinary and in the morning,
Dunn was delighted to find the folder with the citations typed
and waiting for him. Amazingly, there were no glaring typographical
errors or incorrect social security numbers. He hurried off to find the
Major, fully expecting him to be well pleased.

"Sir," he said, spotting the commander, who was outside his hooch
and looking nattily attired in another set of new camouflage fatigues,
"I wanted to personally deliver these to you before I have to take off in
the 0-1. These are the valor medal's recommendations for the men who
were in yesterday's contact."

"Great! Let me take a look right now. Let's see...you know...it's a
goddamn shame about Bevis. But you don't give a goddamn Bronze
Star to somebody just because he was in the wrong place at the wrong
time and gets shot. Lieutenant, I heard from the team...I know what
happened. But, we'll see.

"Now, as far as William Armstrong...this may be a bit premature. He
has only been with the unit a few days, and you are already putting him
in for a goddamn medal. You may be doing this young man an injus-
tice...as that's a lot for him to live up to for the rest of the year. By the
way, I don't want to see him wearing those goddamn love beads either.
I've heard about them.

"I am also surprised about Roger Goldstein. He has been with the
unit a long time and has not particularly distinguished himself. What
about the team leaders? You have nothing for the ones who led these
teams? Who looks out for the team leaders?

"Anyway, Dunn, I will give these proper consideration and will dis-
cuss this with my Tactical Operations Officer and with the Executive
Officer. In the meantime, consider what I have just told you. That's all,
Lieutenant." With that one-sided conversation concluded as far as he

was concerned, the Major swept past Dunn and headed into the TOC with the folder.

Stunned, Dunn just stood there as he realized he would not hear any more about these requests and just didn't understand. *Doesn't the Major want the men to get medals? Didn't he give specific instructions for the platoon leaders to put the men in for medals? What more should I have done? Put the team leaders name in for a medal whenever any of his team members is put in? I don't understand...whom else can I talk to?*

It would do no good to confront the Old Man, because he constantly gives me mixed signals. Well, Army regulations require the Old Man forward any recommendations, so there is still a chance the men will get their medals with or without the Old Man's positive endorsement.

No, even if the Old Man gives me grief, certainly he would send them forward with his concurrence. At least I hope so. To me, it seems obvious that the commander would look pretty good if a lot of the men he commanded received valor medals. So, of course, the commander will forward my recommendations with concurrence. But, why did he act as if he didn't intend to? Joe argued with himself.

§

"Good Morning, Jim," Dunn acknowledged after he watched the Birddog land, taxie over to him, and Wails beckoned for him to climb in. Putting on the flight helmet, he immediately switched on the intercom. "I had a great breakfast, so don't go showing me any fancy maneuvers today.

"There will be four choppers up this morning on a reconnaissance and we'll be involved in a team extraction this morning and one this afternoon. The rest of the time I hope will be smooth and uneventful so you can work with me on my flying lesson so I can work some more on becoming a rated pilot."

"Absolutely, Joe. I will have you flying as well as I do by the end of the day. There is a control stick fastened to the sidewall of the rear cockpit. When we have some spare time, I'll have you plug it in. In a few short hours, I can definitely teach you how to fly this beautiful bird. In the meantime, whenever we take off or land, I will talk you through exactly what it is I do. So, listen up, fly straight and rockets away!"

The events of the day unfolded without incident and the two extractions were performed almost routinely. In contrast with the hectic preceding day, this day could almost have been described as "boring."

Except to Dunn, it was exciting. The thrill of flying was an unexpected pleasure for him as he operated the plane from the back seat with the control stick between his legs. He learned the plane was yawed horizontally right and left by right and left pedals. A vertical stick placed in a shaft on the floor, like a gearshift in a car, dropped and pitched the plane forward and back and rolled it left and right. He performed the same maneuvers that had made him light-headed just the day before. Only now, when he actually was the one piloting the craft, he felt nothing but exhilaration.

Now, whenever he listened to or watched Wails, he did so with a different perspective, keener senses and a deeper respect. He had discovered a new love...flying. Now flying C & C was another form of escape for him.

With flying there was always something to do, something to keep his heart pounding and his mind racing. The ever-changing topography, alone, presented a map-reading challenge he relished. But all too soon, his foray into the wild blue was concluded, and his Ranger feet were trudging back up Charlie Ranger Hill.

The challenges and briefings of the day passed much too quickly, and he found himself in his tent, alone. However, the solitude right then was what he wanted as the first mail for him had arrived and was waiting on his cot. There were three letters from Marie as she had promised to write to him every, single day. He read and reread the letters over and over, savoring each word and especially the endearments. She wrote about their honeymoon in Mexico, Japan and Thailand and so he allowed his mind to wander and refresh his tired body. He escaped to a place far away, and yet, he had been there such a short time ago...

Funny, how different it was now. Just a short time ago, he was in this same part of the world without a care in the world and feeling as if he were the happiest man in the world. Marie had trusted him implicitly. Other than visiting relatives in Philadelphia, she had never traveled outside of New York. Heck, he had even seen more than she had of Long Island, where she had lived all her life. Now she was not hesitating to go to foreign countries without a set schedule and without set tickets. The first part of their honeymoon had been arranged. As a wedding gift, his folks gave them airline tickets from JFK Airport to Acapulco, Mexico.

It was after one o'clock Sunday morning by the time the newlyweds reached the JFK Marriott. Pops was going to have somebody drop him off later that day to pick up the car from the hotel parking lot.

Marie was shocked at the ferociousness with which Joe yelled at the night manager as he pointed at the hung painting of Mr. Marriott and threatened to call him directly. "It's 1:30 a.m." she pleaded with him, "What difference does it really make which room they give us?"

What she didn't know was Joe had secretly flown up from Ft. Bragg a month earlier to personally select and pay for the room where they would spend their very first night as husband and wife. The suite he chose faced east so the rising sun would shine through the expansive red curtains thus illuminating the entire room with a hue of red-Marie's favorite color.

It turned out the suite he chose was made up and available, after all; so he had wondered why they had caused him to display his temper. However, the stewardess on the flight to Mexico seven hours later more than made up for the hotel fiasco. She moved them to First Class, jokingly saying she had to balance the weight on the plane.

In 1965, Dunn's father was stationed at Camh Ranh Bay in Viet Nam and was cited for saving the life of a young soldier whose wealthy dad owned a summerhouse in Acapulco. The house was within view of a hacienda owned by the actor, John Wayne. As an additional wedding gift, Dunn's father arranged for the couple to use the house for a week, and it included use of a personal cook. The private location with its own pool and veranda was the perfect romantic setting for the start of their honeymoon.

After that first week, they flew to Mexico City because Marie was excited about visiting the Aztec pyramids, the Temple to the Moon, and the Plaza of the Sun. Since, at that time, Mexico City was hosting the World Championship Soccer Tournament and Mexico was a finalist, the taxi driver took them to the only place he knew had space-a converted convent.

Marie didn't mind and loved the quaint charm of the old buildings that formed a quad around an open garden. Dunn was less impressed with the lack of modern amenities, like screens on the open windows. Mexican soccer fan chants of "May-hee-co...May-hee-co!" and pesky mosquitoes only insured a sleepless night for Joe. The next morning he unceremoniously announced to Marie he refused to stay a moment longer in that convent. As Marie's long hair had screened her face from the mosquitoes, she slept like a baby. But she didn't mind where they would stay because she was looking forward to visiting the Mexico City Museum and the Aztec ruins.

There, they met up with another honeymooning couple from Canada and decided to join them for dinner at a bullfighting-training ranch. One side of the stadium served as an open restaurant where tourists could dine and "Ole'!" the neophyte matadors.

"Are there any brave-hearted guests who wish to experience the thrill of fighting the bull?" it was announced over the speakers.

Dunn couldn't believe he could fulfill a lifetime fantasy when he heard the announcement. Before Marie had a chance to stop him, Joe immediately volunteered... of course he was the only one brave enough, or stupid enough.

He was led below the stadium into a locker-style dressing room. Some ranch hands slapped him on the back and commended him in Spanish as they strapped full body-length leather chaps on him. He doubted body armor made of half-inch leather would offer him much protection but at least they did not restrict his ability to move or to run, if necessary.

One ranch hand placed a silly matador hat on his head. Another handed him the red cape and, with some smirking, offered some suggestions on its proper use. As they ushered him outside to the muddy pit, he understood their final laughing warning was not about the bull but was to watch where he stepped.

When he made his appearance, the small, tourist crowd of dining patrons gave him polite applause, which he acknowledged with a wave. He was glad to see two ranch hands on horses, and he noticed two others dressed as clowns near exit slots. On both sides of the horses were also draped leather protection. When he was escorted to the center, he was directed toward the gate at the north side. His escorts quickly retreated into the exit slots along the walls.

The bull was young as promised, but much, much larger than he had expected and with horns at least four inches long. The 300-pound bull did not charge, but simply meandered out into the evening sunshine. Dunn stuck the cape out far from his body and shook it. No response. Taking a few steps closer to the bull, he repeated the motion...still no response.

"Hey, Toro!" he finally shouted, as he vigorously shook the cape. That did it. The bull charged, lowering its head as it plowed through the cape. The crowd cheered. Repeating the same procedure brought the same results and the same cheers. Only this time, as the bull sped past, Joe flamboyantly swept the cape over the bull's back. He took the following pass on the other side of his body. As the bull thundered by, Dunn leaned his mid-section toward the bull, making it appear as if he were actually touching the massive animal. The tourists loved it, which egged him on. He extended his body as if doing a squat thrust with his left knee bent and his right leg nearly straight but his right knee actually touching the ground. They cheered wildly even before the bull made its clean pass. Then, making certain to keep his body perfectly still, Dunn dropped to both knees and waved the cape, jumping to his feet as soon as the bull's head passed him. When the bull turned to face him this time, he walked directly up to the head of the bull. There was no way he was going to push his luck or foolish bravado any further. Then he turned completely around and walked away, raising his right hand in triumph and dragging the cape on the ground behind him. What a ham he had been.

The crowd gave him a standing ovation. He threw a kiss to Marie. The clowns presented him with two bouquets of flowers that had been thrown into the ring. It was a good thing that Marie took some snapshots, or nobody would have ever believed him.

Back in Monterey, California, the newlyweds found themselves, upon their return from Mexico, sharing his folks' house with two bachelor officers attending the Naval Postgraduate School. The bachelors were "house-sitting" for Dunn's parents, who were now enjoying the Acapulco villa.

Marie was understandably nervous and uncomfortable. In addition, each arm had just received three separate vaccinations, including Yellow Fever and Bubonic Plague, which the army required before she could get on any "space available flights." So, Joe took her out to dinner at Fishermen's Wharf for their lone-nights stay there. He nursed his one glass of wine but kept refilling hers... so she felt no pain when he tucked her into bed that night.

The next morning they luckily waited less than one hour at Travis Air Force Base before catching a free military flight to Yokohama AFB, Japan, with a short stopover in Guam for fuel.

His memories of their ten-day stay in Japan were already beginning to blur. Unfortunately, the photo lab ruined two rolls of their film, which included all the shots from Japan. Kodak merely sent back a letter of apology with a certificate for two new rolls. Big deal and thanks for nothing!

While in Tokyo, they stayed in a swank hotel that also served as the Army Officers Club. Joe savored the Kobe steaks in the Genghis Kahn dining room and Marie enjoyed the thick, ice cream shakes served in the snack bar.

On the second night there, they were nearly caught up in aggressive anti-American demonstrations. He was still amazed at how well outfitted, how well trained, and how fiercely the Japanese Police Force dealt with the angry crowds. Not too many countries, he suspected, had military armies as proficient as were the Japanese Police.

The shopping in Tokyo had been fantastic and they purchased his and hers Seiko watches for twenty dollars each. He was wearing his now. It glowed in the dark and never needed winding, so it was perfect for use in the jungle.

He remembered how happy Marie had been when he absolutely insisted she purchase a double strand necklace of Mikimoto pearls. It was one of only two luxury items on the whole trip that she allowed him to buy for her.

She thought he was just being terribly patient, but he really enjoyed watching her meticulously search, measure and gauge the quality of each pearl used in stringing her necklace. *Lucky pearls! The chosen ones would gain luster and beauty each time she clasped them on to grace and adorn her exquisite skin,* he mused.

Some schoolgirls in Kyoto spotted her beauty and twenty or thirty of them separated the couple, surrounded her and squealed for her autograph. She had been wearing a black wig with a short, pageboy cut that made her look surprisingly oriental and with her porcelain, white face, had blushed at the adoration of the young fans, and she had pleaded for him to intercede. Left unnoticed, he had just laughed and proclaimed this was just more proof she was adorable and irresistible. He insisted she was the reason the Japanese people had remarkably and courteously provided them extra space on the sardine-packed trains.

Marie cheered when she learned the bullet trains had Western style bathrooms. But, she was slightly dismayed to discover the simple method in which one determined if the bathroom was in use-one merely peered through the diamond-shaped window in the door. So, she made him stand guard duty to block the window.

Their treatment at the Expo, however, was not as pleasant due to the fact they were not treated with any special politeness in the lines of the pavilions, which happened to be in Osaka while they were there.

The ten days in Japan evaporated as if they were only a single day. All too soon they were headed back to Yokohama AFB to wait for space to fly to Thailand. The day they first arrived in Japan, they had signed up. So, after ten days they found they were now at the top of the list. But, unfortunately, the flight had only one passenger seat available. Since dependents were not allowed to fly unaccompanied, he took the free flight and Marie agreed to take a taxi back to the commercial airport in Tokyo. There, she would catch the next plane to Bangkok.

Thinking about it now, he was amazed she so readily agreed to those arrangements. There she was in a foreign country, couldn't speak the language and the taxi drivers didn't speak English. Then, since she had no luggage with her, the customs agents found that very strange. Also, she didn't have any phone number or any ways to even contact him. Good thing he figured out what flight she would be on and met her upon arrival or she would never have forgiven him. As it was, her plane made a stop in Hong Kong, so now she had been some place in the world where he hadn't.

Thailand was special because it was exciting, interesting, and different. The first thing they noticed was the noisy traffic. The Thai government tried unsuccessfully to slow the growth of traffic by imposing a 150% import tax on cars. But, in one generation, the Thais went from the backs of elephants to stomping on the gas pedal and blaring the horn. There seemed to be an unwritten code..."He who hesitates on the streets of Bangkok is quickly run over."

Bangkok was once known as "The Venice of the East" and canals still run through the entire city. While today most of the canals have been covered and turned into roads, there are still some areas accessible only to the slim long tail boats called Rua Hang Yao.

While in Thailand, they stayed at the Royal Garden Hotel located on the bank of the legendary Chao Phraya River adjacent to the Bangkok Bridge. On the first day there, they visited Johnny's Gems, a jewelry store Dunn's dad did business with and could be trusted for quality and price. There, he convinced Marie to buy forty rings they would take back to the States and sell, and thereby be able to reimburse themselves for some of their honeymoon expenses.

Dunn also purchased a genuine blue star sapphire, originally from India, which he had set into his West Point ring. For Marie, he purchased a diamond and blue sapphire princess-cut ring.

While Marie sorted through the topaz, emeralds, jade, sapphires, rubies, fiery opals and diamonds, the young girls working there, feted Dunn with Thai beer. They offered him a plate of food and giggled as they watched him eat. The pungent aroma of the Thai plate instantly cleared his air passages from his nostrils to his lungs as he savored the first taste. But then, unbidden tears streamed from his eyes and he felt his face turn crimson and his pores flush to cool the burning throughout his entire body. He didn't have to ask for beer as they kept bringing him fresh, tall glasses.

When he finished the plate heaped with food, the six or seven girls watching him clapped and squealed approval. He politely indicated for some more, and they all ran off. Soon the owner approached him, followed behind by the girls. Joe's first thought was, *What have I done wrong? I just simply accepted their hospitality. Sure, I was drinking too much, but the beer was an item of critical necessity with this food.*

"I am Tutan, the owner of Johnny's Gems," the man spoke in excellent English. "Is what they tell me true? Did you eat all our food on the plate given you, and did you ask for more?"

When he nodded affirmatively and before he could say or explain anything, Tutan shouted, "Congratulations! You are the first American to finish a plate of our food. And you have asked for more! You shall have more. Plus, everything you buy in the store today shall be half the price. You shall be my guests for all the tours in Bangkok this week and my tailor shall make a dress for your wife from any material she brings him. I will arrange everything. I insist. But, first," he said to the girls, "bring us both more beer. And here is your second plate of our food!"

As a guest of Johnny's Gems, they visited the Royal Grand Palace, then went through the dazzling Wat Phra Kaew with its revered Emerald Buddha, the Golden Chedi, Pantheon of the Chakri Kings, a miniature replica of Angkor Wat in Cambodia and the eight colored towers.

Also, they took a motor launch trip along the bustling Chao Phya River and quiet klongs (canals), passing picturesque scenes of Thai river life. They also visited Wat Arun, the Temple of Dawn; Wat Trimit with its golden Buddha; then they went through Chinatown to the flower market, Pak Klong Talad. After that, they saw Wat Po, the temple of the Reclining Buddha, drove past the Royal Grand Palace along Ratchadamnerb Avenue, passing the Democracy monument, various ministries and government offices, the Royal Plaza, and the Marble Throne Hall. All this before visiting the Marble Temple and its galleries where the most beautiful Buddha images in various positions were kept.

On their own, they toured outside Bangkok and visited the Bridge on the River Kwai, and Dunn did some temple rubbings at the Angkor Wat. Marie got to ride on the back of an elephant and Joe took some pictures of her with a giant boa constrictor wrapped around her neck and shoulders.

Some Aussie soldiers took some pictures of her and exclaimed they wouldn't do what she was doing for a whole lot of Quid. Finally, she begged for someone to remove the snake because of its weight. She was surprised the boa was so cool and dry.

The ten days the lovers spent in Thailand became loving memories that were to last a lifetime. Also, they were going to help him endure a year alone without his precious Marie. After forty days of adventure as a new, loving couple and forty nights of embracing as a new loving adventure, they were now going to have only their letters and their memories for a full year.

Dunn fell asleep clutching Marie's three letters.

9
A Routine Day

DUNN LOOKED FORWARD TO SPENDING a "routine" day at the Charlie Ranger Hill site. The men of 2nd Platoon would be busy cleaning weapons and performing a huge assortment of preparedness activities as the Old Man wanted to penetrate and saturate some new sectors of the Tiger Mountains. There were three teams in 2nd Platoon, and equal numbers from the other platoons as well that were slotted for insertions in rapid succession.

Joe also wanted to get together with his platoon sergeant; something he faulted himself for not having done long ago. As a rule, platoon sergeants enjoyed a special camaraderie with the men, a camaraderie that is never, ever shared with an officer. But he wanted his platoon sergeant to open up to him, teach him things about his men that would help make him a better leader. Dunn was not interested in making things "easier;" he simply wanted to become a better platoon leader. He knew he would be a good student and a good listener.

On his way to breakfast Joe thought, *If only I could get my platoon sergeant one on one in a lengthy conversation, I'm certain there will be a wealth of information revealed to me. Plus, Wilson owes me some lists I have requested. Personally, I think it's a disgrace that so many proud veteran Rangers have to wear faded, torn camouflage fatigues, especially when I know for a fact, there are plenty of new ones in the rear supply. Surely, John Roberts must have received the request and passed it on to Beaver in supply by now.*

After enjoying his favorite meal of the day, Dunn spent some time in the TOC. Always curious to listen in on the goings on in the field, Joe also was just a little bit curious as to how well Lee was doing flying C & C. Sometime when he did not want to be alone in his tent or with the crowd at the 3rd Platoon Bar, he promised himself that he would spend off-duty time with the crew at the TOC. Everyone had a story. He bet they had some doozies.

Heading back to the 2ndPlatoon area, he expected to find Wilson since the conex was open. However, some of the men told him Wilson was at forward supply arranging rearmament of munitions for the teams. Others indicated Wilson had told them he would be gone to take care of pay problems for the Kit Carson Scouts. Looking around, Dunn felt a special pride to be their platoon leader. They didn't need to have their hands held or be told what to do in a nit-picking fashion because, on their own, they *are* productive. When there was a job to be done, they did it. When they went into the field on a mission, they were prepared. They were prepared because they used their time in camp doing all the little things. They understood what was at stake. They knew and they worked hard.

I bet when the time comes, they can play even harder than they work, he thought and smiled as he looked around at the men.

"Lieutenant Dunn," said Roger Goldstein, the E-4 that he and the Professor had recommended to the Old Man for a Bronze Star with "V" device, "may I speak with you in private? I have spoken with my team leader and with Wilson. They both told me to go directly to you."

"Absolutely, responded Dunn. "Let's go grab some coffee from the mess. Then, we'll find some shade and talk privately."

The two men walked over to the Mess Section, which was making final preparations for the upcoming noon meal. Only Dunn filled a cup with coffee. Goldstein shook his head, and said, "No, thanks." Then they moved over to an area where they would not be disturbed.

"Sir," said Goldstein, almost angrily, "I will not go into the bush any-more."

"Do you mind telling me what caused you to make this decision? This is your second consecutive tour with Charlie Rangers. Isn't it?"

"Yes, sir, I have been with Charlie Rangers for twenty-two straight months. I have been to the field dozens of times. I have been in fuck-ing contacts more than most of the men in this unit, and I have always done more than my job in a contact. I am not even a sergeant. I never complain, and I am not complaining now. I just don't want to go to the fucking bush anymore. I believe I have earned that right."

"Is there something more that you can tell me? Does it have to do with the make-up of the teams or the team leaders? It would help me as a platoon leader to understand what factors might cause a man, especially a seasoned veteran like yourself, to not want to go into the field any more."

"Sir, I just don't want to go any fucking more. It doesn't have anything to do with the rest of the platoon or the team leader. This is just me speaking. I won't go anymore. I don't think anybody should be forced to go on a mission against his will so, please, don't ask me."

"Alright, I will talk to your team leader and to the platoon sergeant. I just wish you would let me know all the stuff that may be bothering you.

It would make it a lot easier for me to understand this request. Just out of curiosity, have you taken your scheduled R and R?"

"Yes, sir, I went to Bangkok and had the greatest time of my life. When you get your choice, that's where you should think about going on R and R. They treat American soldiers great there!"

"Actually, I went there on my honeymoon before coming to 'Nam. I have to agree with you that it is a great place to visit."

"Wow! That's a far out place for a honeymoon. But, I guarantee it is an even better place for a single guy looking for a good time away from home... if you know what I mean."

"Talking about home, isn't Mississippi your home state?" Sensing that he was gaining some rapport with Roger Goldstein, Dunn hoped through this angle to be able to delve more into the motives behind the soldier's dramatic request.

"Yeah, my parents are from Mississippi. I haven't picked a home state yet. Charlie Rangers has been the closest thing to home for me. But now, you have got to get me out of any more missions. I would prefer not to leave the unit for the couple remaining months I have left In Country. If that is the only way for me not to have to go to the damn bush, then that's the way it will have to be. Sir, if you don't have any more questions, I would like to get back." Goldstein didn't wait for a response and hurried off.

Halloway, Goldstein's team leader, had earlier observed the two men headed towards the Mess. The Professor figured, correctly, that Dunn would expect his input concerning Goldstein's resolute request to be removed from bush, mission assignments. So, a short time later, when he spied the lieutenant alone, he was not at all surprised when Dunn asked him to join him for lunch. They retreated to a quiet corner to eat and talk.

David Halloway respected and admired his platoon leader and wanted very much to get to know him better. "Sir, Goldstein is a good guy. In the field he is all business and no nonsense. He has a lot of experience, and it shows. Man, he knows what he's doing. Before this last mission, though, I could tell he was freaked out. He was freaked about having to go to the boonies with a team where nobody else but him had ever been in an actual contact.

"You would think that most guys in that situation would be looking out for their own ass. Not Goldstein. He took on all the risks. He acted as if he were the only one there to shield all the other guys. Man, the damn guy was fearless...you should have seen him. Also, he did what he had to do. I mean, you know, shooting the gooks. I tell you, sir, killing gooks is not what is bothering him. He didn't blink when he put a round right between the eyes of a damn woman Vietnamese enemy soldier."

"What about back in camp? Does he have many friends? What is he like?" Dunn asked.

"He is like all the other guys, sir...has his faults, just like everybody. I suspect he uses, although he doesn't drink. But, he *never* uses to excess and *never* before a mission. He gets along fine with all the guys in our platoon but has a few really close friends in another platoon...4th Platoon, I think. About the only guy he can't stand is Pappy over in 3rd Platoon. For some strange reason, Butler goes out of his damn way to ride Goldstein, who is only a Spec Four. From what I know, Goldstein has never done anything to Pappy to cause any of this. Goldstein does his best to simply avoid Pappy. Like I said, Pappy goes out of his way to get Goldstein put on shitty details and to just harass him. But, this has been going on for some time now. I don't see how that has anything to do with his sudden decision not to go into the bush."

"What about Wilson? Doesn't he protect our guys from the other platoon sergeants?"

"Pappy is too smart to make anything he does become a direct confrontation. Besides, everybody knows how close Pappy is with the Old Man; so, any guy who picks a fight with Pappy is fighting the Old Man. That's a no-win situation. Wilson either doesn't realize what's going on or feels there is nothing he can do about it."

"Have you talked with Goldstein about his request not to go into the field? Does he want to be assigned to a different team? Do you have any idea what is *really* bothering him?"

"I have tried talking to him as I don't want to lose him from my team. No...it's not the team. He likes them and they definitely like and respect him. Evidently he doesn't want to go to the boonies with *any* team...he's had his fill and simply doesn't want to go to the boonies, period.

"Maybe you can get the Old Man to assign him to a position in the rear. Man, he doesn't have shit to prove. Like, he has done more than his damn share over two tours. The guy deserves a rear assignment and a promotion, if you ask me. The rest of the guys in my team feel the same way. Probably the whole damn platoon does."

"Thank you, Sergeant Halloway. I appreciate hearing your opinion. I will talk to Wilson. Then, I will see the Major about this. The Old Man has always insisted on volunteers and not forcing anyone to go to the field against his will.

"I know you have a lot of work to do in getting your team prepared for its next mission. So, don't worry. This should be handled quickly," Dunn reassured the sergeant.

When the two men finished their private conversation, Dunn went looking for and found Wilson at the platoon conex. He was busy assisting the three, team leaders getting ready to go on missions and obviously didn't want to be interrupted. However, Dunn requested, "Wilson, I would like a private conference with you regarding a few matters that can't wait. You would only be away for a few minutes."

"All right," Wilson reluctantly agreed then turned to the team leaders and said, "Men, could you please give us a half hour and then come back?" Having plenty else to do, the team leaders seemed pleased to be dismissed to handle their own affairs.

"Sergeant Wilson, have you heard about Goldstein's request not to go into the field?" Dunn asked straight out.

"Yes, sir," Wilson quickly answered. "I know all about it. I told Goldstein to talk to you. What I have to say is no Ranger should be forced to go out on a six-man ambush mission against his will. If that fucking happens, it will raise hell with the rest of the men. This is supposed to be a fucking volunteer outfit. Right?"

"Good. I wanted your input before I talked with Major Wayne. Next, I would like to have that directory for which I asked you. Also, what is the status of the list of men who need new camouflage fatigues?" As Dunn spoke, he noticed that Wilson diverted his eyes and clenched his teeth. Wilson always sweated profusely, but now the sweat was pouring from his face and entire body.

"Goddamn it, sir!" Wilson spat out. Then his eyes grew large, his lips clenched and curled, his jawbone muscle tightened and his face flushed a dark crimson. He was frustrated with this cherry lieutenant. Wilson's mind raced with thoughts...*This fucking college-educated moron has no clue about what it takes to lead a Ranger platoon. Paperwork! That's what this guy wants. Fucking paperwork! I volunteered to come to this unit in order to escape all the Mickey Mouse paperwork.*

I figured if I avoided him long enough, he'd forget about it. But, no, this candy ass has to hound and harass me, just like he did about the fucking sandbags. That's a job for the local Papasan. Rangers should not be asked to fill goddamn sandbags. Just like Ranger platoon sergeants should not have to waste time on goddamn paperwork. That's a job for a college boy. When is he going to get a clue?

He doesn't care that my wife left me, and that's why I volunteered to come here. Her goddamn lawyer made me look worse than I am, and the fucking judge gave everything to her. He doesn't care that I got a letter today telling me she remarried. Nobody in the whole fucking platoon gives a shit about me. The goddamn heat is getting to me. I feel dehydrated. I need a drink. Not fucking water, I need a few belts of hard stuff...

He looked up, visibly got himself under control but diverted his eyes from making any eye contact with Dunn as he said in a controlled voice, "I have been too busy getting teams ready to do their primary job. I haven't had time to make lists on paper for you. Maybe that's something you are much better suited for than me."

"Sergeant Wilson," Dunn spoke deliberately and slowly, "I requested two lists from you. I asked for a roster of all the men in the platoon with their rank, social security number, date of rank, date of birth, DEROS,

R&R status, religion, blood type, and finally the name, relationship and address of their hometown contact.

"Also, you were to put together a list for me of all the men who need a new set of cammies and include their sizes. You *will* make these two lists. Tomorrow morning before breakfast and in no event later than 0700 hours, you *will* find me and give me a date and time on which you *will* deliver each of my two lists. You *will* determine a reasonable date and time you need to complete this task. You *will* tell me that date and time tomorrow morning. Then, you *will* do both lists, and you *will* do them on or before the date and time that you specify to me. Now is that perfectly clear, Sergeant Wilson? If my instructions are clear, then I have nothing more at this time."

"I heard you," said Wilson, slightly louder than a whisper. "Now, I would like to get back to my work." He again purposely omitted saying, "sir."

When Dunn turned and left, the words, *arrogant bastard!* popped unbidden into his head. Visibly and mentally shaking his head and taking a deep breath, Joe purposely headed back down towards the TOC. He figured he might as well search out Major Wayne as soon as possible, as he didn't know how Goldstein's request would affect the rest of the men in the platoon and didn't want to risk any adverse consequences.

While Goldstein might certainly be entitled to a rear job, Dunn's sole concern was to get Goldstein out of the platoon as quickly as possible. He fully expected Wayne would transfer Goldstein immediately, just as he did with PFC Smith, whom he had sent almost instantly to the 173rd.

"Excuse me, sir, may I speak with you in private?" Dunn interrupted a casual conversation that Wayne was enjoying with Butler outside of the TOC. So, Butler pleasantly greeted Dunn and left the two of them alone as he went inside to talk to Staples.

"Sir, I am advising you of a formal request I received from SP/4 Roger Goldstein. He requests a transfer, as he doesn't want to go into the field on any more combat missions. If there were a rear assignment or a non-combat position available, that would be ideal. Otherwise, he requests an immediate transfer out of the unit."

"Goddamn! Lieutenant, am I going to start seeing your whole goddamn platoon looking to become Legs or REMF's? Didn't I just transfer a new recruit from your platoon to The Herd?"

"Yes, sir. Goldstein is a veteran on his second consecutive tour with Charlie Rangers. He..."

"I goddamn know who he is. He is the same fucking Goldstein that you put in for a goddamn Bronze Star. Now, you are telling me that your goddamn hero has suddenly become a WIMP, WEAK, INCOMPETENT, AND MALINGERING PUSSY! What is it you are doing over there in 2nd Platoon? Are you running a Ranger platoon or a replacement center?"

Then, stepping over to the TOC, Wayne yelled inside, "Hey, Pappy, come on back out here. I need some First Sergeant advice, and you are far and away the best person to give it to me." When Sergeant Butler came out, Major Wayne repeated to him what Dunn had just revealed.

"Sounds to me like he is just malingering," said Butler. "I would schedule his team, *with him*, to go into the field... then, we'll see what he does. Lieutenant, I think he is pulling your chain to get some special attention. I know his type and have seen him on work details, always trying to get away with something. Goldstein always looks for a favor or feels entitled to special treatment. I bet he feels like he is owed a cushy job in the rear just because he's been here for a while. Hell, lots of guys, a goddamn better than Goldstein, have served more than two tours. Schedule him to go into the field. Then, if he doesn't go, we will know he is serious."

"I thank you for the excellent advice, Pappy." Wayne nodded his approval.

"Sir, I disagree," said Dunn. "I don't like the idea of potentially compromising a team by trying to force someone to go into the field that should not go. It's the rest of the team that I am concerned with, not just Goldstein. Won't you just talk to Goldstein and try to discern his true intentions and his state of mind? If he goes into the field in his present state of mind, I fear he could hurt himself or others. Since I am convinced he wants and needs a transfer, I definitely want him transferred out of my platoon."

"You want him transferred? Then, schedule him to go into the field. If he refuses to go, then I will transfer him out of your platoon."

"Sir," politely begged Dunn, "you have always insisted on having volunteers and not wanting anybody who did not want to be a Ranger. I request you reconsider..."

"Goddamn it," hollered Wayne, "I am giving you a goddamn order, Lieutenant! You *will* schedule Goldstein to go to the field on an ambush mission with his team; and, you *will* give him a direct order to go with his team into the field on that mission. If he goddamn refuses, then and only then will I transfer him out of your goddamn platoon. Is that clear, Lieutenant Dunn?"

"Yes, sir," was Dunn's steely response.

He had been caught off balance by his commander's adamant attitude. *Was it that he did not want to lose a good field soldier or was it that he did not like Goldstein? Why wasn't he treating this situation in the same manner that he treated the Smith situation?* Joe wondered and worried as he left the TOC.

From a commanding officer I have been taught to expect consistency... much like a player expects from a baseball umpire. Only with

Wayne, the strike zone is evidently all over the place, and I feel as if I'm constantly striking out....

🍃

That evening at the Operations Briefing in the Tactical Operations Center, there were two items that were out of the ordinary and were rather interesting. Most of the material presented was routine, in that it pertained to the upcoming missions and was information Dunn was used to hearing. He was glad to hear that Lee had done a good job inserting X-ray in its new mountaintop location.

But there was one item of interest that caught his attention mainly because it was so out of the ordinary. It was announced that a company of ROK, Republic of Korea, would soon be on call as a reactionary force. The ROK Company would be ready during daylight hours to be airlifted into any site of a contact in order to pursue the enemy. Once the ROK company was actually on station, its commander had requested that permission be granted to allow a few of his troops to participate with some Ranger patrols. One of Charlie Ranger platoons would be tasked with allowing ROK's to become team members.

Another item of interest that grabbed him was a request to Charlie Rangers from Headquarters, ARVN, the Army of the Republic of Viet Nam. ARVN wanted a platoon from Charlie Rangers to build, start and run a Ranger school in Pleiku. The assignment would last anywhere from four to eight months. It meant that soon one platoon leader with his entire platoon would be dispatched to Pleiku. They would be gone and away from the company for quite a long time.

Phillips concluded the briefing by stating the company would convene an E-5, Buck Sergeant, Promotion Board at 1000 hours the next day at a segregated section of the mess hall. The promotion board was an administrative requirement imposed by the army before a soldier could be promoted from the enlisted rank of E-4 or SP/4 to that of E-5 or Sergeant. Unfortunately, this was rare for the men of Charlie Rangers because the company had to rely on rank allotments from the unit to which it was opconned. Those units generally kept the rank allotments for their own men. Somehow, Charlie Rangers had wrangled five allotments from The Herd.

What Joe heard the Old Man saying was that without seeking any input from his platoon leaders, he had already chosen five out of many qualified and deserving men to report for examination of fitness before the promotion board.

It turns out that two men were from Pappy's 3rd Platoon, two were from Commo and the other was from the TOC detail. Dunn later discovered it was Staples who had pulled in a favor to get the allotments after getting the Old Man to promise to promote his man from TOC.

The last announcement by the Old Man was, "The duty of sitting on the promotion board is assigned to LT Kent, LT Dunn and to SFC Staples. Gentlemen, that is all. Dismissed."

After the Ops Briefing, the four, line platoon leaders, gathered informally to talk over the interesting revelations. Lee was the last to join them because he had already hotfooted it up to the Old Man to let him know he did not want to go to Pleiku.

Lee stated, "Boy, I want no part in running a school for ARVN and was very adamant about it to the Old Man. However, I did say I would volunteer to take the whole ROK Company, two at a time, into the field with my teams. There is no way I want to train Vietnamese wannabes."

Dunn suspected, *The real reason Lee doesn't want the school assignment is because he still has his heart set on winning some kind of valor medal on a mission. If Lee were to go to Pleiku, it would mean no more missions for a long time.*

Then Kent stated, "Pappy and I will do a good job on any assignment and it doesn't matter to me one way or the other."

"Hell, yes," Rod Winthrop chimed in, "I definitely want this assignment. I know how to start and run schools as I've done it before. Besides, the best part is being away, on your own, being my own fucking commander. I don't mind saying it would be wonderful to get away from "The Duke" and his goddamn war stories."

"Let's just wait and see what happens. I don't think it matters what we might want," was all that Dunn said. Then he headed to tell his platoon team-leaders all the news of that evening's Ops Briefing.

Wilson was conspicuously missing, but the rest were absolutely thrilled with his surprise-a dozen packages of Kool-Aid for each team. Marie's care package was a huge hit.

※

Later that evening, Dunn finished another letter to Marie. He was anxious to share with her how enormously thrilled the men had been to receive something that, to many in the outside world, would have seemed trivial. Water was an absolute necessity out in the boonies in the damn heat, but the awful taste from the brown iodine pills used to kill the germs in the water was something everyone hated but had to swallow.

BAM, BAM, BAM, BAM, BAM, BAM, BAM, BAM!

An eruption of loud, ominous and angry cursing and yelling close by, interrupted the droning sound from the gas generators. Bursting through the mosquito netting, Dunn nearly tripped over the ropes securing his tent as he raced down the hill towards his platoon area. *A whole magazine on full automatic! What the Hell?*

He found Wilson with his weapon pointed at the 2nd Platoon hooch. *Thank God his shots have only harmlessly ripped open sandbags.*

Wilson, swayed, staggered and turned his head around to face Dunn, who was now less than six feet away from him. Nearly falling, he turned his body around with the M-16 held in his right hand with his arm fully extended. The weapon pointed in the general direction of Dunn.

"Gooks and Dinks in the compound! I'll kill the fuckers, shir," slurred Wilson, who was still clicking the trigger on the now empty gun pointed directly at Dunn. Closing the distance between them, Dunn reached out and had to tear the weapon out of Wilson's strong grip. That was when Dunn noticed Wilson clenching a banana clip, a magazine with fifteen rounds, in his left hand. The stench of whiskey confirmed that Wilson was definitely drunk.

"It's okay, now, Sergeant First Class Wilson," said Dunn in a calming voice. "The area is now secure. Give me the magazine."

Wilson slowly crumpled to his knees, dropped the banana clip and covered his sobbing face with his hands. The small group of spectators continued to grow and started to stir when Sergeant Butler spoke out.

"There's nothing more to be seen here. Everybody get back to doing your own business. Now!" Turning to Dunn, Pappy continued, "Sir, please have one of your team leaders secure this weapon. I will take care of Sergeant Wilson." Then, the thin, wiry 3rd Platoon Sergeant lifted and carried off the heavy, large, whimpering man as if he were weightless.

Following the incident, Dunn acknowledged the feeling of adrenaline that surged through his body. It all happened so fast. Only now did he appreciate the danger in which he could have been and that he should have been more cautious.

When he first spotted Wilson, he recognized that the man was drunk and was overcome with a sense of sadness and pity. Here was a proud, towering soldier who had risen through the ranks with an unblemished career of service. And, now, for whatever reason, he had cowered and fallen prey to the demons within his mind that had been unleashed by the spirits he increasingly consumed. Dunn also felt a sense of personal loss as he now lost the guidance of a seasoned NCO and the chance to create a professional relationship for both of their developments. Bottom line, he lost his platoon sergeant.

Not in the least bit sleepy, and definitely not in the mood to finish his letter to Marie, Dunn sought distraction by spending time with the night crew in the TOC; he was Duty Officer again that night.

"Hey, sir," said Specialist Fourth Class Ramos, "we heard you captured an M-16 from a hostile friendly tonight. I always thought Wilson was flaky, but then I guess any guy who volunteers for this duty is a real 'dinky dau.'"

"Wilson just had a bit too much to drink, and the pressures must have gotten to him," Dunn commented.

They all kidded him to try and lighten the moment, including Staples, who stopped in with a tall drink, which he was nursing and savoring. It was a fine scotch given to him by the Major from the Major's private stock. Before leaving, Staples pulled Dunn aside for a favor.

"Please be on the lookout for an intelligent, industrious soldier from 2nd Platoon that I could solicit for work as head of the TOC night shift."

Dunn recognized and appreciated this opportunity. He would select and refer his finest enlisted soldier to Staples and would thereby solidify a valuable ally. The position Staples wanted to fill was critical support to combat operations; therefore, it was important to him as well.

"So," turning to the crew after Staples left, he said, "Okay guys, entertain me. Tell me about some of the interesting things that happen during night shift. Anything going on tonight in the field?"

"Not much ever happens around here at night anymore," said Ramos. "Not like the old days. But let me tell you about the time a team called into X-ray in the middle of the night about an enemy tank that was crushing trees and heading right at them.

"The team had huddled in the standard wagon wheel formation below a bramble bush in a dense section of the jungle. They figured nobody could sneak up on them there in the blackness of the night. But, they never figured on an enemy tank. Boy, was the team ever scared. But they were more afraid to try to move in the dark. Fortunately, the Ops Briefings had included warnings of small enemy tanks, so each team carried the M-72 LAW, Light Anti-tank Weapon." (The LAW is a one-shot bazooka-style rocket launcher with a periscope fiberglass tube that was supposed to be discarded after use.)

"The team became more frantic as they worried that their general position was compromised. Finally, they could no longer bear the crushing noise of the oncoming tank and fired the rocket at the sound. The deafening explosion included what the team described over the radio as a 'ghastly' sound. They figured they made a direct hit because after that they detected no further movement. However, they were all too freakin' scared to sleep the rest of the night. After first light, the team got a look at their unfortunate target, the goddamn carcass of an elephant!" Ramos laughed at the story he had just told as if he were hearing it for the first time.

"On another occasion, a team fell asleep at the base of a large tree. Before the sun came up, the entire team was awakened by the hoots and shrieks of large monkeys fighting. Upon closer inspection, the team reported that the tree was filled with Orangutans. In the morning, one of the team members tried to shoo away a rather large Orangutan with his rifle. The Orangutan grabbed the damn weapon and proceeded to hack the soldier senseless before throwing the rifle down and scrambling back up the tree. The team had to be extracted and the Ranger sent to the hospital for emergency treatment. I don't like and I don't trust monkeys anymore."

"Thanks for the entertaining stories, guys. Since it is now approaching midnight, I will leave for my rounds," Dunn said as he arose to leave on his inspections. But he stopped in mid-movement when the current X-ray called in earlier than expected for the hourly check. The calling voice was an excited whisper.

"Hanger Three, this is X-ray. Hanger Three, please come in. Over."

"X-ray, this is Hanger Three. Over," answered the specialist in the TOC.

"Hanger Three, this is X-ray," the voice nervously whispered. "We are being probed. For the past half hour we have been listening to the enemy climbing. The sound is all around us below. Over."

"X-ray, this is Hanger Three, do you hear voices or any other sounds? Can you tell how many of the enemy there are? Over."

"Hanger Three, this is X-ray, they are still too far below us, but they are continuing to climb. We didn't believe anything could climb this to reach us. They have us completely surrounded. Over."

"X-ray, this is Three. Can you see them? Can they see you? Over."

"Three, this is X-ray. No, it is pitch black. Nobody can see nuthin'. But we are sure they can't know our exact position. Over."

"Tell them not to fire their weapons," said Dunn to Ramos, who was on the radio. "The flash and the tracers from their weapons will give away their location."

Ramos passed on Dunn's advice. The scared whispered response asked in a low whisper, "What should we do because the climbing is getting much closer."

Dunn suggested, "Throw rocks at the sound to try to get the enemy to reveal itself, but then maintain radio silence."

"Roger," was the lone whispered word over the radio.

Then there was a long pause of silence before another very urgent, yet low whisper, "They are throwing rocks back at us!"

The prolonged and silent waiting in the TOC was unnerving. Ramos said, "Let's go get Staples or wake up Phillips."

"No, lets wait until a situation develops," Dunn insisted. "If we here at the TOC break radio silence, the sound of our transmission could give away the location of the X-ray radio. We really don't have much choice but to wait"

It was after 0100 hours before the radio again sounded. "Hanger Three, this is X-ray, we have a Romeo Charlie from every papa. Over." The radio relay site was sending in its standard hourly report that it had received a radio check from every patrol in the field.

"X-ray, this is Hanger Three, how about a sitrep on the rock throwing? Over."

"Hanger Three, this is X-ray. Negative, nothing to report. Over."

"Oh, no," Dunn said to Ramos. "No way have I stayed awake on pins and needles to be simply told there is 'nothing to report.' Find out what really happened."

After a bit of cajoling, pleading and threatening, the X-ray team finally admitted to the TOC that they had been the unwitting victims to enemy Orangutans again. Listening to the series of radio responses, the men in the TOC figured the teams in the field had listened in and were having a ball giving X-ray some serious monkey business.

I don't know how many of these "routine" days at Charlie Ranger Hill that I can stand, thought Dunn, as he left to make his round of inspections and to ponder over the many events and feelings of the past day.

10
Map Reading

THE NEW DAY BROUGHT PROMISES OF NEW experiences and new challenges. Some lucky SP/4 soldiers were getting a promise of new rank. To many of them, the promotion simply meant an increase in pay and privilege and when they got back to The World, they would be treated with greater respect and be entitled to use the NCO Club instead of having to go to the Enlisted Men's Club.

To Dunn, this particular promotion was significant because these men were joining the ranks of the Non-Commissioned Officer. For the first time, they would become responsible for other soldiers. They were now in line to become team leaders.

"Hey, guys," said Kent to Dunn and Staples as they arranged the chairs in the area they intended to use to test the candidates, "I think we should ask these soldiers relatively easy and straightforward questions. You know, the field conditions really do not provide an environment conducive to study. I, for one, want these men to get the promotions."

"I agree," said Staples. "I am very familiar with these men and they are all well qualified and deserve promotion."

"Plus," chimed in Dunn, "who knows when Charlie Rangers will be able to extract additional allotments. We have too many men overdue promotions."

Among the questions posed, Dunn designed a straightforward map reading problem. While all the men were in the ballpark on estimating the distance from point A to Point B on the map, Dunn emphasized the importance of map reading by showing each man the exact answer. From their facial expressions, Dunn could tell that some probably thought he was being a "nitpicking asshole." He just hoped they would not be thrust into a situation where a team depended on their map reading accuracy any time too soon, but all five candidates were promoted.

After lunch, Dunn meandered through the 2nd Platoon area and the TOC. There was absolutely no mention or any evidence of Wilson; he was simply gone. The Old Man had evidently taken care of him and covered for him by unceremoniously transferring him out of the unit. Dunn couldn't help but feel sorry for him, but he was glad he was gone and no longer a challenge, a problem or an embarrassment.

Flying C & C, Lee oversaw the insertion of two teams that morning. Since he was scheduled to fly C & C for the next three days, Dunn wanted to go on a recon that afternoon with three team leaders and their assistants. Rod Winthrop would get his chance at flying C & C after Dunn. Lee also told him he was going back into the field with Team 12 the following day. Ranger Hill seemed settled into its hectic routine.

❧

During the VR that afternoon, Dunn lay prone on the steel floor with his head and shoulders protruding outside of the chopper. As they flew over their respective sectors, the team leaders and their assistants took turns along side of him. When they spotted trails or adequate Landing Zones, they had to yell to make themselves heard over the noise of the helicopter and the wash of the blades.

After they had been into the VR for over a half hour, Dunn noticed puffs of smoke on the ground directly behind them on their flight path. "Is that someone shooting at us? No, that's not possible with our irregular flight path. What the hell could those be?" he asked as he pointed out the mysterious puffs of smoke to the team leader nearest to him.

That team leader tapped him on the shoulder and indicated for him to look inside the chopper cabin. There, seated calmly on the floor in the center of the aircraft, was one of the assistant team leaders. He methodically pulled grenades out of a sling bag and yanked the pins but prevented detonation release by stuffing the grenades into a milk glass, which he grabbed out of a second bag. Then, he alternately tossed them out each open side of the chopper. When the glasses broke, they left a trail of explosions in their wake.

"Bombs away, sir!" exclaimed the soldier.

So much for clandestine operations. Phillips was pissed. New sectors were assigned and this time only team leaders went on the second VR with Dunn.

That evening Phillips announced as part of the Ops Briefing, "The Koreans are nearly prepared to function as a reactionary force and 2nd Platoon will be tasked periodically to take some Korean troops into the boonies on ambush missions.

"The Koreans will give us one week notice when they are finally ready to start. Furthermore, in two weeks time, Rod Winthrop will depart with his entire platoon to put together a Ranger school for ARVN in Pleiku."

"Yeeehaww!" Winthrop let out a rebel cheer when he heard the good news. Lee also grinned and exhaled a sigh of relief. Kent and Appier just continued making notes as they had been throughout the entire briefing.

Dunn was not surprised at the decisions. While running a school for ARVN would no doubt have provided some exceptional experiences, he was really looking forward to continuing in his present job. At that moment, he knew he relished being a Ranger platoon leader and felt there was no finer service anywhere in the world for him to perform, and no finer men to serve than the men of 2nd Platoon.

When he got back to his tent, that night after briefing the team leaders and alerting those who were headed to the field, he planned on writing a long letter to Marie. However, the swarm of bugs in his tent was so thick it coated the single bulb and drove him to seek refuge in the dark under his nylon jungle blanket.

In the morning, he made his way down to the tarmac and entered the ready shack, which was used as a place for briefing pilots on upcoming missions. During the day, the pilots hung around it while they waited to be scrambled for mission support. He introduced himself and quickly made friends with Dennis Riley, his new Seahorse pilot of the Birddog.

"I was briefed earlier by Jim Wails, who was your frontseat the other day. I am also familiar with supporting LRRP and Special Forces units. I definitely prefer working for you guys than some of the Ruff-Puffs I have had to deal with lately. By the way, Jim sends his regards. He says you did a helluva job as his observer."

"Thanks. Jim is a great pilot. Just don't tell him I said that, as his head will get too big for that flight helmet of his."

"Well, let's make the most of this gorgeous weather and go help insert some Ranger teams," Riley said, as he headed for the Birddog.

The insertion of the two Ranger patrols went smoothly, and the four helicopters supporting the clandestine insertions headed back. Then, with some free time, Dunn broke out his map to study some of the features. He asked Warrant Officer Riley, his frontseat, to continuously circle the current X-ray site. The heavy team, meaning more men than the regular 6-man ambush team, had been inserted by Lee on a small plateau on one of many high peaks. The location was ideal in that it did look like it was not approachable from below.

However, something about it made Dunn uncomfortable because according to his reading of the map, the X-ray was a full klick to the west of where TOC positioned it on the war room maps. He noted that the two mountaintops and adjacent area were similar in topographical features so Dunn searched for and finally found some clearly identifiable features. Then, he directed his pilot to fly a pattern that allowed him to trace back to the X-ray site from those clearly identifiable features. Once again they repeated the pattern of investigation until he was 100 percent, grade A certain. *X-ray was not on the mountain where TOC thought it was.*

Since it was time to refuel and have lunch, he decided to wait until he was back to personally advise Phillips and Staples.

Skipping lunch, Dunn hurried to TOC so he could brief Phillips and Staples of his concern. Major Wayne was present and listened intently.

"Goddamn, you lieutenants need to get your shit together," interrupted Wayne. "What makes you think you are right and that TOC has it wrong?"

"Sir, the grid lines on the map and the terrain on the ground around these two mountains look almost the same. However, I can show you how I identified some specific spots and followed them from the air to confirm my suspicions about the real location of X-ray. If I am right, then Robert Lee could also have been off by the same distance when he gave TOC the coordinates of the teams he inserted. The teams might not be where they think they are."

Dunn then proceeded to explain in detail the steps he took to determine the actual placement of X-ray. He showed and described the distant features that would be easily and definitely identifiable from the air and pinpointed on the map. Then, he showed the paths of the traces to the X-ray site.

Staples readily accepted Dunn's findings and sought to correct the map. Phillips, however, was not convinced and chose not to make any changes until he had an opportunity to verify the location for himself. He determined to go on the recon flight that afternoon, as he wanted to personally verify Dunn's findings before allowing any modification to the map placements.

So, Dunn made some quick sandwiches from the mess and joined Riley to head back to the tarmac. When the Birddog was aloft, they listened to transmissions that chronicled a huge tragedy that was thankfully averted. Two Charlie Ranger patrols ran into each other. Both teams were scouting the same dry riverbed in which to set up an ambush. In a miraculous turn of events, just as the point elements of both teams were about to collide and fire each other up with mutual killing force, one Ranger recognized the distinctive favorite green beanie bush headgear of his best friend.

"Charlie Rangers! Hold your Fire!" He yelled out just in the nick of time, probably saving the life of his best friend as well as, most likely, his own teammates. Team 43 had been inserted the day before by Lee and had run into Team 31, which was inserted that morning by Dunn. Team 43 Team Leader insisted his team must have been inserted a full kilometer west of where he was positioned on the map. Fortunately, this lesson in map reading wasn't paid for more dearly. After that, TOC wisely decided to insure there was a buffer zone between sectors in which any teams thereafter worked.

War is a job for the soldier. There is no such thing as on-the-job-training for war. The ongoing training received by a soldier is generally for conventional warfare. The soldier is taught to react in certain situations, not to think or ponder. The soldier is expected to unquestionably follow orders.

A Ranger must be more than just a soldier. He must anticipate and cannot afford to simply react or even to wait for orders. When you are one of only six men completely surrounded by hostile forces, every decision of every man affects the lives of all six. The war becomes a frame of mind, of heightened senses and of dependent reliance on your fellow Ranger. If war is hell, then the deepest bowels of hell are too hot for all except Rangers. But, putting Rangers in a predicament where they can kill their own is a place in hell where they should never go of their own accord.

At the Operations Briefing in the Tactical Operations Center that evening, Captain Phillips noted the corrected locations of X-ray and some of the teams. Without elaboration, he mentioned that the two teams met in the field, and he reiterated the importance of accurate map reading. Phillips also advised the Korean forces had delayed for a month or two in becoming a reactionary force or accompanying teams to the field. Dunn was glad Lee was in the field already and thus spared the humiliation he would have obviously felt about his error.

Staples warned, "The teams in the field will most likely be plagued with foul weather tonight.

Of special note to Dunn was the fact that Team 23 was scheduled for insertion the following afternoon after a recon in the morning.

Phillips told Butler, "Check in with the team leaders of 2nd Platoon since there is no platoon sergeant at the moment."

After the meeting, Wayne pulled Dunn and Butler aside and stated, "I want Butler present when you order Goldstein to go into the field."

"Yes, sir," Joe responded in a less than enthusiastic voice.

Dunn turned to do as Major Wayne had ordered. He called out for Goldstein and when the man came to him ordered, "You are being ordered to accompany Team 23 into the field tomorrow."

Goldstein did not say a word but his eyes spoke volumes. He looked at Dunn with searing anger, a sense of abandonment and a resolute resentment. Before retiring back into the hooch, he shot a purposeful but furtive glance at Butler.

Sergeant Halloway started to say something to Dunn concerning the situation, but Dunn prevented him by tersely saying, "Please meet with me privately at a later time."

Later, in private, the Professor reiterated his feelings he previously expressed about Goldstein. "Sir, I feel Goldstein is a model field soldier who should not be forced to perform any further ambush missions. Change of subject. I wish to advise my platoon leader that the Kit Carson Scout, Nguyen Trang, has become a permanent member of my team."

The Professor was disappointed that Dunn made no response whatsoever about the Goldstein situation and wondered, *What was he thinking? What made him give that order? Have I misjudged our lieutenant?*

Halloway obviously thought Dunn had created this awkward situation by ordering Goldstein into the field. *I was sure he would stick up for the men in our platoon. It looks like I am wrong. He is either a lackey for the Old Man or wants to impress Pappy and the Old Man at our expense. Well, as team leader, I won't let it affect my team. Goldstein is not going into the field, and I am not going to make him go against his own wishes. I sure as hell won't be a lackey for this lieutenant,* he decided.

The next morning Dunn was pleased to note Goldstein's field gear was not with the rest of the team. *Good*, thought Dunn, *the team will go to the field without Goldstein. This way the Major will transfer Goldstein out of the platoon. There will be no further repercussions. I definitely do not like the way the Major is doing this, but I suppose he has his reasons*

Dunn said nothing about the Goldstein situation but spoke with the teams to insure they were all prepared and there were no problems requiring his attention. He was not surprised or disappointed Pappy was not around to serve as an acting platoon sergeant. He suspected last night Pappy had been sent only to insure he precisely followed the Duke's orders. He also recognized the team leaders were capable and preferred not to have the assistance of an outsider, the 3rd Platoon Sergeant.

Riley was once again Dunn's frontseat. He said, "The only reason I came back was to enjoy the superb food served at the mess." Pancho's reputation was quickly spreading.

In between the three uneventful insertions, Riley allowed Dunn to pilot the aircraft from the back seat. Privately, Riley was favorably impressed with the skill with which Dunn piloted through a series of maneuvers. He pointed out to Dunn, "Since you have not taken off or landed yet, any flying skills you have developed are not worth public mention. Of course, you probably won't get a chance to take off or land from the back seat," he jokingly reminded Joe.

In the afternoon, Dunn decided to do a flyby of the area being worked by Team 12, the team with Robert Lee. The sky was increasingly looking threatening, and Riley warned him they might have to terminate early due to the weather.

Calling the team, Dunn recognized Lee's voice over the radio. From the description Lee gave him about the team's location, Dunn had no trouble spotting them. The team had already broken down their ambush site and had been following a wide trail Lee described as a "super highway," but then had found itself between a river and a vertical ridgeline with nowhere to go but back up the trail from which they had just come.

On instinct, Dunn instructed Riley to fly in a route that gave him a look up the trail. Then he warned, "Sinker Three, this is Sinker Twenty-eight. Scramble gunships! I say again, scramble gunships! Four zero to six zero unfriendlies approaching Sinker One Two in a bad spot. Scramble gunships, over." Team 12 was in a tenuous position.

"Sinker One Two, this is Two Eight. Find cover. They are one zero time away from your location. Do you copy? Over."

"Two Eight, this is One Two. Roger. Over." Only there was no cover and only one, large, lone oak tree behind which to hide six men.

※

Andy Garrett, Devil 45, was hanging out in the Pilot Scramble Hooch with his good friend and partner, Martin Ivor, Devil 47. After seeing how swiftly the weather closed in, the air base supervisor already closed the runway to all non-mission essential aircraft. Most likely, they would not be needed again today. Martin explained to him the LRRP teams from Charlie Rangers had probably already gone to "groundhog." That was a term they used, meaning they would hide and avoid any contact with Charlie. Whenever the weather was so bad that air support was impossible or whenever another team was in contact and using all available aircraft, the teams in the field went to groundhog.

Suddenly, a high-pitched siren wailed, shocking them into action. A team was in trouble. Every time they got a "Tac-E," Tactical Emergency, to provide cover for those guys, it was an emergency. Andy had flown a lot of convoy cover and spent more time than he wanted to recall flying cover for RF/PF units, a very different experience from these missions with the LRRPs. RF/PF were Regional Forces and Popular Forces of South Vietnam, also known as "Ruff-Puffs." Before they could get to the Tarmac on the run, a second wail of the siren sounded.

Andy said to Martin, "Some poor guys must be in deep shit. If I ever get an ulcer, it will be because of those guys in Charlie Rangers."

By the time they mounted the pair of Cobras, the siren wailed for an unprecedented third time. He had never recalled even hearing about a triple blast from the Scramble Siren. This meant the situation must be awful. Martin, who was flying lead, put in a cursory call to the airfield commander and lifted off, totally ignoring the response that the airfield was absolutely closed due to the horrific weather. Punching the burners on the two large birds of prey, the two Cobras sped off towards the Tiger Mountains. They prayed they would be in time.

They made contact with Sinker Two Eight, the Forward Observer in a Birddog. The FO said a team was hidden under a tree between a river and a ridgeline with nowhere to go and a platoon of NVA coming down the trail in front of them. The Ranger team was sure it would soon be discovered and could respond only by breaking squelch on the mike, depressing the send button on the radio transmitter. The FO authorized the two Devils to communicate directly with the team on the ground.

The team is obviously scared out of their skins, thought Andy, *because they will only answer us with a squelch.* Andy and Martin arrived at the same conclusion of the required course of action at about the same time.

Thank God the FO gave us an accurate sitrep or we would never be able to even attempt the maneuvers we know we have to do. Martin and I will have to be, definitely, creative in our approach to this job.

Martin was lead and they decided to go IFR, Instrument Flight Rules, and solo to see if they could break over the ridge. He made it and then talked Andy into position to where he would climb, go IFR, and break out right behind the NVA patrol. It worked and he explained to Andy, "I know the NVA heard me, but probably thought it was some milk run slick. The last thing they expected was a gunship coming in hot out of the clouds. They were so surprised they didn't even take cover until they heard me fire the first four rockets, which literally came out of the clouds right at them."

The result was 31 NVA killed on one pass by a single ship. The FO requested, "Devils Four Five and Four Seven, guide in a slick that has also braved the weather to pick up the guys. I need you 'cause now I can't see a thing through the heavy ground clouds."

Devil 45 did so with pleasure. But, Andy had to wait for the team as the guys actually took the time to confirm the kills and retrieve weapons and intelligence data. When the team was finally extracted, the FO called to tell Devil 45, "Sinker One Eight," the platoon leader who was with the team on the ground, "has a 'Red Star,' souvenir, for you." This was a Chinese pistol.

Naturally, Andy promised to visit Charlie Ranger Hill that night. When Martin and Andy showed up, they were treated royally. *Rangers sure eat well,* thought Andy, *and can they ever down their liquor. Lee, the guy whose ass we saved, posed for some pictures with us wearing a Black Beret, but he didn't live up to his promise about the Chicom pistol. Seems the Ranger commander enforced some policy of sending all captured weapons to the rear. The Ranger commander probably wanted it for himself. Oh, well, the FO was a nice guy by the name of Dunn and has recommended Martin and me for a Silver Star and Distinguished Flying Cross.*

Actually, they both were downgraded a notch because they broke regulations by splitting up a gun team and going IFR.

When the Cobras reported they had concluded and the team was safely extracted, the Birddog checked out of the commo net and headed back.

"Are you sure you don't want to shut it down and spend the night here?" Dunn asked Riley when he finally came to a stop on the small runway after dropping out of the clouds that had made visibility nearly impossible.

"No. I have some time off coming to me and I want to get back to Tuy Hoa now. They have a tower there, so landing won't be as scary as it was here. Let me get going before they try to make me park it," concluded Riley

Dunn spotted Lee and the other five members of Team 12 looking grungy in their camouflage make-up and looking elated. They were hooting and hollering with the two Cobra pilots, who had just joined them. They were all about to load up onto a deuce and a half truck to take them to Charlie Ranger Hill. Dunn joined them.

The meal that evening was a lot of fun. The Rangers swapped war stories with Andy and Martin, the two Cobra pilots from the 134th.

"We once took some LRRPs out on a mission to capture a prisoner northwest of Tuy Hoa," Martin recalled. "We picked them up a couple of hours later, and the LRRPs had a badly wounded prisoner. Actually, he died about 5 minutes later in the helicopter and the LRRP's threw his body out at around 2000 feet over the area where they captured him. I have to admit you Rangers are a pretty scary bunch of guys-even for us."

Dunn collected information from Andy so he could submit requests for medals for these two legitimate heroes to their commander. He genuinely liked Andy Garrett and got him to promise to take him for a ride in the Cobra. *I'll definitely have to remember to take my camera for that. The Cobra is such a sleek, awesome flying fortress.*

The group hammed it up, taking pictures as a keepsake memento, as if they really needed pictures to remind them of what had happened and what nearly happened that day. While the officers retreated to the TOC for the Ops Briefing, the rest of the team ushered their guests to the 3rd Platoon Bar.

After a relatively routine briefing, Wayne pulled Dunn aside and told him, "Restrict Goldstein to the 2nd Platoon area until I decide how to proceed."

Dunn asked, "When can I expect the transfer?" since he did not like keeping Goldstein in the platoon.

Major Wayne did not answer him. Instead, the Duke wrapped his arms around Lieutenant Lee and told Lee, "Your team is a brave example for the rest of the company."

As Dunn left the TOC, he heard Wayne asking Lee, "From among the souvenirs being shipped to the rear, could I have the pistol for myself?" He didn't hear the response

After briefing the team leaders who were not already in the field with their men, Dunn paused to spend some time talking to a few of the guys hanging out around the hooch. Somehow, they always seemed to make him feel better. The conversations were never earth shaking and no solutions to life's problems were ever discussed. They were usually about girls, baseball or somebody's hometown. And they always made him feel good.

Again skipping the party already in full swing at the 3rd Platoon Bar, Dunn retreated to his tent. He could always use the excuse he needed his sleep because he was flying C & C tomorrow. The heavy, musty smell of the old canvas tent was even more familiar during periods of rain or overcast weather. Some wooden boards served as a floor ever since the incident with the bamboo viper. In addition to stacking sandbags around the tent, the men of 2nd Platoon dug a six-inch ditch to help divert the rainwater.

Today, there was no letter from Marie waiting on his cot. She was good about writing every single day and some days he would receive two or three letters while other times, like today, he received none. Swearing to himself he would do better, he penned a short letter to her. He meant to write more often as he knew how important his letters were to her. Also he knew she needed to hear he was fine and that he loved and missed her.

Turning off the bulb, he stripped out of his cammies and lay back on the cot. The air was cool and moist, which caused him to shiver. But he wanted his naked body to feel cold-a kind of personal retaliation against the insipid heat of the day. When he felt as if his teeth were about to chatter, he finally pulled the nylon blanket up to his chin, turned on his side, curled up his knees and let his thoughts drift to his escape zone....

With his mind somewhat relaxed, he purposely chose to dwell and remember what it had been like *after* he had made long, slow, and wildly passionate love to Marie. They would lie together on their sides, like two spoons fitting perfectly together and he would put his right arm around her. She would take his arm and tuck it in with both her hands as if she were tucking in the corner of a blanket. Then, when he adored how close she felt along his whole body, she would manage to snuggle even closer. Of course he loved the sex with Marie, but what he missed, what his body anguished for, were the tender touches and the two spoons. He needed, he wanted, he longed for the tender little things she did that were the real essence of love.

That night he discovered what all the poets and writers throughout history sought, the true meaning of love. To him, the definition of love was the empty anguish and hurt felt by a lonely heart that knew a distant heart felt the same way. Only a simple spoon-like cradling would comfort the yearning. The two hearts must feel the heartbeat of each other.

He totally loved Marie and had to strongly will himself to sleep as a temporary relief from the lonely heartache that punished his mind and body.

11

The Essence of C & C

WHEN DUNN GOT TO THE AIRSTRIP THE following morning, he spotted two Birddogs parked at the south end. Standing in the front of the 0-1 aircraft were two pilots outfitted in their standard Nomax fire retardant flying suits. As he drew closer, he was happy to recognize the smiling face of Jim Wails, who was going to be his frontseat for only that morning.

"Let me introduce you to Mr. Larry Hill, a young man who is a great pilot and has recently joined Seahorse," said Jim. "When Larry pilots for you this afternoon, it will be his cherry mission assignment In Country. The weather is great and visibility is good... so here's hoping the morning will be uneventful. How would you like to take advantage of my excellent tutoring and practice your flying from the back seat?"

Dunn laughed as he said, "Hey, we're wasting precious flying time. Good to meet you, Larry. I look forward to flying with you this afternoon. It will be a real treat to fly with somebody who is actually a good pilot." He couldn't resist taking a little friendly jab at Wails.

No such luck about having an uneventful day. They were aloft less than forty-five minutes when the excited call came in from the RTO of Team 43 alerting them to the first contact of the day. The situation report advised, "...that the team ambushed three, armed, enemy soldiers and there were no friendly casualties." Then, almost immediately following the situation report, the team frantically radioed for an emergency medical evacuation.

The assistant patrol leader was checking out the kill zone of the ambush site and had been wounded with three shots in his right leg, fired at point blank range. He approached the fallen enemy soldiers caught in the ambush. However, he did so without first firing additional shots into the heads of the fallen enemy. When he knelt on one knee along side a mortally wounded enemy soldier, the soldier managed to fire three shots before expiring. All three shots ripped into the Ranger's leg. He would probably have lost the leg if one of his team members, a man nicknamed "Doc," had not expertly applied an emergency tourniquet. He was lucky since Doc's secondary military specialty was that of a medic.

No sooner had Team 43 been successfully extracted and all the support aircraft returned to the airfield when Team 23 announced, "Contact!" The Professor's team came across a way station of sorts, a shelter with barrels of rice and other food items. Once again, young Billy Armstrong, with the help of the Kit Carson Scout, Trang, saved the team when they hastily fired upon an approaching superior force that would have otherwise caught the team in an open, vulnerable position. The enemy force, probably thinking they were opposed by the lead element of a large U.S. force, immediately retreated and dispersed.

Since U.S. forces nearly always moved en masse, in large numbers and units, the Viet Cong and the North Vietnamese would not have suspected only six men opposed them. Therefore the team destroyed the contents within the way station. The extraction of Team 23 then proceeded without further incident.

That was fortunate because immediately afterwards, Team 12 initiated contact on a lone-armed enemy soldier and ended up in a fierce short firefight with what they suspected were three or more others. Since Charlie was using only small arms weapons, the responding gunships were actually delighted to be fired upon as the green tracers used by Charlie simply pinpointed their location.

The gunship pilots cheered, hollered and made all sorts of nasty insinuations about their targets over the radio when they reported the details of their reign of terror upon Charlie to the C & C. For good measure, Dunn called in an artillery fire mission from one of the two firebases, which had been both delighted and anxious to join in with their support.

Just after Wails advised him the Birddog was running on fumes and they had to head back, Team 31 called in with an alert. "The Kit Carson Scout with us is nervous and wants the team to retreat from its present course. He insists the team is approaching a fortified camp."

Even though the team leader wanted to proceed cautiously, he agreed to hunker down and wait until the Birddog returned and was back in the air to provide support. Dunn promised, "We'll be back as quickly as possible, Three one."

Wails alerted Larry Hill by radio to be ready to roll so Dunn would be able to jump out of the one Birddog and into the other one with no waste of time on the ground. Since Hill was a cherry pilot, Dunn openly directed him back to the area above the Team 31 sector. He notified the team they could Charlie Mike because he was on station.

Fifteen minutes later, the team leader screamed, "Contact!" Dunn immediately notified the TOC to scramble the choppers.

"Knuckle Two Eight, this is Three One, get us the fuck outta here, now! They are dug in with big shit! .51 cal heavy machine gun and .30 cal machine guns! Smoke out. Which way to the closest LZ? Over."

Since the team was receiving fire from heavy caliber weapons at dug-in positions, it had clearly chanced upon a main camp. The Kit Carson Scout had been right with his premonition and warnings.

"Knuckle Three One, this is Two Eight, I identify cranberry red smoke. Lima Zulu is one hundred south. Can you break contact or hopscotch? Over."

However, he did not wait for their answer. Instead, he switched frequencies twice to call in a fire mission to each of the two supporting artillery firebases. Since both firebases were due south of the team's position on the ground, he called for the first round from each to land well to the north and away from the team. He set up one to fire on an axis to the east and the other to the west. Then, he switched back to the team's frequency.

"Two Eight, Two Eight, goddamn where are you? Knuckle Two Eight, this is Three One. Over!" the team leader was screaming over the radio.

"This is Two Eight. Over."

"Fuck! Stay on the radio! Don't leave us! We're gonna die! We can't move! Fucking shooting from our entire front. Get the fucking gunships! I don't want to get killed! Fucking gunships! Now! Over."

"Three One, this is Two Eight. I will not leave you. I am calling in Red Leg and the gunships. Just hold on. Over."

Dunn switched to the intercom to instruct Hill, his frontseat, to maneuver the 0-1 to provide him a better view. Dunn then switched to the frequency of each artillery firebase. He purposely placed their first rounds to the north and far apart so he could accurately adjust the rounds fired from the two separate bases. He had to creep the rounds to land closer to do any damage to the entrenched enemy. After making his second set of artillery adjustments he heard from a pair of Devil gunships. They were now only moments away from joining the fight and he called the Three One team to tell them to pop another smoke so the gunships would know their exact location.

Then, he switched back to the Devils to establish a sweeping circular pattern on the east side only. He had to make certain that the Devil pilots did not fly within the arc of the artillery fire from the south, otherwise the helicopter gunship could be blown out of the sky by friendly artillery fire. When Dunn was satisfied the Devil gunnies understood the approach pattern he established for them, he switched back to the Three One team frequency.

"Fucking Two Eight! God damn it! Come in! Over." The team leader was screaming a string of obscenities.

"This is Knuckle Two Eight, go ahead, over," Dunn deliberately spoke calmly, hoping to help settle the team leader.

"Goddamn it! You have to stay on the radio with us or you're gonna get us killed! We are able to crawl...but very slowly. The fucking world is blowing up all around us! We can't be sure we're headed right. Fucking stay on the horn! Please stay on the radio with me! Please! Over."

"Three One, this is Two Eight, keep heading south. You have to go a full one hundred meters. Over."

"Roger, but please stay on the radio with us," pleaded the team leader in a plaintiff voice.

Dunn ignored the flashing on the Devil frequency for the moment since he could see the two gunships were making excellent gun runs on the pattern he had established. Instead, he called in one more adjustment on the eastern artillery. Next, he called for the western base to "Fire For Effect." Then, he switched to the Devil frequency and was surprised to hear from two "Tigersharks" which were two Cobras from the 192nd Assault Helicopter Company out of Phan Thiet.

The Tigersharks had monitored and were on station and ready and eager to assist, and their Cobras were on the west side of the zone. Dunn thought, *Excellent. I can set them up in a pattern on the west side to avoid the artillery and lay down killing fire on that side for the team.*

He also called the Devils to let them know they were doing a damn good job. The Peter Pilot, the Assistant Commander, for Devil 70 was scared as hell he might get the mini gunfire too close, and the AC, Aircraft Commander, was equally concerned about getting the rocket fire in too tight. In fact, when Dunn switched back to the Three One team, he heard the team leader report taking some shrapnel from the rockets. But, when the AC asked if they should back off, the answer was a resounding, "No!" The team leader begged, "...keep laying it on!

"Damn it, Hill!" Dunn yelled to his frontseat. "Quickly turn this around so I have a view of the contact site. Keep me so I can see the spot where that red smoke was." He had had to switch onto the intercom to direct his cherry frontseat. The guy had been flying due south, away from the action between the artillery arches. Larry Hill was afraid to turn for fear of flying into the artillery.

"Three One, this is Knuckle Two Eight, we have two sets of gunships and artillery working for you. Keep moving south. We will get you out of there. Over." Dunn knew he had to keep talking to the team periodically.

"Please, Two Eight, please stay on the radio. We're now moving. How much further do we have to go? There's fucking explosions everywhere.

You have got to get us the fuck outta here! Now! Goddamn it! Stay on the radio! Over." The team leader was now beginning to sound hoarse.

Secondary explosions! thought Dunn, his heartbeat racing even faster. *Yes, those are definitely secondary explosions!*

The series of secondary explosions he saw and heard had been caused by the western firebase with their battery of rounds. This meant the artillery explosions set off some ammunition or something to cause additional explosions. Dunn quickly called for the eastern base to also fire for effect. Just as he felt comfortable with the pattern of fire for the two Cobras, Hill, his frontseat, told him that an Air Force Forward Air Controller wanted to talk to him.

Dunn quickly dialed the FAC frequency into the fifth radio bank. "This is Wolfman One Zero," said an Air Force Captain flying in an OV10 airplane, "please be advised I have two fully loaded 'Fastmovers,' a flight of God's finest Phantom F-4s, looking to join in on the party. Over."

Dunn quickly briefed Wolfman on the situation: the location of the team on the ground in relation to the enemy, the patterns of the now active gunships on the east plus the Cobras on the west and the locations of the two firebases providing support. Wolfman suggested runs down the middle from south to north for the Fastmovers. Dunn instantly concurred.

So, now he had two parallel arches, like the McDonald Restaurant arches, of artillery rounds being fired from two different firebases. He had two sets of gunships and Cobras, each in a flat circular pattern outside of the arches, making passes with mini-guns and rockets. And, now, he also had two Phantoms descending between the arches, dropping bombs and napalm to the north of the team. To maintain contact with the team, each support element and his frontseat, he had to continually juggle and switch radio stations.

Meanwhile, the team managed to crawl nearly forty meters south of the point of contact. Miraculously, other than some flesh wounds suffered by two Rangers, there were no friendly casualties. Finally, the team got up and ran the remaining distance to the LZ, where they were safely extracted.

Dunn stayed on station in the air above the general location of the contact for another hour as he mopped up communications with all the supporting elements, giving and receiving laudatory feedback.

He was told to expect three companies of South Vietnamese troops to be inserted as a follow-up reactionary force. However, they did not arrive before he decided to finally head back. It would be after 1800 hours by the time he finally got back to the Hill. Although he had not eaten since 0630 hours, he wasn't particularly hungry; he was drained, both physically and emotionally.

When he pulled up to the company area, he noticed the men were engaged in a rambunctious game of volleyball. A net and court had been set up outside the TOC in the flat parking area. Everyone was either bare-chested or in undershirts and having a great time. The Major, still nattily attired in his full camouflage fatigues, greeted Dunn and invited him to join in the game.

"Sir, I would rather not...I'm just too tired," replied Dunn.

"Goddamn, Lieutenant, after sitting around for three days in an airplane, the exercise will do you good. I am giving you an order to play.

This isn't just for you. This is good for the goddamn morale of the men. Now, stow your gear right here in the TOC, and play some volleyball with the troops. That's an order."

Staples, who was listening and already sipping from his tall glass of Jim Beam, nodded to Dunn. After depositing his weapon and gear inside the TOC, Dunn emerged to watch the duel then in progress. The officers and headquarters elements were outgunned by a collection of all-stars from the platoons. An excellent volley ended with a point for the all-stars by a vicious dunk on the head of Rod Winthrop. Following the lost point, the officers called for Dunn to join them on the court. Before he could strip off his shirt to do so, Staples, who had momentarily before gone into the TOC, came back out and called to him.

"Lieutenant Dunn," shouted Staples, "sir, you have a telephone call in the TOC."

A Captain with Battery C, 32nd Field Artillery, located at a hill designated Firebase 6, was on the phone. The Captain requested a detailed recount of the incident involving their fire support for Team 31 that afternoon. So, Dunn gladly took his time to narrate the events of the entire contact. Naturally, he elaborated on the accuracy and devastating effects of the artillery rounds and when Dunn described the series of secondary, major explosions, the Captain was elated.

"I want to thank you guys for calling us," said the Field Artillery Captain. "Not enough Forward Observers take the time afterwards to call and report the effect of our fire support. When the gunners hear all you have told me, Lieutenant, they are going to be really excited. This is great. Thanks. We are glad to have helped out your team. Call on us anytime. We'll deliver for you."

"Here, Lieutenant," said Staples, handing Dunn the written routing information for connecting by the landline to A Battery, 7thBattalion, 15th Artillery, located at LZ Crusader. "I'm sure they would also appreciate a call telling them about their fire support today. Then, when you finish with them, I would like for you to tell me the whole story, too. After all, I could only monitor certain portions of the transmissions. While it was all going on, I could only guess at what was happening. You can fill me in on the details. I hope you don't mind you'll probably miss volleyball."

Staples smiled and saluted Dunn with his tall glass of Jim Beam. Dunn smiled appreciatively and made another call from TOC, this time to A Battery.

That night, following an especially spicy but tasty pork meal, a relatively concise Ops Briefing and a short meeting with his team leaders, Dunn relaxed by writing a long letter to Marie. In it he mentioned he felt proud of his contributions to the men in his unit and the job he was doing. He assured her that he was not in harm's way and was safe. In the balance of the letter he told and described his feelings for her. At the end he did ask her how Pop was enjoying being a guinea pig. This was because Pop had to endure a year of Marie learning how to cook.

Dunn slept soundly that night.

12
Surprises

THE FOLLOWING MORNING, DUNN WAS FAMISHED. He thoroughly enjoyed a hearty and leisurely breakfast and sat with a group of the men from his platoon. The rumor mill was in full swing, or else their informal lines of communication were simply more efficient...

"We're getting a new platoon sergeant soon."

"Yeah. I hear he was a fucking Ranger instructor in the mountains of Dahlonega, Georgia." If they were correct, then Dunn would be delighted.

"The officers coulda used ya in the game last night, sir. We kicked their butt!"

"Any truth to the rumor there's going to be an R&R tour to the World over the Christmas holidays?" If that were true, it would be a wonder for some lucky Ranger.

Dunn heard "Rusky" Gregorov was getting ready to go to Australia on his third R&R. Gregorov first volunteered to fight Communism as a Russian citizen for the U.S. Army, but recently had finally gotten his wish to become a U.S. citizen. Just last month, his former commander made this possible, and Major Wayne and Captain Phillips conducted the small ceremony.

Gregorov had been In Country continuously probably longer than any other soldier in the unit, having volunteered for Viet Nam in 1968. Rusky joined Charlie Rangers at the end of 1969, and distinguished himself innumerable times in contacts while in the field. Although still a bachelor, Gregorov was older than most of the men in the platoon. Even though he didn't join them with their drinking or drugs, they liked and respected him. The rest of the men generally looked up to him because of his maturity, his proven combat skills and his unwavering principles.

But Rusky did make good use of vodka; and because of it, his feet were probably in the best condition of anybody's in the unit. He frequently poured vodka on them to kill any possible fungus.

While most of the men were, at times, confused about the real reasons they were in 'Nam, there was never any question about Rusky. He was there to help defeat Communism and had volunteered to serve his newfound homeland even before he became a US citizen.

During an enjoyable and extended conversation, Dunn had been favorably impressed with Rusky's wit and intelligence. When he'd discovered Gregorov also possessed a Top Secret security clearance, he realized he had the perfect candidate for Staples in TOC. Dunn decided he would wait until Rusky returned from R&R before he advised him of his new job.

I know his team leader will be upset, but with Rusky in the TOC, he will be better able to serve the unit, thought Dunn. *Staples is going to be delighted with Rusky and really surprised he was unaware of his Top Secret clearance. Maybe Staples can help Rusky get a long overdue promotion.*

Just then the Major's driver interrupted them. Pulling Dunn aside, he advised Dunn the Old Man wanted to see both him and SP/4 Goldstein in the TOC as soon as possible.

Excellent, thought Dunn, *The Major is going to keep his word. Goldstein is finally going to be transferred out of my platoon. Great! Goldstein has just been sitting around waiting for the proverbial other shoe to drop. Morale has been adversely affected ever since I gave him that order to go into the field. The men did not like that one bit. Everybody can see themselves in his jungle boots.*

After serving as a volunteer for a couple years on combat ambush tours, a veteran Ranger should be allowed to say "enough" without having to cry "uncle." Perhaps a position has opened up in the rear for Goldstein. That would be a fitting conclusion to this uncomfortable situation, especially since his DEROS is less than a couple months away. Dunn hurried off to collect Goldstein from the platoon hooch.

"Sir, Lieutenant Dunn reporting with Specialist Goldstein, as ordered."

"At ease, Lieutenant," barked Wayne, who was seated at a small field table that had been set up just inside the TOC entrance. Butler stood behind the Major, and Staples was sitting at one of the radios further inside. No one else was present in the TOC.

"Specialist Goldstein. Step front and center. I asked your platoon leader to bring you to report to me because I want you to hear what I have to say, directly from me. I want you to understand exactly what I have to say to you. Is that understood?"

"Yes, sir," said Goldstein without any show of emotion.

"You were given a direct order by Lieutenant Dunn to accompany your Team 23 into the field on a mission. The team went into the field without you and, in fact, made contact with the enemy without you.

You deliberately chose to violate a lawful order. Sergeant Butler was a witness to the direct order you received. Sergeant Butler witnessed your wanton and willful violation of the lawful order given to you.

"As commander, I am responsible for the discipline in this unit. Also, I insure that all lawful orders are obeyed or the violator is punished. Therefore, I have advised First Field Force, this day, that I have formally requested from the 173rd Airborne Brigade the convening of a General Court Martial. I am hereby charging you with a willful violation of a direct, lawful order. You will shortly be provided with an officer who will be your defense counsel. Your defense counsel will advise you of your rights and defend you at the General Court Martial. Until such time as I otherwise direct, you are restricted to your platoon and the general confines of the company area. Do you understand everything I have just told you?"

"Yes, sir."

"Do you have any questions?"

"No, sir."

"Good. You are dismissed." Then, turning to Dunn, who had been observing and listening with steely silence, "Lieutenant. You are also dismissed."

When Dunn left the TOC, he headed over to the 1st Platoon area hoping to find Robert Lee, as he needed to talk to somebody about what had just happened. In the TOC he had been absolutely speechless and unable to think of a thing to say. He felt as if he had been sucker-punched by his own commander. The last time he similarly felt as if his breath was unexpectedly and suddenly sucked out of him was when he first stepped off the plane upon his arrival in Viet Nam. This incident, he felt, was probably going to prove as incessant and insidious as the oppressive heat.

However, as he approached the 1st Platoon area, he spotted Lee in conversation with the Team 43 Leader. Overhearing just some of the one-sided conversation, he realized this was not a good time to seek Lee's advice.

"Goddamn it, sir. There is no fucking excuse. I almost fired up my fucking best friend! Both teams could have fucked up each other. If you can't read a map, you have no goddamn fucking business flying C & C for us." The team leader was still furious over the map-reading incident, which had placed the two teams onto a collision course. His reaction was understandable and appropriate.

So, rather than retreating to his own platoon area, Dunn returned to the TOC and found that neither Wayne nor Butler was present. But, the place was active with a half dozen soldiers working on maps, radios or the field telephone.

Phillips was trying to get information from ARVN on the base camp that had been discovered by Team 31. Staples was talking on the radio with Winthrop, who was up in the 0-1. The three companies of South Vietnamese had finally been inserted as the reactionary force. However, Winthrop confirmed that after nearly two hours on the ground, they had not yet moved from the Landing Zone, where they were actually eating lunch. After all this time, there probably would not be much reaction from the reactionary force.

After a while, Jack Kent and Kelvin Appier stopped by the TOC on their way to lunch and invited Dunn to join them. Even though he had no appetite, Dunn decided to tag along. During the lunch Kent explained that two days before, he had observed what he considered as suspicious, activities by two of the 3rd Platoon hooch maids.

"I became concerned when I noticed the two hooch maids were walking in different areas of the company...there was no reason for them to be out of my platoon area. After watching them acting suspiciously, I soon realized what they were doing-pacing off the distances between all the structures and then making written annotations and secreting them on their persons when they thought no one was looking.

"I told Staples to alert the 173rd Criminal Investigation Detachment, who then apprehended the two hooch maids. Both hooch maids were arrested as Viet Cong sympathizers. The written annotations turned out to be detailed diagrams of the entire compound, showing distances and dimensions of the structures as well as the number of men and type of equipment in each. The detailed drawing would have been a treasure map for enemy sappers or a mortar attack. Well, the two, sweet, frail-looking young Vietnamese girls are now on their way to take up residence in 'The LBJ Ranch,' the Long Binh Jail."

"I, for one," said Dunn, "sure hope this incident does not affect the company retaining the help of all the other hooch maids. I have actually come to appreciate the few little creature comforts, such as clean uniforms, they provide."

"Since everybody else feels the same way, we should not be surprised when it has no effect," Lee agreed with Dunn's sentiments.

The afternoon passed quickly and relatively quietly. Dunn performed some administrative tasks for a few of the men in the platoon and straightened out some apparent discrepancies in ammunition allotments. Since he did not yet have a replacement platoon sergeant, he helped out the team leaders, who were preparing their teams for the next series of clandestine insertions. There was no mention by anyone about the serious situation facing Goldstein.

"So, tell us about your first day of flying Command and Control from the backseat of an 0-1. How do you feel?" Dunn started the conversation that evening at supper with his question to Rod Winthrop.

"I don't know where you guys got the notion that the pilots try to make their backseat barf on a cherry flight. Sure, my stomach was queasy the entire day, but my pilot purposely kept the aircraft smooth and steady," extolled Winthrop.

All the other lieutenants, including Dunn, argued otherwise but indicated the queasiness would soon fade with experience. They took turns describing the ordeals of their first day as observers in the 0-1.

Then, Winthrop admitted it had only been his frontseat's second mission. Larry Hill, his pilot, had described to him how hectic it had been for him on his first day of piloting for Charlie Rangers. According to Hill, the fierce reputation of Charlie Rangers was quickly spreading among the Army aviation units. Charlie Rangers was hailed as the finest of all Ranger units, having conducted the most missions, the most productive missions and the most widespread insertions in all of Viet Nam.

That evening, the operations briefing in the Tactical Operations Center, by Phillips, turned out to be interesting and informative. "The South Vietnamese reactionary force reported Team 31 uncovered a huge base camp used by the enemy as a training site and as a hospital complex. In fact, the damn camp is the entire mountain. They have a massive complex of underground caverns that are interconnected by an immense number of large tunnels tall enough for a man to walk upright.

"When the reactionary force went in, they found the enemy had hastily retreated, leaving behind operating tables with evidence of recent use, large caches of medical equipment that weighed over 2,000 pounds and hundreds of unopened boxes of medical supplies. Also found at the training site were training manuals, mock-ups and propaganda leaflets.

"Also, the reactionary force reported there was evidence of four, destroyed ammunition bunkers. But, incredibly, the pounding from the artillery and the Phantoms had not disturbed much of the underground portions of the complex."

Phillips then concluded with a series of special announcements:

"Charlie Rangers has received notice it will be provided one R&R tour back to the states over the Christmas holiday season. This experiment is the first for an R&R to the States. Furthermore, the commander is permitting an extra two travel days, thus extending the leave time for the R&R from the customary seven days to nine.

2nd Platoon has the three men with the longest time In Country without having yet taken an R&R. Therefore, the lucky person to go to the States over Christmas will come from the 2nd Platoon. Dunn, I request you consult with me within the week as to who will be the lucky man.

"Next, the unit shall continue working in the Tiger Mountains through-out the following week. Then, the Fourth Platoon will leave us to set up the ARVN Ranger School in Pleiku. At the same time, the rest of the unit will stand down for a period of up to ten days in Nha Trang. This means there will be a temporary halt to missions.

"You will be glad to know the unit will be moving into permanent-style buildings with running water and hot showers. The men shall then be free to go to the Enlisted or NCO Clubs and the officers to the Officers Club. Also, they may be able to go to a movie theater or shop at a PX. This 'stand down' is a reward for your successes in the field.

"When the unit, less the 3rdPlatoon, then returns from Nha Trang, the unit will move to a new camp yet to be determined. It will probably be set up in the vicinity of the Tuy Hoa airfield. Tuy Hoa is a town located along the coast of the South China Sea. In the past, most of the assets supporting Charlie Rangers have been based out of Tuy Hoa anyway, so this move makes a lot of sense from that perspective.

"Charlie Rangers is still going to be under the operational control of The Herd. The real reason for any move would probably be the 173rd wants us to work our magic on another range of gook-infested moun-tains," concluded Phillips.

A move would mean learning new topography and more map-reading challenges. The new terrain will also be better for the safety of the teams, thought Dunn. He also felt strongly that if the ambush patrols worked any concentrated area too long, then Charlie could get wise to their Ranger tactics. Surprise was the Ranger's greatest ally. If Charlie did become aware of their presence, he could form Ranger hunting parties or react in force against the lonely six men. In any case, Dunn looked forward to everything being new, including the new challenges.

Naturally, the team leaders were pretty excited about all the news that came from the Ops Briefing. Dunn started out by telling about the base camp discovered by Team 31. He also described for them the series of explosions he had witnessed from the air caused by the eruptions of the munitions bunkers from the artillery strikes.

Then, he singled out Halloway, the soldier in their company who had been the longest In Country without having taken an R&R. Halloway was to let Dunn know the name of the lucky soldier that was to spend Christmas at home-the mainland-United States.

Whenever an R&R tour was announced, the soldier longest In Country without an R&R had first choice. That soldier could then choose to accept the R&R tour to its particular destination or pass it up to the next soldier in line. If the first soldier passed it up, then he again had first choice on the next R&R destination. Some soldiers wanted Hawaii; others wanted Australia; and others chose Bangkok. So, Halloway had first choice at going to the States for his R&R.

Finally, Dunn told them about the stand-down in Nha Trang being given to the men by the Old Man after one more week of missions. When the Ranger cheers subsided, he also told them to be prepared for the upcoming move to Tuy Hoa or to wherever they would be sent.

Some of the guys indicated they were going to sorely miss their present hooch maids, while some of the others cheered about hiring new ones. Since they did not have a replacement platoon sergeant, they all volunteered to do the interviewing process to pick out young hooch maids. Each of the team leaders also expressed relief at getting away from the ugly terrain of the Tiger Mountains.

That night Dunn wrote Marie a long letter. It was not typical, as in this letter he was not sentimental. But rather, it was an outpouring from his heart. She would probably not understand why he was writing about the incident, but she would instinctively know it was bothering him. Even though he left out details about the combat missions, Dunn felt better after writing an analysis of the Goldstein situation. He needed an outlet where he could vent his frustration.

Dunn was angry because he allowed himself to be in a position where he had been used. *Since I gave the actual order as a henchman of the Duke, I should have recognized the series of prior moves that would intimate this power play. Perhaps...had I played my part differently, I could have avoided Goldstein's situation. Well, I'm not yet checkmated. Somehow, "the pound of flesh" might still be protected from the Major's decision. However, I can't foresee a solution to the problem that has me so vexed.*

Dunn's mind then wandered to another thought, a quote from Shakespeare: "The world is but a stage; full of sound and fury, signifying nothing." Before he fell asleep that night, he forced himself to calm his brooding, inner anger.

The following week quickly passed. Two more teams made contact, but none during any of the three days in which Dunn flew C & C. Fortunately, there were no Rangers wounded. There were also no additional trophies from the two contacts to be sent to the armorer in the rear.

On each day he did fly C & C, Dunn used his map-reading skills. The teams would signal with a mirror or a color panel to him in the plane and when he spotted the locations, he relayed the coordinates of their locations to them.

Dunn was happy to use his in-air time in the 0-1 to practice his map reading and also as a backseat pilot. Since his frontseat was different each day, he collected different pointers and helpful hints. He thought all the aviation warrant officers were great guys.

Three nights before the unit was to split up and break camp for the stand-down, all his team leaders were present for the briefing. There was only one team each from 1st and 3rd Platoons and the X-ray Team left in the field, but they would be extracted the next day.

Following the short briefing, Halloway announced to Dunn that the platoon had reached a consensus concerning the Christmas R&R. "Sir, the platoon has unanimously agreed and decided. PFC William Armstrong will spend his Christmas on R&R with his family in Topeka, Kansas. We know he hasn't been In Country longer than most of us, but nobody loves his country with quite the zeal and passion that he does. And, nobody has proven his Ranger courage and combat effectiveness faster than Kansas. We are tired of hearing all about his mom's hot apple pie plus his God and Country rhetoric. Sir, you have to send him home for the holidays. We don't think the rest of us could stand being stuck with him here over Christmas."

Dunn was stunned and immensely proud of his guys. Here was Halloway, initially absolutely against taking this 18-year-old boy with love beads into his team. Now, he had galvanized the entire platoon into recognizing and rewarding the young man's courageous deeds and patriotic fervor. Halloway not only gave up his opportunity to use the R&R for himself; but had also convinced all the others entitled, to do likewise. These guys were really special heroes.

KA...BLOOM! The sudden and loud explosion initially stunned the group of team leaders. Some of them quickly grabbed for weapons as the rest, led by Dunn, raced off in the direction of 3rd Platoon.

"That sounded like a fuckin' frag grenade," yelled Ski and that was exactly what Dunn thought.

When they got to the 3rd Platoon area, Dunn spotted Pappy lying face down on the ground about fifteen feet from the platoon hooch. Wayne was bent down assisting Pappy, who staggered to his feet with the help of the Major. Lieutenant Kent used one end of the hooch as his private quarters; Pappy used the other end. The men of the platoon slept in the middle section. The end that was used by Pappy had been completely blown away.

"That fucking pot-head! That dope user, Goldstein, tried to frag me!" Butler shrieked. Dunn could not understand the rest of the incoherent ranting by Pappy as the Major led him away to his private quarters, but what he had heard sent a shiver up his spine and tied a tight knot in his stomach.

"Sir, I think you should secure the area of the blast and report this incident to the 173rd Criminal Investigation Detachment immediately," said Dunn to Phillips, who emerged from checking the hooch.

Fortunately, the building had been empty at the time of the blast because Kent was having a platoon meeting in the mess hall at the time and nobody else was in the hooch. "This is a serious criminal matter now," Dunn concluded.

Just at that moment, Goldstein walked up to Dunn and said, "Hey, sir, there is no way they can try to pin this on me. I had absolutely nothing to do with it. This is fucking bullshit!"

"This is a matter for the C.I.D. to handle now. If they feel it necessary to talk to you, I am sure they will. Until then, you probably should not discuss this matter with anybody... including me," Dunn told him.

Phillips dispersed everybody back to his own area and instructed Staples to cordon off the damaged section of the hooch. Then he headed for the TOC to call the 173rd Criminal Investigation Detachment by landline. Dunn headed back to the relative safety of his own tent.

❧

Early the next morning Dunn left on a whirlwind tour to fulfill his most recent assigned extra duty. He was the paymaster for Charlie Rangers that month and being paymaster afforded Dunn one small benefit-he would miss the busy work of coordinating the company move to Nha Trang.

One hundred forty men and thirteen conexs would move by air, and eight vehicles with twelve men would travel by convoy. Joe was glad he would not have to be with the convoy, as it would be an all day trip besides being very dangerous.

Jack Kent was in charge of the convoy. The Major probably would have sent him to pick up the money earlier, but the weather had not cooperated. It was strange how typhoons would hit different areas of Viet Nam at different times.

The Old Man wanted the troops to have the money from their pay in order to spend it during the downtime in Nha Trang. Dunn would be able to pick up the Piasters there at LZ English to pay the indigenous personnel and the Kit Carson Scouts. However, he had to travel to Phu Tai Military Base by way of Phu Cat Air Force Base to pick up the scrip, the MPC, Military Payment Currency, to pay the troops. Dunn was taking Smitty, a Spec-4 in his platoon, with him as an armed guard.

Then he would have to stop at Ahn Khe to pay the rear area personnel, the hospital at Quin Nhon and then to Camh Ranh Bay to pay those recovering at the 6th Convalescent Center. Next he would have to stop in Pleiku to pay 4th Platoon, who was establishing the ARVN Ranger School. Finally, he would meet the rest of the company in Nha Trang to disburse the balance of the money. He would also be bringing back with him a finance records team to straighten out all the pay problems and complaints of the men in the company.

Dunn was concerned about making efficient travel connections because of the weather. He knew the men would be furious and disappointed if they did not have their pay so as to better enjoy every moment of free time. He knew flooding south of LZ English had already cost the lives of four hundred Vietnamese. Roads were washed out and impassable and air traffic in certain sections was at a standstill. However, one moment there was a deluge and the next, sunshine. Somehow, he would have to find the sunny route.

13
Stand Down

AFTER PICKING UP THE FINANCE RECORDS TEAM, and the sum of Thirty-six thousand, seven hundred and forty-three dollars ($36,743), Dunn and his armed guard headed for the terminal at Phu Cat. There, he ran into LT Richard White, one of his West Point classmates. White was in the Engineers and had just gotten into country.

"I'm on my way to my first assignment In Country, to the 173rd Airborne Brigade. I thought I was going to be one of the first in our class to make it to Nam, but you beat me by a few months. Man, I wish I had run into you sooner. We could have downed some brew and laughed about how bad the Corps of Cadets has gone to hell. The monsoons have stranded me at this terminal for three days," enthused White to his buddy.

After a short and sweet reunion, the weather cooperated fully, and they all got flights out. Three days after originally leaving the unit, Dunn and party completed their appointed rounds, arriving in Nha Trang about eight hours after the unit was settled. Each man was required to sign for and collect his payment, which Dunn counted out to him. Despite his best efforts at being careful and precise, Dunn found himself short the sum of one hundred eighty-seven dollars ($187) when he concluded paying everyone and surrendered the balance to the finance team.

He hated to have to tell Marie in his next letter to her, since the amount was nearly half of his full month pay, including the extra for combat and airborne status. The Army would deduct the shortfall from his next paycheck.

Dunn was having his entire paycheck deposited into a savings program that offered a high interest rate to soldiers in a combat area. He and Marie were saving for a car and figured this was a good way to have the funds upon his return to the States. Whenever Dunn needed money, he would negotiate a check at one of the bases. At home, Marie continued working as a lab technician and it was her money that supported the two of them while he was in 'Nam.

Well, he had not planned on any of the expensive revelry in which most of the men would soon be engaged. So, now, he had additional incentive not to spend money foolishly.

〜

The Major insisted Phillips deliver a class to the entire company on the perils of venereal disease. In his talk, Phillips indicated he arranged for a local medical outfit to provide plenty of penicillin shots on an "as needed" and "confidential" basis.

Next, he mentioned while on the base, the men would be required to observe traditional military customs, such as saluting any officer.

Finally, the men were instructed to present themselves at all times in complete uniform or suffer the loss of freedom. This meant the men were required to wear hats and have their boots bloused, that is, the pant leg of their camouflage fatigues had to be neatly tucked into their boots. Also, this meant the Charlie Rangers were going to appear more strac than the REMF units stationed there. Most of the local soldiers they had seen did not take any pride in their appearance. The local soldiers seemed to work at strutting and looking crass, trying to look as if they had just come out of the bush.

〜

The Charlie Rangers were more than delighted to comply with the Old Man. After all, they were now living in relative comfort in wooden billets with running hot and cold water and regular latrines.

"Hey, sir." called out the Mad Swede to Dunn. "Did you hear about the first thing Snake and Crush did when we got here?"

"Oh, no," reacted Dunn, "what trouble could they have got into already?"

"Well, the first thing they did was to rush in the barracks and flush all the fucking toilets."

Dunn doubted there could be anything that would dampen the high festive spirits of his men. Of course, 2nd Platoon had always managed to perform the unexpected, so he wondered what mischief they would undoubtedly pull here.

Joe knew most of the men would be heading to the front gate or to the various clubs. It wasn't long before they literally stunned him with their transformations. Their appearances were not only disarming, they actually looked quite military with clean fatigues, clean shaves and polished boots.

The town of Nha Trang was off limits to all U.S. troops and also to the Kit Carson Scouts, who were paid in Piasters, which they could not spend at the U.S. facilities. Supposedly, no one went to town, but the men could sign in "Vietnamese Ladies" into the front gate between 7:00 p.m. and 10:00 p.m. daily.

The attraction at the front gate was obvious. Earlier in the day, Dunn witnessed an ocean of bicycles and crowds of women assembled. There were hundreds of young, local Vietnamese women dressed in their finest silk ao dai gathered just outside the gate.

An American GI simply walked out among them until he found one who appealed to him. Then, he would accompany her through the heavily sandbagged entrance as her escort. These young girls were thrilled and anxious to show their appreciation, as they could earn more in one night pleasuring an American GI than as a laborer in an entire month.

There were also plenty of other activities for the troops to enjoy. There was the PX for shopping, bowling alleys, craft shops, movie theaters and clubs. Joe intended to take advantage of the MARS Station, Military Affiliate Radio Station, used by soldiers to call home via Signal Corps and ham radio equipment. The service was free and on a first come, first serve basis, weather conditions permitting. Since there was an eleven-hour time difference, he wanted to call at a time that improved his chances of reaching Marie. Therefore, he figured he would call when he knew she would be asleep, which would be during the day in 'Nam. He didn't care if he had to wait all day.

That night, while the men enjoyed their new playground, the officers of the unit ate together at the Officers Club where they were also treated to a wonderful show put on by a traveling Australian band that happened to be performing. The REMF sure had a good life. For every one soldier who was actually involved in combat, there were probably twelve soldiers living in relative comfort at the rear in a support role.

The next day, Joe waited for six hours to place his MARS call, and sure enough, he awakened Marie out of a deep sleep. Her mom answered the phone and first talked with the female ham radio operator who helped to place Joe's call.

It was strange to relay his message through another person. "He says he is fine and he loves you," she relayed Joe's message. Then, a moment later the ham operator told him, "She says she will always love you."

Joe could barely hear Marie's voice, even though he could not always make out exactly what she said. But he definitely heard her when she yelled, "Over!" at the end of her sentences. So, he was sure she had been able to hear his voice, too.

The ham operator had been adorable the way she had helped translate. Joe felt the two-minute phone call had been worth the six-hour wait. Right then, he felt there was nothing that could possibly ruin his great mood.

But, early that evening, the Major dispatched him to the local jail operated by the Military Police. They had locked up eight Rangers, all from 2ndPlatoon, of course. The MPs had failed to search their prisoners. Consequently, the Rangers used their K-Bars and other devices to totally dismantle the jail from the inside out!

By the time Dunn arrived at the jail, the men had already escaped. Probably more out of embarrassment, than from any assurances from Dunn, the Captain in charge of the MP jail decided not to pursue the matter further.

"Lieutenant," said the MP Captain sternly, "I am cutting your men some slack because I know you are a combat unit. They have probably been stuck in the field, and this is their first freedom period in a long time. But, this area is just like being stateside...you must control your men. They do more damage than the enemy. Any further incidents, and I will personally see to it they are put in chains and escorted to LBJ."

Turning to view the extensive damage the Rangers had done to his jail, the Captain did not ask any questions. So, Dunn did not even try to respond but took the opportunity to quickly depart.

〴

That night, SSG Reginald "Peace" Parvis and SSG Lars "The Mad Swede" Swenson were at the Enlisted Men's Club when some rowdy GI's tried to provoke a fight by ridiculing the Rangers. The GI's were assigned to the Engineer Companies in 1stBattalion, 22ndInfantry. Peace managed to talk The Mad Swede and friends out of doing anything rash. Nothing happened, except the bouncer threw out the rowdy group of GI's.

Later, as Parvis and Swenson walked out of the club, fifteen guys jumped them. Parvis' face was badly cut up by a broken bottle before the bouncer and others from inside the club were able to disperse the fight before more damage could be done to the two Rangers.

Having been notified, Dunn arrived at the hospital while the doctor was still working on the twenty-eight stitches Parvis' face needed to repair the damage done by the bottle. *Not a pretty sight*, thought Dunn. *I know I could never be a doctor.*

〴

Later... about 0100 hours, the *entire* 2nd Platoon slipped away in a truck, loaded with plenty of CS grenades which were filled with a riot-control gas that burns the eyes and mucous membranes. Abandoning the vehicle at a safe distance, Dunn sent four men to scout the entire perimeter of the target. When they returned, they provided a detailed description of the two billets of 4thEngineer Company and the locations of four Military Police jeeps whose occupants seemed to be sleeping.

The Military Police had been alerted much earlier of a possible incident and had responded because they already had the prior unfortunate dealing with the Rangers.

After stealthily securing the doors on the billets, the 2nd Platoon members popped dozens of the CS grenades in about five seconds time. Then all hell broke loose. Those trapped in the billets really suffered. The Stars and Stripes, the Armed Forces newspaper, later reported that twenty-nine GI's were injured, six requiring hospitalization.

Four jeeps activated a loudspeaker system and their last words were, "Okay. They are in the area. We've got them surrounded." Then, all four jeeps were simultaneously gassed and the MP's took to full flight. The few Engineers, who did manage to escape from the billets, wound up with a club over their head.

"A perfect surprise ambush," praised Dunn, "I don't think people from that unit will gang up on a Charlie Ranger again."

While the Stars and Stripes later reported the incident was a racial brawl, the fight was actually nothing more than wannabe REMF's against true combat soldiers.

The following morning, the Base Commander summoned the Duke and politely requested the Rangers stay in their own company area or soon depart the base. Surprisingly, the Major did not even feign being upset. Instead, he publicly championed the men, praising their appearance, conduct and unity. As a result, the men responded by gladly welcoming the return to the field environment.

Earlier, all of the men, including the officers, decided not to be seen again at any of the clubs on post. A club system official ruled the indigenous personnel-the Kit Carson Scouts-were not allowed in the clubs, not even as a guest, for a lot of cockeyed reasons. The clubs rolled out the red carpet and welcomed the red light ladies who were escorted by the REMF troops. However, they slammed the door in the face of the men who lived with the Rangers, fought with the Rangers and died with the Rangers. Therefore, the tight-knit family of Charlie Rangers looked forward to returning to their home in the field, an environment where the supposedly elusive enemy was more clearly identifiable.

The rest of the day was devoted primarily to the task of moving to a new base camp. Phillips called the senior Non Commissioned Officers and the Officers together to present a concise briefing: "The company will move back to Phan Thiet. While we probably will only be there for about three weeks, I admit we do not know for sure just how long it will be. The 192nd Assault Helicopter Company, the Polecats and Tigersharks, will supply slick helicopter and gunship support while we are in Phan Thiet. The Birddog pilots will come from Dong Ba Tin, a base near the port of Camh Ranh Bay. Details on artillery support, enemy disposition, radio frequencies and all other mission essential data will be provided later, once the unit is established in its new tent city."

After the terse briefing, Wayne and Phillips called Dunn over and introduced him to his new Platoon Sergeant, E-6, Promotable, Frank C. London. London was awaiting his promotion orders to the E-7 rank of Sergeant First Class.

Dunn was ecstatic as he remembered London from the second phase of Ranger School. London was the principal instructor for all of the mountain training exercises, including rappelling. He remembered London to be a master with ropes and knot tying. Also, he remembered that London had been an inspirational and motivational leader to both the students and the other cadre personnel in Ranger School. Dunn felt if he had his choice from the entire Army, he could not have selected anyone better qualified.

"Sergeant London, welcome to 2nd Platoon. You are going to love working with the men, and they are going to be glad to have you as their platoon sergeant. I know I am," greeted Dunn.

"From what I hear, I think we'll make a great team, sir," London nodded with a grin and a firm handshake. "Now, I've got a lot to do to get your platoon ready for this move," he said.

London was the same height as Dunn but with a stockier build and a chubby face that was nearly always smiling. He was also about ten years his senior. This was London's second tour to 'Nam. His first tour had been in the Mekong Delta river region with the 9th Infantry Division.

"One more thing, Lieutenant," Wayne said, turning around to face Dunn. "Your man, Goldstein, visited JAGC, Judge Advocate General Corps, office yesterday. Evidently, he convinced a goddamn military attorney to represent him in his upcoming court martial. I don't know why the Army is wasting time and money on a goddamn malingerer. The case is open and shut. Goldstein disobeyed a goddamn direct order. Anyway, sometime today you have to go to JAGC. Ask for Captain John Edgerson, the attorney for Goldstein. He wants to talk to you about the case. Whenever you are ready, see Staples. He will assign a driver to take you to JAGC."

"Fine, sir. I will talk to Staples now."

"When you talk to that goddamn attorney, just stick to the facts. You gave Goldstein an order, and he disobeyed it. There is no reason for me, as the commander, to be dragged into this waste of time. But, I am supporting you on this, Lieutenant. If it is absolutely necessary, I will meet with this attorney.

"Goddamn attorneys are worse than Charlie. They don't care I have a war to wage, that I have to look out for what is best for the entire unit. God forbid I have to *enforce* a lawful order. I suppose they think I should just cancel a mission whenever one of my troops doesn't feel like going into the field that day.

"If you are going over there now, tell Staples you can take my driver. I won't be needing my vehicle for the next three hours, and you should be back long before then."

When Dunn found Staples, he was just returning with Specialist Ramos from the Class 6 Store, where he had purchased a re-supply of Jim Beam. After explaining the Major's message, Dunn pulled Staples aside.

"Tell me, Sergeant Staples, what were the results, if any, on the investigation of the fragging incident involving Butler?"

"Sir, the Criminal Investigation Detachment of the 173rd did a thorough job and submitted their findings to the Old Man. He never released the results and officially declared the matter terminated. However, the whole unit is aware of what actually happened. Pappy tried to put the blame on Goldstein.

"Well, Goldstein had an airtight alibi and had absolutely nothing to do with the incident. The C.I.D. determined that Pappy, himself, was the only person who could possibly have set off that grenade. They also found the grenade was from a lot under Sergeant Butler's lock and supervision. He was also drunk at the time of the grenade's explosion. However, sir, as I said, according to the Old Man, the incident is now officially closed. There is to be no further discussion of this unfortunate 'accident.'"

Ramos handed the bag containing the bottles of Jim Beam to Staples and then turned to Dunn. "Where to, sir? I understand I am to be your driver for the next couple of hours."

"Thanks, Ramos. Please take me to the JAGC office. It is next to the Provost office. Do you know where that is?"

"Roger that, sir. Airborne All The Way! Hop in and let's go. It's within walking distance of the PX. I passed right by it earlier today."

They reached the small building that housed the Provost and the JAGC officers in less than ten minutes. Since Dunn had no idea how long he would be, he asked Ramos to wait there for him.

"No sweat, sir, I am used to waiting. I've got a couple of college correspondence courses with me I am working on to keep me occupied."

Dunn entered the wooden building and was immediately impressed with how orderly and neat it appeared.

"May I help you, sir?" asked a young female soldier. She was the first round-eyed girl he had seen since the stewardesses on the plane when he came over.

"I am looking for a Captain John Edgerson."

"You are in luck. He is in that office directly behind you, sir."

Dunn knocked on the door that was not closed all the way and through the windowpanes on the door he saw a good-looking man reading a book. The man was seated behind a desk piled high with stuffed manila folders. Looking up at the knock, the man beckoned him to enter.

"Come on in. Close the door behind you and have a seat. How can I help you?"

"Sir, my name is Lieutenant Dunn with Charlie Rangers. I understand you are representing Specialist Goldstein."

"So, you are his platoon leader. You are the one who gave him a direct order that he subsequently disobeyed. Right?"

"I am his platoon leader. I did give him an order to go to the field on an ambush mission with his team. He did not go on the mission."

"Do you know why he did not go?"

"No, sir. But, I do know that he did not want to go into the field anymore."

"So, before you gave him the order to go into the field, he had already told you he wanted to be relieved from having to go on any further ambush missions. Isn't that correct?

"Yes, sir, it is."

"Tell me something. Do you have any personal dislike for Specialist Goldstein or any particular reason to consider him a substandard soldier?"

"No, sir, quite the contrary. Shortly before this matter, I met with his team leader concerning his exemplary performance on his last mission with his team. Based on the testimony of his team leader, I recommended Goldstein for a Bronze Star with Valor Device. I had no reason, prior to his request to be removed from the field, to consider him any differently from all the other men in the platoon."

"Does Goldstein know you submitted him for a valor medal?"

"I never said anything to him. However, I feel certain his team leader would have told him he was submitted for it."

"Did you know he was approaching his DEROS on his second consecutive tour of performing combat missions with your unit?"

"Yes, sir."

"Please tell me, Lieutenant Dunn, why is it that you ordered him to go to the field when he had already asked you not to send him anymore?"

"Based on his application not to go to the field, I requested Goldstein be transferred out of my platoon. The commander stated he would not grant the transfer unless he was confident Goldstein was earnest in his appeal. He directed me to give Goldstein the order to confirm the resolve of Goldstein. I simply wanted Goldstein transferred. His frame of mind, his intentions and his reasons are his own business and he has chosen not to reveal them to me.

"However, the rest of the men still choose to perform missions and I am concerned with their state of mind. So, I want him transferred. I don't want his situation to adversely affect the rest of the men. This situation is already having a negative affect and I just don't know the extent or what toll it will eventually take. Quite frankly, sir, I hope you can help him; but what is even more important to me, I just hope this is resolved quickly."

"So, you're not looking to get him busted?"

"No, sir. As I said, I hope you can help him. I'm not sure how all this works. Major Wayne thinks this is pretty clear-cut. Goldstein was given an order that he disobeyed. Perhaps in a civilian courtroom, you would have room to maneuver. But, here you will have a panel of military officers. The setting is wartime. The order on its face is not only lawful but also is ordinary for our unit. I think you have an uphill battle, sir."

"When I was graduated from law school, I didn't expect to change the world. However, I always hoped to serve as the champion of the little guy. In my own way, I believe I help save lives. Your Goldstein is the type of little guy who deserves a champion. This incident could very well mess up his life. Tell me one more thing. Why is it Major Wayne decided on a court martial instead of administrative punishment? After all, he could have simply given Goldstein an Article 15 and demoted him without question or interference of his judgment."

"I have no idea, sir. You will have to ask Major Wayne that question."

"Dunn, when you came in here, I expected an adversarial if not a hostile attitude. I am delighted you possess an open mind and actually appear to want to be helpful. Is there anything you can suggest for me to use in preparation of a defense for Goldstein?"

"Yes, sir..."

"Let's drop the 'sir' now," interrupted Edgerson, "and please call me John. The Army gave me a sweet financial incentive package, which meant I have to serve for a couple years; But, I'm not even certain I pin on my rank properly. So, let's concentrate on facts helpful to my client and dispense with the military formalities. Shall we?"

"That works for me. It seems like this whole country has dispensed with military customs anyway. So, what I suggest is you speak with members of his team, the men in the platoon and men in the rest of the company who know him. Establish he is an excellent combat soldier who is worthy of valorous recognition, not punishment. Make the issue his right to voluntarily terminate his field combat role. Perhaps you can possibly void the whole issue of not following the order given by me."

"Can I rely on you as a primary character witness?"

"Actually, no. I don't really know Goldstein. When I tried to talk to him, he wouldn't open up to me. So, I don't know him. I have never personally witnessed him in the field. Plus, I have another problem."

"What's that?"

"Well, I work for Major Wayne. He is my commander. He rates me, which means he controls my future in the Army. After this is over, I will still be working for him."

"I understand. He gives you an OER, Officer Efficiency Report, so you want to avoid making him mad by your testimony."

"Don't get me wrong. I will not hesitate to answer truthfully to any question. I also want to do what I can to be helpful to your client. However, my strongest desire is to insure the situation does not adversely affect the rest of the men in my platoon. To a much smaller degree, if I can escape without damaging my working relationship with my commander, then I would also like to do that as well. Plus, as I said, I do not think I am the best-suited person to establish what you need for your client. There are many men who will personally attest to Goldstein as a hero and lifesaver."

"You are quite insightful. I really appreciate your suggestions and plan on following up on them."

"I have been giving this considerable thought. I feel responsible for the way this thing got out of hand and want to help resolve it the best way possible," replied Dunn.

"Joseph, you would make a good attorney. Have you ever thought of a change in profession?"

"John, in truth, I have always considered the Law a noble profession. I also recognize I don't aspire to become a general. I took some law courses in college and really loved them. So, yeah, I have thought of becoming an attorney."

"Hell, if you're really serious, the Army has a program where they pay for law school. You then owe them two years of service for every year of school. Where did you get your undergraduate degree?"

"The Military Academy at West Point. How about you? Where did you go to law school?"

"I went to the University of Virginia for both undergraduate and for law school. I was in R.O.T.C. and got a partial scholarship from the Army to help pay for law school. In return, I owe the Army three years service. But you, being a West Pointer, could have a real shot at this new program. If you're serious, why don't you take the LSAT, Law School Admission Test? The next test is December 19th, and I just happen to have an application right here."

"How am I going to take the LSAT in Viet Nam?

"The test is being given at the Educational Center in Saigon. I am going to be there as a monitor while the test is administered. You have two months to prepare. Here, take the application. The fee is only six dollars. You can buy a money order and mail it from the PX, which is right across the way outside. Who knows, maybe they will give you extra credit for taking the test in a combat zone."

"Thanks, John," said Dunn, as he took the application and filled it out right then and there. "I really do wish you well on your representation of Goldstein. I suspect this case is near impossible for you to win on his behalf."

"Maybe and maybe not. At least you have given me the first indication of a possible defense. See you in two months in Saigon."

Dunn departed and asked Ramos to make a quick stop at the PX before heading back to the company area. Ramos was surprised to note Lieutenant Dunn was whistling and relatively cheerful. Not too many people visiting the Provost office came out happy.

I must remember to ask Marie to send me some books with practice LSAT exams to study from, thought Dunn. *I hope I can make the time to study in between everything else.*

14
Phan Thiet

W HEN CHARLIE RANGERS DEPARTED NHA TRANG for Phan Thiet, it happened to be a Saturday. As each day in Viet Nam was just like any other day of the week, one could easily lose track of the date or the day of the week. The "Short-timers," those close to their DEROS, could always tell the date and day of the week. The shorter they became, the more accurately they could give the number of hours and minutes until they were to leave Viet Nam for the States.

The daily Operations Briefings helped Dunn keep track of the date, but the letters to and from Marie forced him to constantly follow the calendar. She wrote to him every single day, so he kept track to insure he received each letter. The exchange of letters helped him envision he was part of her daily life, and they were growing closer together while they were actually apart. Some days the courier mail plane simply did not arrive while other days it did not carry a single letter for him. Then there were days like the day he broke the company record for receipt of mail. Once he received eighteen letters: fifteen from Marie, one from her little sister, one from his aunt and one from his folks. But now they had diverted to Phan Thiet, they probably would be without mail for at least the first week. After that, mail was going to be delivered to them only twice per week.

Whereas they had left Nha Trang just prior to the beginning of its monsoon season, the monsoons were nearing their end at Phan Thiet. Nevertheless, for the first three days they were there it rained non-stop. Phan Thiet was in the southern-most part of the Central Highlands, the Area of Operational Responsibility (AOR) owned by First Field Force. The company was located about one-quarter to one-half mile off the South China Sea and was on the outskirts of a compound that was slowly fading into oblivion. Fortunately, there was some grass where their tents were located. But, unlike Nha Trang, they were going to be living in tents without electricity and other relative comforts. However, like Fort

Ord in California, the ground was all sand, which meant the rain turned the ground into a sea of mud.

On their first full day there, at the request of Phillips and Staples, Dunn trudged through the rain and mud to a Quonset hut that served as the central headquarters for the compound. Dunn was to provide the Charlie Rangers tactical call signs and agenda as well as to coordinate for administrative support, such as the re-supply of food, munitions and fuel.

"Sir, can you direct me to the person I need to speak with to coordinate the activities of my unit, Charlie Company, 75th Infantry? Charlie Rangers arrived at this compound yesterday."

"Hey, Lieutenant Dunn! How the hell are you?"

"Major Caldoon! What a pleasure it is to see you, sir." enthusiastically returned Dunn. Caldoon had been one of Dunn's English professors during his senior year at West Point.

"Great to see you, too. You are with a terrific unit. Charlie Rangers has a top-notch reputation as a first class combat outfit. We're glad to have you in the compound. The good weather is right around the corner, even though it might not look like it right now. When your guys aren't out killing Charlie, they are going to love our Waikiki sandy beaches. Well, let's get to our dealings. We'll take good care of you guys."

After nearly two hours of introductions, negotiations, coordinations and careful deliberations, Dunn trudged happily back to the company area. It was a pleasant surprise to have run into his former English Prof. Back at the company area, he found the men were busy settling in to their new base. In spite of the weather, they seemed unreasonably happy in this relatively dire setting.

"Hey, sir," called out SFC Randall Carreuthers, Lee's 1st Platoon Sergeant, "I hope you have a damn nice gift for your new platoon sergeant tomorrow. Have you heard the news? The Duke authorized London's request to host his promotion party for the entire fucking company. Since it is supposed to rain all day again, word of the party has definitely raised everyone's spirits.

"Man, I don't know how London and Pancho fucking did it, but somehow, the two of them managed to scrounge up about twelve hundred choice steaks and hundreds of pounds of chicken, hamburger and hot dogs, plus who fucking knows what else. This is going to be a rockin' Ranger party, sir. I volunteered 1st Platoon to be responsible for starting a barrel of fucking Jungle Juice," the veteran sergeant both explained and informed Dunn.

"What, pray tell, is Jungle Juice?" asked Dunn.

"Sir, as far as Jungle Juice goes, everything goes! Jim Beam, vodka, beer, you name it. I have seen guys squirting in lighter fluid in the absence of any other alcoholic contribution. The medics empty bags of plasma, cooks do their thing with beef bullion and oranges, and the engineers use some fucking chemicals to make frozen ice chunks from the river water containing frozen fishies. My God, man, the stuff is 'Number Ten,' fucking awful...

"The main thing to remember is that everyone equips themselves with a gallon can from the mess hall's veggies and uses it as their 'glass' to dip into that Jungle Juice drum."

The remainder of that day and the majority of the following day the men of Charlie Rangers worked tirelessly to get their new camp established and to be prepared for the next series of missions. Morale had actually been at low ebb in Nha Trang, but now they were ready and able to raise hell and just be themselves.

Everyone had a blast at the party, and as word had spread throughout the compound, no guests were turned away. The event by everyone's standards was a spectacular success.

Dunn presented his newly promoted E-7 platoon sergeant with an elegantly carved mahogany pool cue stick. The crest was a dragon's head atop a three-foot portion of the stick around which was an intricately carved and winding snake-like creature. The base was made of brass, which unscrewed to reveal the remaining two portions inside. These portions fit together perfectly, with rings of ivory to conceal the joining. Dunn had won the stick from a pilot in a dice game, and London was thrilled with his unexpected gift.

"So, let's hear from the new Sergeant First Class London!" Dunn grabbed the attention of all the men and saluted his new E-7 with his "glass" of Jungle Juice. "Platoon Sergeant, it is time for you to lead the company in a toast!"

"Lead, follow, or get the fuck out of the way!" bellowed London.

"Hoooahhh! Hoooahhh! Ahhoogaa!" responded all the Charlie Rangers in unison.

It was a good thing it rained again the following day, because just about the entire compound needed that extra day to recover from the Ranger party or more specifically the Jungle Juice.

Another good reason for the rain and thus a day of recovery was at the Ops Briefing held before lunch, the Old Man made it clear he intended the unit to become aggressively involved in their new Area of Operation right away.

"Lieutenant Dunn," stated Phillips, "we want to employ all the operational teams in your platoon. How many teams can you have ready to be inserted tomorrow?"

"Sir, all six of my teams are ready for deployment. I will be taking Team 21 to the field since Parvis is still recovering from his hospitalization in Nha Trang," responded Dunn.

That meant for the next four to five days, 2nd Platoon would be in the field. The entire platoon, made up of six, six-man teams, would be deployed concurrently on six separate missions. Only London, Parvis, who was on a medical profile, and Goldstein would remain in Tent City.

Continued Phillips, "Six teams. That's excellent. Lee, I want three teams deployed from 1st Platoon. Kent, the same from your platoon-three teams. Appier, you have to put together two heavy X-ray teams for insertion tomorrow. I will be flying Command and Control. The reconnaissance flight is set for all team leaders at 0700 hours and the 192nd Polecats and Tigersharks are giving us aviation support. We have an aggressive timetable and a hectic schedule tomorrow. Therefore, I require everybody's commitment. Staples will now brief you on the requisite tactical data."

The questions were always reserved until the entire briefing was concluded. Normally, the briefings were so thorough that questions germane to the group were unnecessary. Staples shared with them the considerable intelligence data on the AO he had amassed concerning enemy dispositions, terrain, weather, supporting assets, call signs, radio frequencies and analytical anecdotes. He warned them to be prepared for the sudden return of unbearably hot weather.

"That's fine," remarked Dunn. "Just so long as we can avoid hot LZ's."

The rest of the day was an organized "cluster-fuck." Everybody seemed to be running this way and that. But after being with the unit for such a short time, it was amazing to see London so unbelievably organized. He seemed to anticipate the needs of the team leaders, and they responded energetically to his lead.

By midday, the sun was already beginning to dry out the equipment and the earth, and the energy of the men was heating up as well. Dunn was delighted with London's help in making sure all the teams, including and especially the one he led, were fully prepared. London helped ease the stress of his having to work out all the details of the overall and specific operation on his own. Thus, it left him sufficient time to get himself ready as well.

"Sergeant London," said Dunn, "what do you think about arranging some test-firing of the weapons for the men?"

"Way ahead of you, sir. Staples reserved the firing range on the outskirts of the compound at 1500 hours for us. I invited 1st and 3rd Platoons to join us. I figured we could have some friendly shooting competitions. There are three trucks with drivers scheduled to take us."

In comedic fashion, London had drawn caricatures of the three platoon leaders as targets at which the men would shoot. Bragging rights were equally spread around, as the men were all expert sharpshooters. They took special delight in shooting out each individual facial feature of their platoon leaders. The competitive atmosphere still continued while the men cleaned and cared for their weapons.

"Peace is gonna be fuckin' proud of his Team 21," bragged Specialist Jeffrey Matthis, "The Dog," as he was called. "We've got the Looey with us as a good-luck charm so, we are guaranteed to make contact first and be back with our team leader in Tent City before any of you other guys even find a fuckin' Tango."

"You got that right," chimed in SP/4 Albert "The Cuban" Rios. "I bet we get a fucking trophy for Lieutenant Dunn on this mission with 21."

"Oh, yeah," retorted The Mad Swede. "The only trophy for you is the special fucking Cuban cigar between my legs for you to suck on."

"Fuck you and the Charlies we're gonna burn!"

"Put your money where your fuckin' mouth is. I bet you guys do as you usually do. You'll fucking hide out for four days and claim your sector is empty of gooks."

Why is it, wondered Dunn, *that these intelligent men cannot speak without using the word, "fuck," in every single sentence?*

The creative expletives and laughter never subsided as the Ranger family bonded in its own unique way. Actually, it was truly amazing they didn't kill each other, the way they screamed obscenities and called one another: "Spick," "Nigger," "Wop," "Chink," and other terms even far worse. But what was most amazing to Dunn was the apparent lack of any real racial tension between such diverse ethnic groupings of men.

⟨⟨

The heavily laden reconnaissance flights early the next morning proved Staples correct about the terrain-thick, triple canopy jungles blanketed the mountains. Since dense forests so effectively camouflaged the earth's surface, it made detecting the trails difficult from the air. But fortunately, there were sufficient clearings available to serve as Landing Zones.

About three hours later, Dunn's legs were dangling outside and above the skids of the Polecat chopper as it zipped along just above the tops of the trees. This reminded Dunn of his last week of Jump School at Fort Benning. He couldn't remember actually jumping out of the plane on his first jump; he had simply reacted to the Jumpmaster's commands as a result of the highly disciplined, intensive training. But by his fifth jump it was much scarier because, by then, he was more alert and aware. It was as if he had stepped off the ramp of the C-141 "Starlifter" jet in slow motion and was both frightened and exhilarated at the same time. Just like now. He was leading these men into unknown territory owned by the enemy. Then the adrenaline rush kicked in full force as reality also struck home, *We're going out hunting the hunters.*

Suddenly, the head of the bird on which they were riding rose upward and the craft braked in mid air. As it started to descend, the helmeted door-gunner pointed to the team and then held his palm up to them, as if to say, "Get ready, but not yet."

Dunn hopped down onto the skids, effortlessly lifting the 65-pound rucksack on his back. It seemed so much lighter without the Prick 25 radio, which was carried by his RTO, The Dog.

Matthis was already standing on the skids beside him. Rangers learned to detect the slight bounce when the helicopter came to a hover right before it reached a landing. The teams always jumped from the aircraft before it fully touched down. They sensed more than felt the correct moment and the two of them were off and running around the chopper where they joined the rest of the team and headed for the nearest wood line even before the helicopter lifted off again.

On the edge of the forest was a trail they had not seen before. "Fucking shit!" SGT Robert Godfried, his assistant patrol leader, yelled and pointed. "Look!"

A North Vietnamese soldier was running on the trail away from them. Evidently, he had been surprised by the sudden appearance of the helicopter and had watched their infiltration. As the team rushed unknowingly and directly toward him, he panicked and was now running away.

Both Dunn and The Cuban raised their weapons and fired a couple of shots at the fleeing figure. The pith helmeted NVA in black trousers and a green military shirt never broke pace. He barely glanced back as he hoisted his AK-47 with just his right hand and pointed it in the general direction from where he had been. A single shot went harmlessly into the air but the distinctive "pop" sound of the enemy's shot was enough to cause the team to take cover. This gave the NVA time to disappear into the thick woods and on over a hill.

Godfried, a compact bull of a young man, had, appropriately been given the nickname, "Bull." He had been the first to spot the fleeing enemy soldier, but had not even fired off a single round with the cut-off M-60 machine gun that he toted.

"Well," said Dog, "shall I call in a fucking 'contact' on this Charlie?"

"No," Dunn said curtly. "Absolutely not. Make your routine commo check and then advise the Oscar One that a single Charlie observed our insertion. Tell him the Charlie is now 'di di mau.' Then advise him we are going to 'Charlie Mike,' and go into 'Groundhog' for a while."

Bull asked, "Don't you think we are compromised? He saw there are only six of us and that fucker could bring back a large force."

"He doesn't know if we are only a lead element or even if we are staying here. They are not expecting or even aware of any Ranger operations in this area. I think that guy was so scared he didn't have a chance to figure out anything. What do you guys say? We clear out of this area, hide out, and then tomorrow we set up a good ambush site? So, what do you guys want to do?" Dunn asked, wanting feedback.

"I say we 'Charlie Mike;' that fucker is 'dinky dau.' He ain't comin' back," agreed Dog.

The team unanimously agreed to continue the mission. Dog called in the commo check and reported the incident to the 0-1 Birddog as Dunn instructed.

"I want you to be extra careful walking drag," said Dunn to The Cuban. "Have the man in front of you watch your rear as I want you to completely erase our tracks." Then, speaking to the whole team, "We don't want anybody to know we were even here or which way we went. So, when we move out, we will move very slowly and deliberately. Watch carefully where you step and what you touch. Try not to disturb anything in order to make as little work for the Cuban as possible."

By the time the team spent three and a half hours of painstaking, laborious and slow movement through dense forest, they were exhausted. Dunn looked around and noticed a spot that looked like a natural log cabin. Three large trees had fallen a long time ago and had formed an interlocking base. A couple more trees nearly collapsed upon the fallen trees but were still rooted and a huge living tree formed the cornerstone. Within the confines of this natural formation, a deep base of leaves and sediment made for a comfortable bedding area. To complete the perfection of the site, he saw it was surrounded on all sides by thick, nasty brush that would provide a perfect barrier when it was coupled with the absence of any light.

Dunn allowed Godfried to determine the placement of the protective Claymore mines. However, he carefully watched him and was favorably impressed with the full circumference and interlocking lanes of covering fire he established.

Bull paid particular attention to the obvious approach paths dictated by the terrain. Unless the enemy traversed the tree limbs like monkeys, they would not be able to reach the team's nighttime hideout without mortal injury.

Settled in, the team members took turns eating their LRRP rations, carefully burying any discard. Then, huddling together, they quietly slept.

It is really amazing a Ranger who usually snores loudly is silent in the field. Probably because sleep in the field is not deep; it is not sound; it is not secure. Sleep during a combat mission is simply a state of guarded rest.

As team leader, Dunn was allowed the final watch duty from 0400 to 0500 hours. Nevertheless, he was acutely aware of the hourly commo check. He figured Dog probably drove X-ray crazy with his requests for a time-check every two or three minutes. But he understood the reason was that it helped him stay awake.

Their internal alarm clocks had everyone on the team awake long before 5:00 a.m. However, it was nearly 0700 hours before the team had sanitized the area of its night camp and was ready to continue the mission. Dunn broke out the map to ascertain the locations of adequate Landing Zones in proximity to their present location. Ideally, he preferred to initiate contact close to a place from where they could be safely and quickly extracted. When he was confident he had refreshed his recollection of the topography from the map, they started out.

After a little more than two hours, the team skirted a large clearing, when they chanced upon a hard-packed trail. They had come upon the trail just where it took a dogleg away from the clearing.

"I told you that you were a good luck charm," whispered Dog to Dunn. "Where do you want to set up the Hatchet and the claymores?"

Dunn liked having direct access to the clearing without having to cross the hard packed, open trail. However, this particular spot provided very little concealment and even less cover. So he motioned outstretched arms into his chest for the entire team to huddle so they all could have a view of the discovered trail. He responded to Dog's whispered question and to all of them to remain silent by raising his finger across his lips. With palm outward hand signals, he beckoned them to remain prone there under the concealment. Then he signaled them by pointing outward from his eye, to watch the trail and to cover him.

Dunn wanted to find a place that would better afford cover protection from small arms fire, not just concealment. Further up the trail, Dunn felt it was too close to the clearing and he could not afford for the team to be spotted from far away or even from the far side of the clearing. What he hoped was the trail would soon bend away from the clearing. In either case, he needed to take a good look to determine which way to go to find a suitable ambush site. The team instinctively seemed to understand his thought process and automatically did exactly as he instructed.

Satisfied they all understood and seemed to agree with his tactics, he rose in a crouched position. He had only taken four noiseless steps when he froze and dropped into the prone position. There was some vegetation to serve as concealment from the unsuspecting, but there was absolutely no cover at his present location. He quickly gave the signal meaning approaching sounds coming from up the trail. They understood and repeated the signal.

Deliberately and noiselessly, each man switched off the safety on his weapon and nimble fingers found, checked and caressed the accessible location of additional loaded magazines and grenades. They hadn't had time to put out any claymores because they had not, as yet, scouted the area for a prime killing zone. While they were huddled in a spot that did not provide adequate cover, they could only wonder at the size of the force that was approaching. To make the situation tenser, they had no flank security or early warning mechanisms and were bunched together without adequate and separate fields of fire. Plus their view was limited to less than twenty feet of the trail. However, they did have the element of surprise on their sides.

Surely, all the men in my team are having the same flashing thoughts. Dunn silently prayed, *God, please protect the men of Team 21.*

The approaching, animated, high-pitched voices grew louder. *Good. They are unsuspecting,* Dunn thought. *The laughter means they are not alert. This has to be a hasty ambush.*

As Dunn trained his right eye on the sights of his CAR-15, beads of sweat trickled down his forehead and nestled precariously and uncomfortably on his right eyelashes. Tiny beads of sweat momentarily blurred his vision but he dared not move...not even to blink away the drops of sweat. Three NVA soldiers appeared in his sights, wearing dark green uniforms with soft caps. He could tell one was an officer as the other two were laden with burgeoning knapsacks that slightly bent them over. All three carried different type rifles on slings over their shoulders.

No. No one else seems to be behind them. There are only three of them. Good.

Dunn placed the aiming point on the sight of his weapon at the head of the officer. He figured the burden of the knapsacks carried by the other two would help deter or slow their response. As he was the closest to the approaching enemy, the team knew to wait for him to initiate contact.

The enemy officer walked on the side closest to him so Dunn waited until he was only eight feet away before he consciously and deliberately squeezed the trigger. Dunn could have sworn the officer looked right at him when the sound exploded in his ear as the shot exploded in his temple.

The simultaneous eruption of fire from the rest of his team sounded like a mad minute from a company-sized force. Dunn fired two more shots; each carefully placed into the head of the other two soldiers who were already dead.

Then Dunn signaled for the team to cease-fire and to remain in place and for absolute quiet. He wanted to wait and listen for any potential response. For a long time, the only sound he could hear was the mad thumping of his own racing heart. To him it was so loud that he was certain his team would notice. After what seemed like an eternity, but was actually only five minutes of otherwise eerie silence, he called for Bull to put out flanking security up and down the trail.

"Oscar One is asking for a sitrep," Dog had called in the contact.

So Phillips, in the Birddog wanted details. "Tell him 21 has three confirmed with three trophies. I'll call out to you the rest as soon as I check out the bodies," Dunn relayed. He was anxious to see what was in the knapsacks... "Tell him we also have two rucksacks full of mortars!"

The three weapons carried by the enemy soldiers were an SKS, Simonov 7.62 mm semi-automatic carbine, an AK-50 and a wooden, German made, bolt-action rifle. There were no other noteworthy documents. In the breast pocket of the young officer was a rainproof packet with a picture of a smiling Vietnamese woman holding an infant child.

Dunn ordered, "Collect the weapons, Bull. Grab the two rucksacks and call in the guys from the flank. Team 21 earned these three trophies as we saved the lives of friendlies through the confiscation of these mortar rounds.

"Hey, Dog, as soon as you hear from Oscar One that we have inbound, pop and throw some smoke out into the clearing."

"Roger that," responded Mathis. Out in the field, they referred to each other by nickname or last name. They never said "sir" or a rank, which is probably why nearly everybody in the unit had a nickname. Also, it was quicker, more personal, and showed the bonding of the team.

"The SKS is your personal trophy," said a beaming Bull to Dunn. "You dropped that gook officer with a single shot."

"Just remember you got it with Team 21!" Dog exclaimed.

"Here. We want you to have this, too," said The Cuban, as he dismantled the triangular bayonet from the AK-50 and handed it to Dunn. When used, the "illegal" triangular bayonet would leave a sucking wound that could not be closed. "You get more fucking letters than anybody I've ever seen. This will be a great letter opener. Every time you use it, you will think of Team 21."

"Thanks. It has been a privilege to be in the bush with you guys." Dunn gratefully accepted the SKS and marveled at the foot-long, steel bayonet with its three grooved edges. Its cylindrical base extended out to a sharp, flat, screwdriver-like point.

The Cuban spoke up, "I say we also take this new fucking AK-50 back and present it to Peace. I know he wishes he had his bad black ass out here in the bush with us." They all agreed to give the trophy to their team leader.

"Hey, Two One has its shit together," said Bull. "It's because of Peace, our TL, that we are the best team in the company. You are a great platoon leader, and Peace is gonna be proud to hear we took good care of you. Man, you did a fuckin-A job out here in the field with us. You're alright for an 'occifer.'"

Dunn was surprised the Tigersharks did not make a gun run around the perimeter prior to their extraction. Perhaps Phillips didn't think it necessary since the clearing was so large. Anyway, Dog popped yellow smoke and a Polecat chopper just came directly in to pull them out.

The two rucksacks filled with mortars were unbelievably heavy and Dunn helped lift the smaller one onto the chopper. It was so heavy he was amazed to think the diminutive North Vietnamese soldier had carried it so effortlessly and cheerfully.

The NVA was fiercely committed to some cause. Before the Americans, who were now in Viet Nam, they had fought the French. The present generation of Vietnamese had not known a time when they were not at war.

On the short chopper ride back, Dunn feigned a cheerfulness he did not feel. His actual somber and reflective mood did not affect the rest of the team. They hooted, hollered and celebrated like victorious warriors returning from a mighty campaign. They didn't stop cheering until the

3/4-ton truck, from which they were hanging out of, reached the TOC. Their yells drew a crowd and they gleefully emptied the rucksacks and spread out the spoils for the crowd to view. The Duke appreciatively picked up and examined each mortar and captured weapon.

Dunn quietly retrieved the SKS and entered the TOC. "This was the only item in the pockets of the dead enemy," said Dunn as he handed the picture to Staples. "The picture was in the breast pocket of the NVA lieutenant.

"I put a tag with my name on the SKS, as I am keeping it as a trophy. As directed, I am turning it in for shipment to the armorer. You'll have to check with Godfried about the other two weapons."

"Commendable job out there, sir," said Staples. "I'll see to it the SKS is logged in as yours and sent to the rear for safekeeping...unless you want to keep it with you. Do you want to keep the picture?"

"No, thanks, you can keep it. I'll follow the Old Man's instructions concerning trophies, too. You can send my SKS to PFC Martinez at Ahn Khe," said Dunn.

Staples continued, "The guys in the team are out there talking up your shit as if it don't stink. Of course, you know I prefer having you in C & C."

"I know. I'm ready to fly starting tomorrow if you want," responded Dunn.

"Great, because I need Phillips back here in the TOC during the day to deal with all the friggin' officers in the supporting units. They don't understand what we are all about.

"By the way, Gregorov is doing a fantastic job running the TOC night shift. Thanks for giving him to me, Dunn. At first he gave me a hard time, as he didn't like the idea of being pulled away from combat missions and his team. But now he realizes how critical and important he is to the whole company in his present role. He is good, very good. I should have spotted Rusky earlier myself."

"I told his team leader not to expect him back, as I knew you would appreciate Gregorov's work. Please excuse me, as I have to go take a shower. By the way, has the unit received any mail here?" asked Dunn.

"No, we haven't had mail in six days."

With that disappointing news, Dunn's somber mood returned. He was really feeling blue and was glad most of the platoon was still in the field, because he knew he wouldn't be good company for anybody.

No one else was around at the makeshift showers, so he took his time. Normally, he would have taken a quick shower but this time, he washed himself and then washed again. When he had finished rinsing the second time, he held the chain so the water continued to cascade onto the back of his head and neck.

But try as he might, he could not wash away his thoughts... He had volunteered to come to Viet Nam and had volunteered for this combat unit because he truly believed his extensive training prepared him to save the lives of his men. The notion of killing the enemy without truly appreciating what that meant, he had just accepted. Now, he had to accept the fact of killing another human being became personal. He had killed, but he did not hate.

One cannot hate a person one does not know, he thought. *But, then, there are men in the platoon who do hate-those who have lost good friends and buddies; those who have witnessed other Rangers killed by the enemy; these men do hate. The war became personal when they lost someone close due to an enemy action. I hope and pray to God I do not lose a single man.*

What Dunn hated was being away from Marie. He hated the politicians, not the generals. *What policy put me halfway round the world in a position where I have to personally kill? Today I pulled a trigger and exploded a young family's life.*

Why is it the most powerful country in the world has to sneak around in the jungle, six men at a time? Why Viet Nam?

Staples, who arrived ready to take a shower with a full glass of Jim Beam and a cigarette in his mouth, brought him back to present reality. After Dunn got out, he glanced back and noticed Staples standing under the water holding the glass in one hand and the shower soaked cigarette in the other. Everybody had his own way of dealing with reality.

A late plane arrived in Phan Thiet that evening carrying a change of mood for Dunn. He received five letters from Marie, a newspaper clipping from his dad, a sweet letter from his wife's next door aunt, and a cute card from Mike, Marie's little brother. He really got a kick out of the card from Mike. On the front of the card was an alligator wearing a beret. Receiving the mail certainly made a big, big difference in his disposition.

"Oh, your Sugar Reports sure make one hell of a difference," he whispered out loud, as if Marie were there. "They mean so much to me."

That night he actually used his new letter opener.

⧯

First thing the next morning, Dunn was to brief the pilots in the ready shack at 0630 hours. So, just before 0500, he meandered over to the mess.

"Hey, Lieutenant," called out Pancho, "come on over and join your Papa Sierra. London is always my first and best customer of the day. I'm making my special Spanish omelet. How's that sound to you?" he asked as he handed Dunn a cup of freshly brewed coffee.

"That sounds like just what my body craves. When you get back home, you should get out and start a cooking school. You'd make a fortune."

"I doubt it," laughed Pancho. "Other than for a prison, who needs to learn how to cook for a few hundred guys?"

At precisely 0630 hours, Dunn arrived at the ready shack only to find it locked. It wasn't until 0800 that the pilots showed up, so he was forced to cool his heels as the day quickly heated up. His frontseat, Sandy Thomas, was the last pilot to show as he had just flown in from Dong Ba Tin in the Birddog.

The schedule for the morning called for the re-supply of both current X-ray sites, the insertion of two ambush patrols, the extraction of four teams and two visual reconnaissance sorties. Despite the late start, Dunn took his time in briefing them since he was not certain how well they understood Ranger tactics. But as it turned out, they were as eager, efficient and just as capable as the previous pilots with whom they had the good fortune to work. Luckily, the programmed events came off quickly and smoothly to make up for some lost time.

Later, on their way back from the last scheduled exercise that morning, just as Thomas happened to be flying the Birddog over its sector, Team 14 below them announced, "Contact!"

"Spitter 14, this is Spitter 28, I have Red Leg, Polecats and Tigersharks on station. Contact sitrep. Over."

"Sandy," said Dunn, flipping on his intercom while he monitored and waited for the team's reply, "you did a great job of flying for me this morning. Now, we're the big Ranger-in-the-sky in the perfect location to provide Command and Control for this team. Thanks!"

"This is Spitter 6. I repeat. This is Spitter 6. Spitter 14, Spitter 14, this is Spitter 6. Over," called Major Wayne to the team. He was on the helicopter with team leaders on a VR. The crew chief had provided the Old Man with a flight helmet so he could monitor and make FM radio transmissions during the flight.

"Spitter 6, this is Spitter 14, please stand by. Spitter 28, please stand by for the Tango Lima. Over."

"This is Spitter 6, goddamn it, talk to me! Over."

"Spitter 28, this is Spitter 14, we have four unfriendly confirmed with one trophy; two unfriendly have didi maued to the west...no Zulu (report). There is still sporadic incoming from the west of our location. Do you want us to pop smoke? Over."

Dunn could tell from the changed voice, the authority and the control of emotion that the team leader was giving the situation report. He probably did not realize that Wayne was even on the channel. Thankfully, the Zulu report meant there were no friendly wounded.

"Spitter 14, this is Spitter 6. This is Major Wayne on a chopper. Talk to me, goddamn it! Pop some smoke so we can come in and get you, son. We got an empty chopper so we can come in and get you out of there. Soon as we see you, we can lead you to a spot where we can pull your team out. You guys have done your job. Now, talk to me so I can arrange to get your ass out of there!"

So much for proper radio procedure, Joe mused. *The Duke is sure excited and taking over in a blaze of ignoble glory.*

"Spitter 6, this is Spitter 14, smoke out. Over."

"Okay, Spitter 14, we see your smoke. We see yellow smoke. I am going to tell the pilot of this helicopter to have the gunships with us provide you cover. The gunships will fire up the goddamn gooks. You guys are close to a spot where we can come down and get you. What's your status? Can you break contact and move? There is a clearing where the pilot says we can land without a problem. If you can move, I want you to goddamn move! You only have to go less than a football field length from the smoke. The landing zone is a little bit to the north and a little bit to the east of your smoke. You should be able to pick up the sound of my helicopter. Can you see us? Over."

"Spitter 6, this is Spitter 14, we are moving north east. Tell the gunships to hit the area sixty meters due west of our smoke. Over."

"Spitter 14, this is Spitter 6. That's a big goddamn Airborne Roger on that! My pilot says the gunship is going to make his run now. He just wants you to tell us if the mini guns get too goddamn close to you guys. When you get to the clearing, pop another color of smoke. When we see the new smoke, we're going to come down and get you. Your whole goddamn team is going to get on the same chopper with me. I'm on the one that's going to pull you goddamn heroes out of there. Do you see the clearing? Can you pop smoke? Is the gunship fire too close? How are you guys doing? Over." There was a slight pause with no transmission sound.

"Spitter 14, this is Spitter 6. What is your situation? Where are you now? Can you...I've got you. We see red smoke! We have red smoke! Goddamn it, Spitter 14, we're coming in! Get ready to climb aboard! Over."

Dunn was annoyed because the Old Man should have let him do his job. *The Old Man had only one radio and was lucky to have an FM radio at that. If it had been required, he would not have been able to call in artillery or coordinate air support because he didn't have those frequencies. There is no sense complaining as there is no one to whom I can complain. The important thing was the team, and they were safe...* In actuality, Dunn was more than annoyed. He was pissed.

Later in the afternoon of that same day, two more teams made contact. But he and Sandy Thomas were plagued with radio equipment problems on their Birddog while another one had engine trouble. Fortunately, all the teams came out of their situations in good fashion. It was another hell of a day.

Famished because he had not had time for lunch, Dunn returned to the company area after 1700 hours, ready and eager for some of Pancho's delicious cuisine. But, he returned to discover the Duke had challenged officers of another unit to a volleyball game from 1700 to 1800 hours. Since the Rangers had only five officers, including Dunn, against their six, he missed supper. Even though he wasn't really in the mood after the hellacious day for a game of volleyball, he gave it his best and ended up having a good time in a hotly contested losing effort.

Then came the greatest hurt of the day. He spent an hour before darkness, searching but to no avail. "I now sit here writing to you," he penned to Marie, "and around my neck is a lonely chain, lifeless without the weight of my little lost medal that has *constantly* been with me whenever we have been apart...." The silver medal was a thorny-crowned head of Christ on a square cross.

Another tragedy-some of the guys in his platoon came by to rub it in that Army lost to Virginia by a score of 21 to 20. "What a day," he cried, "Army had better beat Penn State."

"Hey, sir," said Slant, "we brought you some pizza and two rock lobsters from the South China Sea. We want you to know you are welcome to go back out in the field with Team 23 anytime."

Chief chimed in, "That goes double from us guys in Double Deuce."

"These lobsters are simply dee-delicious. Thanks, guys." Dunn said.

※

When Dunn got up the next morning, he was looking forward to a restful and uneventful day. As Lee was flying C & C, he hoped to spend some downtime with London. There was always plenty of paperwork, and he also had been assigned the additional duty of being the forward Supply Officer for the company. In addition, there was always somebody ready to DEROS home, while a new soldier was just starting his tour of duty. Also, there was always somebody coming from or going on R & R leave. Then there usually was one or more of the troops with pay problems, personal problems from home, "Dear John" letter problems, medical problems, especially foot problems or just plain problems.

London was proving to be an invaluable asset and had already taken on the task of securing new camouflage fatigues to replace the terribly tattered ones. It was Dunn's personal opinion the personnel in the rear were involved in the Black Market, since it was so hard to get supplies of any kind moved forward. Already, London had presented him with a Platoon Notes Record Book containing all the same lists and information he originally wanted from Wilson.

Suddenly the TOC loudspeaker blared, "Contact! Team 26 has reported it is now in contact! Stand by for the incoming Situation Report."

"SSG Lucky Nate's Team," Dunn said instinctively, heading to the TOC from the mess without his coffee.

"Negative results," said Staples, looking up at Dunn, who had just entered the TOC. Staples was wearing a set of earphones and seated in front of a bank of radios. "Seems like Two Six ran into a couple of VC soldiers who dropped their gear and ran off. Team 26 captured two more rucksacks filled with enemy mortar rounds. The team was due to be pulled out tomorrow anyway, so Lee is extracting them now."

"What do you hear from Rod Winthrop?" Dunn turned to Phillips. "Last night he checked in with us right on time on the landline and sounded frustrated. Nothing seems to be going right for him. Being his own commander is not the picnic he expected, I guess. He is finding the ARVN really difficult to work with or to get anything done. Also, his own men are giving him a real hassle too. But he'll work through it, as he has no choice. I doubt we'll be seeing 4th Platoon back with us anytime soon, though."

"Contact!" Staples interrupted. "Ramos, announce on the loudspeaker that Team 24 just made contact; no sitrep yet." All ears in the camp tuned in and concentrated on the anticipated report.

"Captain Phillips, I think you should send in the rest of 2nd Platoon as a 'React' to help out Two Four. The team is presently pinned down by heavy fire from fifteen to thirty Viet Cong. Lee is going to need our immediate help on this one. I'll scramble choppers to take in 2nd Platoon. Then, I will alert the ARVN Company that is supposed to be our reactionary force. Fortunately, I met one of the U.S. Advisors with the ARVN Company. Damn, I hope I can get them to react in decent fashion."

"Ramos," ordered Dunn, "announce over the loudspeaker for the entire 2nd Platoon to assemble at the conex. Prepare to deploy as an immediate relief for Team 24." Dunn did not wait for instructions from Phillips but raced for the platoon area after grabbing his CAR-15 and web gear.

"I am issuing weapons and ammo, sir," London told him. "Including you and me, we have eleven men ready right now. Here's your magazines and grenades." He handed Dunn a stack of eight magazines and as many fragmentation grenades. All the men were busy stuffing munitions into the baggy pockets of their cammies and attaching grenades to their web gear.

"What the fuck! Let's go!" shouted Ramos who was waiting for them with a deuce and a half truck to take them to the two choppers already scrambled with blades whopping.

The two birds with the reinforcements lifted off and were soon descending together into a large field. However, the chopper in which Dunn was riding, suddenly bucked, swayed and lurched forward. Both choppers quickly rose back up into the air.

What is going on? What is happening? the men thought as the tail of the chopper whipped back and forth. They held on to each other and to anything they could grab as they rode the steel, bucking bronco as it flew through green tracer lassos.

Suddenly, gunships flashed by them and went into violent action in the zone the choppers had just vacated. It was Halloween day and the gunships didn't appreciate the treat given by the VC to their sister slicks, so they dished out some nasty tricks of their own.

The cowboy at the helm of Dunn's wounded steed valiantly regained a modicum of control. But the pilot was forced to auto rotate into a more distant LZ, landing with a crumpling "thwamp."

The men of 2nd Platoon required no commands. With unrehearsed precision, they left the crippled chopper unassisted and headed off toward the unmistakable sound of battle. Not even twenty minutes had passed since the first cry of "contact" had come from Team 24. A pair of Tigershark gunships "brapped" the area with mini guns. An occasional rocket impacted with a thunderous roar. The second Landing Zone was a full 250 meters from the embattled team.

"About fucking time," screamed The Mad Swede when he first saw Dunn and his men. "We were fucking running out of goddamn ammo. They're in bunkers and shit. But, I think they are pulling back. Can you see those small bunkers there?"

"Got it. Break contact. Pull your men back and leave your radio with me. A chopper is waiting to pull Two Four out. Get going! The LZ is 250 meters back."

Then, Dunn turned to the men who had arrived with him. "Take up blocking and defensive positions to provide covering fire for Team 24 as it withdraws. We will stay here until the reactionary force arrives. Use single shots. Try to pick out targets."

"Chief," yelled out London. "I need your M-60 over here! Blue, set up over there with your Thumper!" London was organizing their defensive position, even though the volume of incoming enemy fire had dramatically declined with their arrival. However, they continued to exchange sporadic fire for the next fifteen to twenty minutes.

"Curveball 28, this is Husky 5. Curveball 28, this is Husky 5. Over." Dunn hoped this incoming call was from the ARVN reactionary force as they should have been on the ground by now. He had been talking with Lee in the Birddog and Lee told him to expect their call anytime.

"Husky 5, this is Curveball 28. Over."

"Curveball 28, this is Husky 5. We were told you would be here to give us a sitrep. We are supposed to be in the same place you landed. What is your present situation? Can you come to where we are? We are at a clearing with a downed chopper. Over."

"Husky 5, this is Curveball 28. Roger. We can come to you. Just make certain we are not greeted with any weapon fire. We are coming to you from due north. Over."

"Roger that, Curveball 28, nobody will fire. Come on down! This is Husky 5. Out."

Dunn and the ten other Rangers withdrew to the large field where they had been inserted. "Americans! Hold your fire!" They yelled before stepping out of the trees. Three U.S. Advisors with a company force of about eighty ARVN soldiers were rather casually waiting for them. Husky 5 turned out to be Captain Lilly. He and two sergeants with him were serving their tour of duty in Viet Nam as advisors to a South Vietnamese Battalion.

Dunn briefed Lilly on the direction, distance and disposition of the enemy force while the Rangers moved to the rear of the ARVN force. They vigilantly waited for about 30 minutes while the ARVN force regrouped. The ARVN Company then deliberately headed towards the point of the enemy contact and the Rangers followed.

Without any further confrontations, they eventually uncovered a Viet Cong base camp. Dunn was amazed at the volume and variety of food they had grown out there in the wilderness. There was corn, watermelon, cucumbers, squash, potatoes and numerous other items unfamiliar to him. The cave complex was another marvel.

2nd Platoon pulled out that evening leaving the ARVN to exploit the situation. But before they left, the men of 2nd Platoon began distributing their remaining frags to eager South Vietnamese soldiers who, they discovered, had very little ammunition and no grenades.

"Don't do that!" Lilly shouted and waved his hands as he ran to stop the distribution. "They won't use those against the VC! They'll simply save the grenades to use when they go fishing."

Our government cannot possibly expect or believe that the South Vietnamese Army will ever win this war, Dunn thought as he told his men to stop distributing the grenades.

❦

During the past weeks, it had seemed to Dunn he was always flying C & C or pulling Duty Officer at night. One or more teams managed to get into contact every other day as well. The time flew by. However, in terms of being away from Marie, time always seemed to drag, forever holding him a prisoner of one.

Kent pulled duty as paymaster for the first of November payroll. He had been away for more than a week and claimed the monsoons had wrecked havoc with his travel. Privately, he admitted to Lee and Dunn he had spent some pleasurable extra time in Saigon. He had eaten at a fine French restaurant and enjoyed the company of a very refined lady.

In a feeble attempt to disrupt the use of MPC by the Black Market, the authorities had changed the color and look of the scrip. The supposedly unannounced change was anticipated by the healthy Black Market, which profited even more by the exchange. Rumor had it the rear collected old scrip from local papasans for pennies on the dollar. Otherwise, the papasans would have been left holding worthless paper. Then they and everyone else in the military surrendered the old scrip in exchange for the new "funny money." Dunn was glad he had not pulled paymaster duty this time. He figured his turn would come again, soon enough, the next month.

"Well, guys," said Phillips to the assembled group as part of the Operations Briefing, "I hope you are not too comfortable here. We just received word about our next move. Over the next two days, we'll pull all the teams out of the bush. On the third day, Charlie Rangers is moving to Phu Hiep. To make matters even better, our rear area is also moving permanently out of Ahn Khe. Our rear will now be located at Tuy Hoa, about fifteen to twenty miles from where we will be at Phu Hiep.

A sideline, but immediate effect of our rear echelon's move, is a change in our mailing address. Same-same, except the APO zip code is now 96316 instead of 96294. With our rear area so close, we should start receiving mail quicker, hopefully, anyway."

Recently there had been numerous rumors circulating about the future status of Charlie Rangers in Viet Nam. All equipment, to include airplanes in the Mekong Delta area, had already been turned over to the Vietnamese. There in Phan Thiet, most of the U.S. elements were pulling up stakes and being shipped out or disbanded. The 0-1 Birddogs that had been flying for the Charlie Rangers, were also soon to be given to the Vietnamese. Everywhere there were signs of what the brass referred to as the "Vietnamization" of the war. Perhaps this was a way for the politicians to save face. Anyway, it would be a good thing if it meant the American soldiers could be sent home sooner and American presence there came to an end.

"Oh, one more thing-a bit of bad news," continued Phillips. "It seems we now have a man in LBJ and probably eventually headed for prison at Fort Leavenworth. Private First Class Michael Martinez was AWOL and apprehended in Saigon by the CID. According to the CID, our own Martinez set an all time record. He was apprehended with two hundred and sixty-nine vials of heroin secreted within and upon his body. The really bad news is he stole all the weapons that were trophies belonging to our guys. He sold the trophies or used them to pay for the heroin...all trophy weapons are gone. Even the Major lost a Chicom pistol. So, you have to let the men know. Those who sent weapons back to the rear for safekeeping have lost their trophies."

15
Phu Hiep

THAT GODDAMN COCK-SUCKING SON-OF-A-BITCH!" said The Mad Swede angrily. "He's a fucking bastard!" Dunn called the entire 2nd Platoon together to tell them about the upcoming move to Phu Hiep... and to tell them the unfortunate news about their trophies.

"He's the same fucking WIMP we had to medivac after only fifteen minutes on his cherry mission with my team." said "Slant" Garbo. "Then, the Old Man rewarded him with a cushy job in the rear area. Boy, that really pissed me off!"

"The fucker should be shot as a traitor!" "Lucky" Nate spit the words out with disgust.

"He is a drug dealer who will probably be spending a long time in prison," said Dunn.

"No, sir," said Lucky, "he's a fucking traitor! We all know that Charlie sells drugs to buy weapons. Well, this fucker saved the enemy from having to deal with a middleman. He fucking knew exactly what he was doing and collaborated with the fucking enemy. To get his precious heroin, he gave them weapons and he knows those fucking weapons are going to be used against us. We're not talking about just a couple trophies. He stole a shit load of weapons. Hell, sir, he even got your SKS. He is a goddamn traitor, and he should be shot!"

Most of the men echoed the same sentiments expressed by Lucky and used even more colorful words to vent their anger. The announcement they would be moving again seemed to have gotten lost in the melee of emotions that erupted with the knowledge that one of theirs had not kept the trust and honor they esteemed so highly.

The company moved out of Phan Thiet in good, disorderly fashion. As usual, it was the typical rat race of packing everything and then moving. To make matters worse, when they arrived at Phu Hiep, the monsoons were in their full glory and the torrential rains plummeted to the earth in raindrops the size of water balloons.

The company moved into a deserted Air Force complex and the troops were housed in billets. All the top Non-Commissioned Officers and Officers were put into long buildings that had been divided into separate apartment-type quarters.

"At one time," said London to his platoon leader, "this area must have been plush. But, after the flyboys moved out and some damn ground-pounders took over the compound, all the buildings were ransacked. Fixtures were ripped out, furniture stolen or broken, walls and doors smashed-a crying shame. What a shitty mess was made out of such a once beautiful facility."

"I agree, but I am sure the men will make do," Dunn said trying his best to sooth London's ruffled feathers.

"Naturally, sir, I knew you would feel that way. So, I authorized the men to scrounge what they could from the other deserted buildings. They have begun to build up their personal cubicles to make them as comfortable as possible."

"Tomorrow we start combat operations again, so some of them are going to have to wait to enjoy their new creature comforts. How are the new men doing we picked up for the platoon?" asked Dunn.

London reported, "Everyone is working with a team. The reports I've received back are all good. I know you will be doing beau coup flying starting tomorrow. But, don't worry, the platoon is going to be just fine."

"Thanks. I'm not worried, as there is no one else even near us. There are no facilities or even a PX, which is great. So the men cannot get into too much trouble here," Dunn commented.

Replied London, "The perimeter is manned by a U.S. infantry company, and there is a large minefield all around the camp. So, we are rather safe, and our men are happy they don't have to pull guard duty."

"London, I want you to know you are doing one hell of a good job. I appreciate all you do as do all the men," Dunn praised.

※

At the Operations Briefing that evening, Dunn was glad to hear Staples say the unit was once again being supported by the 134th AHC out of Tuy Hoa. To him, while the pilots in all the units were fantastic, there just seemed to be something extra special about the Devils and Demons. Staples also went on to mention they should be prepared to start working with the Koreans over the next month or more.

"Our unit has been attached to the 17th Aviation Group, whose headquarters is in Tuy Hoa," said Phillips. "The 17th is now our boss. However, we are presently remaining under the control of the 173rd Airborne Brigade. Nearby Tuy Hoa used to be an Air Force base but was recently handed over to the Army. It is a real plush, stateside-caliber post with all the trimmings such as beautiful clubs, indoor theaters, a 'steam and cream' sauna facility and a PX. There is even 24-hour shuttle bus service.

"If the men are good, we'll let them go to Tuy Hoa. If not, no sweat. As it now stands, by 5 December we're supposed to be moved out of Phu Hiep and into Tuy Hoa itself."

"Great," moaned Dunn under his breath, "that area will probably cause me similar or more problems than Nha Trang."

That night, Dunn was Duty Officer and was also scheduled to fly Command and Control for the initial insertions the next day. Weather permitting, the VR was set for 0700 hours.

The next day started out rosy, but began to get rotten, and from there seesawed. Things looked right and went wrong; the wrong was righted; and then the right became wrong.

All of the pilots were on time for the briefing, and the weather in the early morning held promise of a pleasant day. The early VR for the team leaders went off without a hitch, but the impenetrable, triple canopy jungles, dense vegetation and few clearings meant the teams would really have it tough going in their respective sectors. However, they always looked on the bright side and just figured there would be plenty of hidden trails on which to surprise Charlie.

Flying in the 0-1, Dunn oversaw the insertion of the X-ray radio relay site and the insertion of four different teams into their proper Landing Zones. The insertions went well, except for one man that had to be pulled back out. He broke his ankle when he jumped from the chopper and landed, then slipped off a rock.

It was about then Dunn discovered the TOC could not communicate with X-ray, nor could a few of the other teams. The radio relay site was in a bad location for commo-a really bad location. So, Dunn had to pull X-ray and relocate it. This meant he had to first call all the teams to tell them to go to groundhog. Because of all the equipment and the number of men, two Devil helicopters were necessary to extract X-ray. After the X-ray was pulled, the weather suddenly rolled in and practically made the mountain where they were headed, into one big cloudy blur.

"Devil 41, this is Spitball 28, the Lima Zulu and the top half of the mountain are in the clouds. My eyes are of no use to you; I cannot help you. Over."

"Spitball 28, this is Devil 41. We don't want the extra work of retrieving all the passengers from this morning. We have decided to deliver this package. Over."

Well, the Devil chopper pilots did put them in but with a most daring piece of maneuvering. Communication was reestablished, and all the teams Charlie Miked. By the time the 0-1 got back to base, the weather cleared again and X-ray reported the cloud was breaking up there also.

No sooner had Dunn returned to the ready shack, than the Devil 41 pilot, Fred Evans, notified him a landline call was waiting for him from Captain Phillips.

"Joe, this is Phillips, we just got word from X-ray that two Rangers on Team 13 hit booby traps on a trail. They report there is not an LZ real close, and we need to get them out ASAP. We need help right away. What can your guys do?"

"Just a minute sir," Joe told Phillips then turned to the Devil 41 pilot with him in the ready shack. "Hey, Fred, I need your exceptional skills again right away. We've got two wounded Rangers on a trail. Can you rig up a rope ladder or a McGuire rig to drop to them and pull the team out that way? There are no hostiles present as yet."

"Can do! We can leave right now and have it rigged by the time we get there. Which team is it?" Fred asked.

"It was the second team we inserted," Dunn replied.

"Okay. I remember where that sector is."

"Good, I'll fly on the chopper with you instead of in the 0-1," Dunn responded enthusiastically to Devil 41. Putting the landline headset back up to his head, Dunn replied, "Captain Phillips, we can..."

"Joe, I heard. Great! Get going, but I prefer you back up in the 0-1 just in case of anything else."

Dunn grabbed his frontseat and headed for the Birddog. By the time they reached the rendezvous sector, Devil 41 had already located the team and had begun the rope ladder extraction of the six men.

"Spitball 28, this is Devil 41. We have all six hitchhikers. However, one left behind a souvenir, his ruck with beau coup stuff and an item he should never be without."

"Devil 41, this is Spitball 28, please be prepared for a return mission. Out."

"Spitball 3, this is Spitball 28, we have to recover souvenir left by Tango One Three. Suggest my Echo Seven rig Devil Four One. Be advised Tango Lima and his Drag from Tango Two Three can rappel. Over."

Dunn alerted the TOC of the problem. Further, since he knew London was an expert at ropes and rappelling, he suggested London rig the chopper. Devil 41 was enroute and already rigged with the rope ladder necessary for the extraction portion of the recovery. Finally, based on prior conversation, Dunn knew the Professor, the Team 23 Leader, and Slant, the man who walked last in the team file, knew how to rappel.

Ramos, who was instructed to pick up the wounded Rangers and the rest of Team 13, met Devil 41. London and Dobkowski jumped in to prepare and assist; Halloway and Garbo jumped in, ready to rappel. Dunn had a bird's eye view of the operation and was delighted with its progress. The two men recovered the rucksack and weapon and were climbing back up the rope ladder in record time when suddenly, "Demon 66, this is Devil 41. Incoming! I'm taking fire! Find and strafe those bastards! Over."

"Demon 66, this is Spitball 28, green tracers forty meters west of Devil 41. Over." A tracer is a round of ammunition chemically treated to glow or give off smoke so its flight can be followed and adjusted.

U.S. weapons used red, while the enemy tracers were green.

The Professor, who retrieved the rucksack, made it up safely into the chopper. But suddenly, Ski, who had been right behind him on the ladder, clutched at his left shoulder and fell into the chopper. He had been wounded by enemy sniper fire.

"Damn! Ski is shot! But at least he is in the chopper. Now, what's the matter with Garbo?" Dunn was talking out loud to himself in the back of the 0-1. "He's not moving. He's just hanging onto the rope ladder. Oh, my God, he's being dragged through the trees! That's going to cut him up. He's waving up to the chopper! He appears to be all right, but he is still not climbing. Good, the gunship is really blasting that area from where the sniper was firing. I don't see any more green tracers. Garbo is in for a frightening ride if he stays there all the way back."

Garbo strapped the weapon to his back, so it was safely recovered. Going up the ladder behind Ski, the first Garbo realized an enemy sniper was shooting was when he saw Ski get shot in the shoulder. Just then, the snap lock D-ring he used in rappelling snagged on the rope ladder. Fortunately, it didn't let go while he was being swung through the trees but his cammies were lacerated. Thankfully, it turned out there was more blood than there was pain to his body.

He rode suspended below the chopper for the whole way back. Fortunately, at the base, Ramos was there to help him get unhooked while the chopper hovered and waited above him.

Ski was immediately transferred to a medivac and his wounded shoulder turned into Dobkowski's ticket home. Dunn privately prayed no teams would make contact the rest of the day. He had been involved in enough that day and was concerned and worried about Dobkowski's condition. It was encouraging to learn when Ski was medivaced, he was conscious.

Suddenly, the lull was broken by a sudden call, "Spitball 28, this is Three Six. Gunship is firing at us! Holy Fuck! They're trying to wipe us out! Mini's and Rockets! Get them to fucking stop! Our own Gunship is trying to kill us! Hurry! Over."

Why was a U.S. gunship helicopter firing at Team 36? was Dunn's first thought before he sprang into action. "Spitball 36, this is Spitball 28. Roger. Stand by. Over." Then, quickly switching to the UHF universal U.S. pilot frequency for the day, forcefully announced, "Any gunship operating due west of Phu Hiep, cease fire immediately and please respond. This is Spitball 28. Over."

"Spitball 28, this is Warlord 52. Roger, have just ceased fire. How can I help you, Two Eight? Over."

"Warlord 52, this is Spitball 28. You just fired upon friendlies. Why are you in that sector? Over?"

"Spitball 28, this is Warlord 52. Our sister ships just deposited some buddies from the Romeo Oscar Kilo. We were just prepping the area. They claim this is their sector. Be advised they are dressed and equipped to look just like Charlie. Over."

When the Warlord gunship prepped the area of ROK insertion, it had fired its mini guns and rockets within 50 meters of Team 36 and had almost wiped out one of the Ranger teams. Now, the situation on the ground for the team and for the ROK troops was just as dangerous.

"Warlord 52, this is Spitball 28. Roger. Instruct your buddies not to Charlie Mike. I will have my Tango go to groundhog. Over."

Dunn later learned from TOC what had happened was a Korean Major had made an 8,000-meter map-reading mistake regarding his Area of Operations. He put in a force of Koreans dressed and equipped like Viet Cong into Charlie Ranger's AO. So, Dunn had to pull that team out to insure there would not be contact and a firefight between friendly elements.

What an abortion this day's operations have been... just one disaster after another. Boy, what an inauspicious way to begin a working relationship with the Koreans, Dunn thought.

When Dunn returned to the company area, he barely had time to eat before attending the nightly Ops briefing. Afterwards, he spent some time with the guys in the platoon. He praised his platoon sergeant, the Professor and Slant for their participation, by recounting in precise detail the professional manner he witnessed them display and execute during the recovery mission.

Garbo was covered with iodine and bandages, but was no less cheerful for the wear and tear of his experience. He delighted in recounting every detail of the incident as he had a willing audience in the many cherries recently assigned to the unit. Also, plenty of visitors from the other platoons also moseyed over to listen in.

Dunn paid particular attention to the details so he could garner accurate information to use in writing up citations. He intended to put all four of those men in for valor awards. He smiled to himself when he overheard Slant's story.

"The fuckin' Newbies ovah in First Platoon shuddah neva been humpin' on a trail!" Slant exaggerated his Brooklyn accent and loved rubbing it in to the guys present from 1st Platoon. "Of cou'se, aftah they played with da bamboo punji stakes, they needed 2nd Platoon to go in and clean up aftah dem. But, hey, we'se all fuckin' family. Right?"

That evening, after writing the four recommendations for valor awards, Dunn thought about the combat rappels he observed. He would not have minded it at all if he had been on board and had also been one of those to rappel.

ℓ

What a stroke of luck and good fortune for me that the rappelling instructor in Panama broke his leg, remembered Dunn. He thought back to how excited and pleased he had been to be diverted to attend Jungle Warfare School in Panama before shipping out to Viet Nam. Except for the initial night, that first week of the two-week course had been disappointingly...gentlemanly. He had expected the course to be challenging and to fine-tune his combat skills in a jungle environment. But, the first day had been primarily wasted with administrivia.

However, he remembered the first night they were grouped into patrols and sent into the Panama jungle with an "Expert" on a Recondo mission. A Captain Espy accompanied Dunn's patrol. Espy had already completed two tours in Viet Nam as a Special Forces Advisor, first to South Vietnamese units and next to units from the Republic of Korea. He warned the patrol about the Black Palm, a viciously barbed tree indigenous to Panama that caused incredible pain and swelling to any body part that was pricked by its razor sharp barbs. Dunn had then wondered what sort of man-eating plants might await him in Southeast Asia.

That first night, Dunn's patrol was the second of eighteen patrols to successfully reach their objective. However, theirs was the only one to do so without suffering any training losses from booby traps, snipers or any actual casualties from the Black Palm. Three other patrols had gotten lost and never did achieve their objective.

The rest of the week had been primarily bleachers and classroom activity. Then, on Monday of the second week, Dunn was preparing for a hasty river crossing following a demonstration of pontoon bridge construction. When the instructors arrived, they asked the entire class, "Is there anyone here who has experience in rappelling? The rappelling instructor has broken his leg in an exhibition this morning, and there is nobody proficient to replace him."

Dunn was one of only eight students out of one hundred and twenty four that had any rappelling experience. However, it turned out he was the only one who could perform the Australian Rappel and adeptly demonstrated his mastery.

At West Point, Joe had joined the Cadet Rappelling Club and found he absolutely loved the sport. Thereafter, he constantly pushed himself to descend mountain faces faster and with the fewest possible bounds. When in Ranger School, he had even gotten to rappel twice out of a helicopter.

The Australian Rappel method was simply facing downward instead of the usual manner of descending with your back to the ground. One hand was all that was required to control the rate of descent. So, the military value in using the Australian Rappel was obvious as it was definitely an advantage to be able to shoot and to see what you were shooting at if the enemy was shooting up at you while you were rappelling.

The school had been so impressed they not only made Dunn an honor graduate, but also made him an honorary instructor. The rest of the week he relished perfecting the sport he enjoyed while enthralling the rotating teams of students.

"I guarantee you will want to descend quickly if somebody is shooting at you," he told the students. "I further guarantee if somebody is jumping down on top of the enemy and shooting at them at the same time, the enemy will duck or take cover. I encourage you to learn the Australian Rappel as it might someday save your life and the lives of troops entrusted to you," Dunn repeated to each group.

After graduation, the next assignment for nearly all the students was a tour in Viet Nam. The students were all being flown back through either Pope AFB or Charleston AFB. Both of those air bases were located in the Carolinas. Some of the instructors were also being rotated with a tour to Viet Nam, but the instructors were being flown through McGuire AFB, which was located in New Jersey.

Dunn mustered all his persuasive skills to convince the school to reroute him as an honorary instructor through McGuire AFB as well. This gave him two more unexpected, wonderful, love-filled nights with Marie, a God-given second honeymoon. Since Plainview was only about two hours drive from McGuire, was she ever surprised, and it didn't even count against any time off.

In contrast to the first day of operations in Phu Hiep, the day following was a quiet reprieve. After overseeing the insertion of two more teams in the morning, he spent the rest of the day in the Forward Air Controller Shack. He passed the time studying for the LSAT from the book sent to him by Marie or by gabbing and swapping war stories with the pilots.

"So far, this has been one of the most uneventful days I've spent over here," remarked Dunn. "No action by the teams on the ground, no communication problems, no teams lost and needing a fix on their location, nobody sick or out of water and rations-a real exception, this boring day. Well, the day is not over, so there is bound to be something happening with my platoon."

Since his day for being on duty as the flying observer was nearly over, he was about to call to be picked up when he heard a small explosion.

The first event that marred this slow day was most tragic. Two men from 3rd Platoon were returning from the Post Exchange at Tuy Hoa. Joking around, they decided to go over the wire as a shortcut to the Charlie Ranger's area. While climbing, one of the men slipped and his foot hit the ground just below a warning sign. The triangular sign upon the wire he was attempting to climb clearly spelled out, "M I N E."

KA...BLOOM!

When Dunn heard the small explosion, he stepped out of the FAC Shack and saw the smoke. Fortunately, he had just dismissed the chopper pilots, who were ready to head for chow. So, they immediately picked up the wounded Ranger and rushed him aboard their chopper and headed for the hospital.

The fellow Ranger lost the front portion of his right foot. But common sense could have prevented this tragedy as everyone had been repeatedly warned and made aware of the mines and were expressly forbidden to cross any mesh of wires or wire fences.

After the excitement settled down and just as Dunn was again bidding farewell for the evening to some of the aviation crewmen, shock vibrations rattled the shack.

KA...BLAMM!

The men inside the shack instinctively dove for the floor and covered their heads, as the explosion was close and loud.

KA...BLAMM! KA...BLAMM! KA...BLAMM! KA...BLAMM! KA... BLAMM! KA...BLAMM! Six more explosions and each one was louder and closer than the previous one. The last explosion sounded as if it was barely outside the wall where Dunn was seeking cover. It shattered and blew in the glass windows.

Is it mortars? Are we under attack? This shack must be next. God, don't let me die in a mortar attack. There is nothing I can do. Think. What can I do? Wait. No more explosions. Is that it? Is it over? Oh, God, let it be over... were just some of the thoughts that had flashed like lightening through Joe's mind.

Gingerly picking themselves up from the debris-strewn floor, the men rushed outside. Sirens wailed from approaching emergency vehicles as the men rushed towards the open-ended, igloo-looking concrete bunkers that housed the helicopters. Smoke spilled out of the line of bunkers adjacent to the shack.

"Sappers," yelled an MP. "Alert the perimeter to be on the lookout for sappers!"

Dunn had heard stories of sappers who tried to infiltrate base camps to blow up strategic targets. Some were shot when they got caught up in the barbed wire. Others blew themselves up, while some wrecked havoc and escaped. However, he wondered if this mess wasn't caused by the indigenous that worked there and not by sappers at all.

In any event, five choppers were destroyed. There would have been two more if they had not been rushing the injured Ranger to the hospital. Fortunately, the choppers always flew in pairs.

He hadn't needed to worry earlier about 2nd Platoon. Under the platoon sergeant's motherly watch, the brood was doing fine and doing nothing out of the ordinary, as well. Naturally they were curious and angry about the damaging explosions so close to home. Dunn omitted telling them about the panic and fear he had felt being so close to the blasts.

The next day was the day before Thanksgiving. Dunn was again scheduled to fly C & C, provided weather didn't hinder their operations.

"Hey, Captain Phillips," he said into the landline phone, "I'm down here at the FAC Shack, and things don't look good. The clouds are so low I doubt the 0-1 will fly at all today. However, I just spoke to the Devil and Demon pilots on duty with us. They are crazy enough and willing to go to work if you say so and have agreed to provide us an extra chopper for C & C. I suggest we postpone exchange of the X-ray site and just do the scheduled teams."

"Roger that, Joe," replied Phillips, "I'll tell Appier that we are scrapping the exchange of X-ray today. Meanwhile, I'll shuttle all four teams to the tarmac. Do the best you can. The Old Man doesn't want to lose this full day of operations."

After a couple aborted tries, Dunn finally succeeded in vectoring the choppers to the respective Landing Zones to extract four teams and to the other LZ's for insertions of the four new teams. There was some additional excitement during one insertion, when one of the gunships caught a Viet Cong with a weapon out in the open.

"Beanball 28, this is Devil 54. My Peter Pilot spotted a lone Victor Charlie in the riverbed during the approach about four hundred mikes from the bus stop. Request permission to investigate. Over."

"Devil 54, this is Beanball 28, permission granted to investigate, identify and eliminate. Over."

"Beanball 28, this is Devil 54. Roger, we are going down for a closer look. Oh, Charlie is giving us a green tracer reception. Hooo wheee! That's his last mistake!"

A few moments later, "Devil 54 confirms one unfriendly Kilo India Alpha. Devil 54 is now RTB, heading back home. Out."

"Say, Joe," said Dean Manker, the pilot of the C & C chopper, over the intercom, "you messed around out here too long. We don't have enough fuel to make it all the way back to Tuy Hoa."

"Well, Dean," replied Dunn on the intercom, "if we have to make an emergency landing out here in Charlie's country, I'm ready. I'm glad

I have my CAR-15 and not one of those P-38 pistol pea shooters you pilots carry."

"No, no," laughed Manker. "I just didn't want you to get shook up when we divert to the MACV, U.S. Military Assistance Command Vietnam, Headquarters, about six miles out. We can stop and refuel there before returning."

♨

For Dunn the day was far from over as that night he was Duty Officer and was interrupted from his LSAT studies by Gregorov. "Sir," said Rusky, "X-ray reports they have lost communication with Team 33. They request you go up in a chopper to see if you can raise them on the radio, boss."

"How long has it been since they last heard from Team 33?"

"Sir, they said it has been about five hours."

So, at about 2200 hours, in terrible weather and in pitch-blackness, Dunn took a ride in a chopper to find the area above Team 33 and hopefully raise them on the radio. It was Dunn's first night flight and he found it fascinating.

I am probably the only one aboard not really scared, he thought. *The pilots are really good, too, even though they don't like doing this. The poor door gunner looks scared. I only wish the weather were clear. The beau coup flares we carried are really lighting up the sky. This is so cool!*

"Beanball 28, this is Beanball 33." He finally raised the team on the emergency radio. "We want to thank the big Ranger-in-the-Sky for turning the night into day finding us. But, we can Charlie Mike. Tell X-ray we can monitor but not transmit on the regular. We have to use the emergency to send sitreps. Over."

Since they were all okay, they headed back and Dunn finally got to sleep a little after midnight.

As it was Thanksgiving that next day, the mess served traditional turkey with all the trimmings continuously from 1200 to 1700 hours. Somehow, Pancho had even scarfed up some Thanksgiving decorations, and he hung up some "Beat Navy" signs. He was hoping to make another stripe, so he was constantly outdoing himself. If it had been up to the men in the unit, they would have promoted him long ago based solely on his savory preparations.

Dunn was getting excited about that Army-Navy football game. If they won that game and lost all the others, it was still a winning season to him. *It is strange how a college football rivalry plays such an important role in my thoughts when I'm occupied daily with events that have life or death consequences,* he mused.

♨

The following morning, Dunn was going over some things with his platoon sergeant at the platoon conex when the loudspeaker announcement caught his attention. The voice of Staples was summoning him to the TOC.

"Lieutenant Dunn, I want you to meet Sergeant Roy Henderson, Corporal Patrick Burns and Private Sean Keene," said Staples. "These Marines are with the destroyer, the USS New Jersey. She is right off our coast, and this team helps deliver and coordinate Naval gunfire. They are the USMC's ANGLICO attached team, with the Air Naval Gunfire Liaison Office. They'll be with us for at least the next few weeks during our operations here."

"Great! Good to meet you guys," Dunn greeted the marines.

"Lieutenant Dunn is one of our primary observers," said Staples to the marines. "If you want a good fire mission for your ship, he is the best man to get to know. He has called in the most artillery strikes in support of our teams and on some pretty impressive targets."

"Tell me about your ship and their capabilities," said Dunn, genuinely excited about the prospect of working with the Navy.

"The USS New Jersey is a battleship, not a destroyer, and has nine 16-inch guns, sir, each capable of hurling a 2,700 pound shell a distance of 23 miles," said Henderson. "Each shell can pierce thirty feet of reinforced concrete."

"Sir, in 3 1/2 minutes we can fire seven broadsides from our 16-inch guns," said Keene, "equaling the bomb load of approximately sixty B-52 planes."

"The projectiles are so powerful and so precise," chimed in Burns, "that even swarms of B-52 Stratofortresses, America's major warplane, cannot match the New Jersey's doomsday guns!"

"So, how does this work? As the forward observer, if I spot an appropriate target, I notify you of the target coordinates. Then you call in the mission to the ship, and I notify you of necessary adjustments. Right?"

"You've got that absolutely right, sir," said Henderson. "We are in direct and constant communication with the ship."

"Hey, can I send a message to your ship now?" Dunn asked.

"Sure, sir. What do you want to send?"

"Please send this: 'Charlie Rangers welcomes the effective, accurate and lethal Navy gun fire from the USS New Jersey, a valiant ship with service in three wars. This USMA '69 Grad promises to find them a suitable target on which they can wreck havoc. I salute the brave officers and men on board and leave you with one final thought, BEAT NAVY!'"

As it turned out, while flying C & C the very next day, Dunn got a frantic call from Halloway, which provided the perfect opportunity for the New Jersey.

Some aircraft, notably Chinooks, had been complaining about receiving enemy fire from relatively large caliber weapon. The CH-47

Chinook was a twin-engine, tandem rotor helicopter designed to carry a payload of approximately 10,000 pounds. The aircraft complained they were receiving fire in the valley about nine miles out from Tuy Hoa. Reconnaissance flights, however, never revealed any enemy anti aircraft sites.

"Changeup 28, this is Changeup 23. I see hostile Alpha Alpha in my looking glass sending green tracers at a Big Windy. It probably doesn't even know. Charlie appears to be missing his target. I count eighteen unfriendly. It looks like a thirty caliber, water-cooled gun on wheels or tracks. If you hurry, you can catch them in the open before they roll it back underground. Location is in the middle of boulders on the side of a mountain nearly one click from my Tango. Location is Bravo Sierra One Niner Seven Three Foxtrot Victor Four One Eight Two. How copy? Over."

The Professor's binoculars caught an anti-aircraft gun with eighteen enemy soldiers firing at a Chinook. Time was of the essence since the enemy would soon roll it back into the mountain.

"Changeup 23, this is Changeup 28. Roger, I copy. Stand by. Out."

"Tincan 74, this is Changeup 28. Fire Mission! Coordinates Bravo Sierra One Niner Seven Three Foxtrot Victor Four One Eight Two. Antiaircraft with eighteen unfriendlies in the open. Fire for effect. Over."

"Changeup 28, this is Tincan 74. This is highly irregular. We like to fire one shell and adjust. Over."

"Tincan 74, this is Changeup 28. Negative! Target will move inside the mountain in moments. Send the Fire Mission. Over."

"Changeup 28, this is Tincan 74. Willco! Over."

Then, after a brief few minutes, "Changeup 28, this is Changeup 23. Oh, My God! The mountain is gone! We could actually hear the swoosh of the shells. The rumble of the thunderous impact was like the earth opening up all the way to hell! That damn mountain is completely gone! Over."

"Changeup 23, this is Changeup 28. Roger. Thank you. Out."

"Tincan 74, this is Changeup 28. Target has been destroyed. Good shooting. Over."

"Changeup 28, this is Tincan 74. Request a count of unfriendly. Over."

The Marine was actually asking for a body count of enemy soldiers killed by the shells from the New Jersey.

"Tincan 74, this is Changeup 28. You changed the geography. There is nothing left to count. Over."

That night at the Ops Briefing in the TOC, the Naval gunfire support was a highlight of the presentation by Staples.

Phillips followed with his announcement, "This unit is relocating again...this time to Tuy Hoa. More specifically, the unit will be setting up another Tent City in the vicinity of the tarmac."

Dunn thought, *That actually makes more sense than moving the men into air-conditioned billets on the post. Somehow, I don't see the mixing of plush accommodations, with the distractions of the PX and clubs, plus the REMF soldiers and Rangers coming back from field ambush missions, as being anything but an unhealthy and volatile combination. It is much wiser to have the men remain in tents. I feel strongly the daily distractions of the post would definitely interfere with the men's concentration and mental attitudes requisite for combat missions.*

Later, Staples privately revealed to him the Major had tried to secure billets for the unit, but found none were available.

After the Ops Briefing, Dunn overheard the Old Man berating Gregorov. "Goddamn it, Rusky, if the fuckin' Navy asks us for a body count, why in hell did we not give them one?"

"But, sir," pleaded Gregorov, "there was nothing left for the team to report. The whole mountain was blown apart!"

"I am 'sic-n-tarred' of having to fuckin' repeat myself. When the Navy asks us for a goddamn body count, then you give them a goddamn body count. Do you understand me?"

"Yes, sir, boss," said Gregorov.

Dunn was on his way to intervene in the conversation so he could deflect the blame from Rusky, when Phillips intercepted him. "Joe, I just wanted to remind you it is your turn again to be paymaster. Only, in this instance, you will be finished before the relocation to Tuy Hoa even though you will have extra stops at the Long Binh Stockade to pay Martinez and at the Replacement Depot to pay the Liaison Sergeant."

"Thank you for the reminder, sir," responded a rather distracted Dunn. But by the time he completed his brief conversation with Phillips, Gregorov was back at his station and the Old Man was gone.

That evening, when in his pleasurable escape mode and writing another letter to Marie, he chose to detour from his personal narrative to include a paragraph about his platoon: "My platoon is certainly improving-my platoon sergeant, E-7 London, is a good man and a hard worker. I am pleased with his performance to date. He is putting into effect most of the policies I wished to implement. Together, we should be able to adequately handle the myriad of vast unforeseeable and often unbelievable problems the men present us. I am especially pleased London has managed to continue to secure the much needed, new camouflage fatigues for those that have been the most in need of them...."

The following morning Dunn tackled the deluge of ever-present paperwork that plagued an Army platoon leader. In the afternoon, he was accompanying some of his team leaders on a VR when London interrupted him, "Sir, we just got word back from the hospital. Lucky went on sick call this morning and was hospitalized. He has been diagnosed with malaria."

"What? Wasn't he taking his weekly malaria pills? He should know better as he is on his third tour."

"He knew better but just hated taking them, so he stopped. He claimed they gave him the runs. I try to be a mother to these guys, but they don't always do what they are told," complained London.

"Make sure you personally talk to each man in his team. Then, use Lucky as an example for the whole platoon. Also, be sure and stress that *every* man must take his malaria pill *each* and *every* Tuesday. As soon as I finish this report, I'll be getting together with Sergeant Nate's team, as I will be taking Team 26 to the field tomorrow as team leader. I was already planning on going out with the VR."

Dunn decided not to admit his mistake to the team leaders. He now felt he had been wrong when he indicated to them he would break up their chain-of-command when he went into the field. By now, he had come to appreciate the strong bond and cohesion that existed in a team and that emanated from the team leader. Besides, there would be plenty of opportunities for him to replace an injured or sick team leader or to constitute a special team. So he promised himself he would never demote a team leader by taking his place while the team leader was able.

And he had not done so. Since he never intended to do so, there was no reason to even say anything. They were astute; they would notice on their own and appreciate his decision.

###

The next four days he spent in the field admiring the efficiency and effectiveness of a professional Ranger team at work. They were out the full four days because the team did not make contact with the enemy.

On the day after his return from the field, Dunn left on his paymaster duty trip. But the day following his completion of paymaster duties, he became embroiled hip deep in the preparations for the convoy's move to Tuy Hoa.

16
Good Will Towards Men

PERHAPS IT WAS BECAUSE OF THE JUNGLE environment or the oppressive heat, or maybe it was because of the routine of war in Southeast Asia. It was the first week of December, and there was no evidence of any holiday spirit. Dunn was beginning to think maybe the Army actually knew what it was doing when it scheduled only one-year tours in a combat zone. The war was more than a full time job, twenty-four hours a day, seven days a week. There was no respite, no real relaxation.

At first, he thought sleep could provide a degree of escape. But he was wrong as sleep was too easily interrupted. The sub-conscious was ever alert and the unconscious state was plagued with unpleasant scenes played over and over again by an unwitting mind. When the conscious state pushed the demons and reflections of war into the deep recesses of the mind, sleep reached into those recesses and released the demons and reflections.

The Ranger not only had himself to worry about, but he also knew other Rangers depended upon him for their safety. Team leaders bore a direct, defined, and heavy responsibility for the lives of six men. Platoon leaders felt a heavier, expanded burden complicated by the knowledge they could not personally attend to each life or death situation. The higher the level of the leader, the greater became the burden of responsibility. The higher the level the more remote became the impersonal decisions that impacted lives. But the highest level was the Commander-In-Chief, the President, and the President was the servant and representative of the people.

Therefore, the people were ultimately responsible to the Ranger, their defender and champion of freedom. However, the men of Charlie Rangers were too busy and too committed fighting a war on behalf of an ungrateful and irresponsible people to dwell upon the upcoming holiday season.

"Now that we have consolidated our company here in Tuy Hoa, our Area of Operations has not changed except it has increased," said Phillips at the first Ops Briefing after the move to Tuy Hoa. "The most significant difference, starting immediately, is our reactionary force is the White Horse Division, Republic of Korea.

"Beginning tomorrow, fifteen Korean soldiers will be assigned to Second Platoon. Two or three ROK soldiers will accompany each Second Platoon team inserted into the field. The teams are to train the ROKs in the tactics of Ranger ambush patrols. As soon as possible, we want to infill ROK teams with one of our men along as an advisor.

"Next, our Tent City is situated right next to the pilots' Scramble Hooch and the FAC Shack. So, whenever possible, recommend the men mingle with and get to know some of the great aviation guys who support us. The flyboys are always looking for an invite to join us in the mess as Pancho's reputation as a chef is unparalleled in these parts."

"Joe Dunn!" Phillips called out and catching up to Dunn before he left the TOC. "I know you indicated you planned on going into the bush with a team, especially since we are sending in your entire platoon. However, I need you to fly C & C. It's time to let some of your new team leaders get their cherries broken. Rod's Fourth Platoon won't be rejoining us for another four days. Kent is departing in a few days on a religious sabbatical leave for Japan. Lee is still struggling with a bout of dysentery. So, you're my man. Besides, you have a real knack for C & C. What do you say?"

"Sir, that's fine, but I have a favor to ask of you. As you know, the Old Man approved me taking a few days to go to Saigon to take my Law School Admission Test on December 19th. Well, perhaps you can have Sergeant Staples arrange a scheduled flight for both myself and for PFC William Armstrong from here to Saigon on December 18th. Armstrong is going all the way to the States for his R & R. If we could save time by not having to wait for space available, it would be terrific."

"Consider it done. When you get back from Saigon, the Old Man and I may be gone. We're both taking two weeks leave time and are each going home for the holidays. By the way, how the hell did Armstrong get stateside R & R for Christmas? That lucky bastard!"

"I had nothing to do with it. The guys unanimously decided to reward him for his actions in the field under fire and for his incredible patriotic fervor. Remember how he checked in wearing love beads? Well, he has managed to retain his flower-child ideals while performing his Ranger duties in spectacular fashion. He deserves a free trip home."

The following morning Dunn was in the TOC when he heard a commotion outside in the parking area. Going outside to investigate, he noticed most of his platoon and the rest of the company watching curiously as well. The Koreans had arrived-an officer and a First Sergeant accompanied by fifteen troops. The officer never spoke a word but the First Sergeant uttered some short, guttural commands to a sergeant, who screamed non-stop at the men.

"What are they saying," asked the Cuban, "and what the fuck is all this about?"

"I have no idea; I can't speak Korean," replied Dunn, amazed at the scene unfolding before him. Personally, he figured this was staged for their benefit.

When the soldiers were aligned in a precise formation and the sergeant stopped screaming, the First Sergeant barked two more guttural commands. The sergeant walked over to the First Sergeant, who struck him forcibly in the chin with a clenched right-handed fist! Then, the First Sergeant walked over to one of the soldiers and proceeded to pummel him with a flurry of punches. The soldier never even attempted to protect himself. Casually, almost defiantly, the First Sergeant and the officer, who never did speak, returned to the vehicle in which they had originally come and simply departed.

"Wow," whispered Dunn, "their reputation as fierce disciplinarians is well deserved. Too bad they do not enjoy as fierce a reputation as combat soldiers." From what Dunn had heard, the ROK was only slightly better than the ARVN in a firefight.

They never did find out what had been the purpose of the scene enacted in the parking area. However, once the officer and First Sergeant departed, the troops were visibly more relaxed. All fifteen soldiers had been selected because they spoke fluent English. Soon they were laughing and joking with the men in the platoon. Left unchecked, they easily became rowdy.

The rest of the morning was unbelievably busy. The team leaders had to prepare their teams for insertion. The Koreans had to be outfitted and thoroughly briefed. Two sorties of two slicks each were required to ferry all the parties on the Visual Reconnaissance flights. Even the cherries were too busy to display any signs of worry, concern, or fright.

Late that afternoon there was a loud commotion emanating from the 2nd Platoon area. Racing to the spot, Dunn found his platoon sergeant strategically positioned between two warring factions. On one side were ROK soldiers, cursing and spitting. On the other side were the Kit Carson Scouts. Normally placid and silent, the scouts were angrily shouting curses in Vietnamese at the Koreans.

"You the fucking gook," screamed Nguyen Trang. "You no Ranger. You *dien cai dau!*"

"Sir," suggested London, "I think it would be a good idea to give our Kit Carson Scouts a couple weeks off from missions in the bush." Dunn readily concurred but never did find out what had triggered that minor skirmish either.

🕊

At Oh-Dark-Thirty the next morning, Dunn briefed the Devils and Demons on the hectic schedule for the day. They would be inserting two X-ray sites and nine separate teams. Privately, Dunn was annoyed that his Birddog plane had not yet arrived and was worried he might be stuck with an inexperienced pilot.

When he finished his briefing and was ready to go to work, he suddenly heard, "Hey, Oscar One, you hot dog!" blared an exuberant Jim Wails. "Are you rated in a fixed wing yet?"

"Jim Wails!" replied Dunn, opening his arms wide with his fingers spread, as a sign of affectionate reception. "Am I ever glad to see you! I thought they gave your Birddogs to the Vietnamese pilots and figured you'd be flying with them."

"They did. Can you believe it? The Army gave all the 0-1 Birddogs from my unit to the fucking Vietnamese! No way was I going to stick around to be a backseat, especially with them. They are more dangerous to work with than you pussy Rangers. So, I volunteered to come here to fly for you guys.

"Hey, I brought you a gift."

"Thanks, I'm speechless," replied a very pleased Dunn as he accepted a brand new flight helmet with its own carrying case. On the back of the helmet was painted a red C/75 scroll and on the right side was painted, G O D.

"Oh, you're never speechless; I have heard you light up all five radios at the same time. I was going to put 'Oscar' on the side. But, I felt your role for the teams on the ground is closer to that of 'God.' Glad you like it. Now, let's go to work."

That evening the two of them were tired, hungry and happy to be heading back after a busy day of flying. The only break they had the entire day was when they stopped briefly to refuel.

"I would let you try landing," said Wails to Dunn over the intercom, "but Tuy Hoa is much too busy. The Tower is also a real stickler about following bullshit regulations. But the next time we land at a runway without a tower, I'll let you handle the landing of the plane."

"Tuy Hoa Tower, this is Birddog Two Five Seven Three Niner. I request clearance to the main runway for approach from the north. Over."

"Birddog Two Five Seven Three Niner, this is Tuy Hoa Tower. Clearance to the main runway for approach from the north granted. Please maintain current approach pattern and speed. Over."

"Tuy Hoa Tower, this is Birddog Two Five Seven Three Niner. Roger. Over."

"Birddog Two Five Seven Three Niner, this is Tuy Hoa Tower. You are cleared for final approach. Welcome to the base. Over."

Have you ever been driving a vehicle, obeying the speed limit and all the rules of the road? You are driving at forty or fifty miles an hour on a straight road. There are vehicles parked on the side of the road and there is some traffic, but the road is clear ahead. Then, suddenly, out of nowhere, another vehicle pulls out smack in front of you and the only way to avoid a catastrophe is to violently swerve direction, potentially overturning and crashing anyway. Meanwhile, the other vehicle drives on in a cavalier manner. Has that ever happened to you? Did it ever make you mad? Then listen to this:

"Me land now!"

No warning. No call sign. No care for regulations or procedures. A Vietnamese pilot in another 0-1 Birddog plane suddenly announced his intention and cut directly into the final approach path of Jim Wails. Dunn thought he would be thrown through the tiny backseat window. He was hurtled against the side as Jim Wails made a drastic, evasive maneuver to avoid a mid-air collision between the two planes.

"Goddamn, son-of-a-bitch! I'm gonna fuckin' tear him a new asshole!" yelled an outraged Jim.

Dunn could hear Jim clearly even though he was not using the intercom. When they finally landed, Wails turned the plane to taxi to the east side of the tarmac, the Vietnamese side. When he rolled up alongside the interloper Birddog, the Vietnamese pilot was still inside his aircraft. Wails jumped out of his Birddog while it was still moving and raced over and jumped up on the Vietnamese plane and began to flail wildly upon its pilot. It took four mechanics to finally pull him away.

"I bet he won't ever do that again," Wails said, now much calmer as he climbed back into his Birddog. "I guess we should get out of here before I have to deal with the Vietnamese police. I'm hungry. How about you?"

"I'm famished. Say, if you ever want a job as a Ranger, let me know."

"No, you Rangers are too ruthless and scary for me. I really don't like the possibility of hand-to-hand combat."

❧

The following week, Dunn was once again flying with Wails, who had been his frontseat for three of the six days that Dunn had flown. On that particular day, they were overseeing the insertion of three Korean teams, each accompanied by a volunteer from 2nd Platoon. Before they took off, Wails pointed out a couple of bullet holes in the wings of the aircraft.

"The two times I have flown over this one particular location, I have drawn small-arms green tracers... probably sniper fire. The bastard has actually hit my plane a couple times. If we have some free time later today, I'd like to check it out to see if we can spot him.

"You carry a CAR-15, right? I'd love to give him a taste of his own medicine. What do you say, Dunn? Are you up for a little hunting... a little target shooting from a moving aircraft?"

"I'll fly the plane and let you use my weapon from the front seat. Maybe you can scare him, even if you don't actually hit him," Joe replied.

"I'm not a sharpshooter nor have I ever fired a rifle," Wails admitted.

Dunn assured him, "It's not hard. Simply point and pull the trigger and then watch where the red tracers land and adjust your aim accordingly. Squeeze each shot off, just the same way you do with your pistol."

"I think you just want an excuse to fly the aircraft. Okay, but if we spot him and I cannot hit him, then you have to agree to take him out," Wails bargained.

"Agreed, but then you have to teach me to land this thing," countered Dunn.

"Agreed," said Wails, as they took off to go to work.

The scheduled events of the day were performed in routine fashion, including providing a location response to nearly every team. They always requested coordinates of their location because map reading from the ground was even tougher than from the air. The ample daylight and early hour at the conclusion of the scheduled missions provided Wails the opportunity he sought to detour over to the sniper's location. Sure enough, after the second time they traversed the area, they drew the sniper's attention.

"I've got him," yelled Dunn, pointing under the wing below them to the left. "The dummy is in the open field hiding behind that stone well. I bet you can get him to jump into the well. Here's the weapon. Flip the safety off and fire single shots. That gives you greater accuracy."

"I see him. Got it, thanks. Now, it's time for you to take the controls of the plane."

"I have my control stick set and can now take over the flying. Let me know how close you want to go."

"Take it down so that I have a decent chance of hitting the bastard, and do a fly by. Great! That's it! You are getting pretty good at handling this bird," enthused Wails.

BLAMM! BLAMM! BLAMM! "Damn! I missed him. Bring it around for another pass. See if you can get us closer."

BLAMM! BLAMM! BLAMM! BLAMM! "Missed again! One more time, Joe and this time bring it around and make it even closer." But Wails' pattern of fire was random, at best.

"Here, Joe, take the weapon," said Wails unexpectedly just as the Birddog was flying by the sniper on the third pass. Reaching back with his left hand to pass the gun to Dunn Wails said, "I'll take over the controls, and you can... arrgghh!"

His frontseat, Jim Wails, was shot. Dunn quickly pulled the aircraft into a steep climb and banked a turn away from the field containing the sniper.

"Jim! Where are you shot? Are you all right? Can you fly? Dunn urgently inquired of his frontseat.

"My left shoulder... my chest... I can't... ahhh..."

"Jim, hang in there, buddy! You agreed to teach me to land this thing, so that's just what you're going to do! Everything is going to be just fine.

"Tuy Hoa Tower, this is Birddog Two Five Seven Three Niner," Dunn switched to the tower frequency. "Mayday, I say again, mayday. Over."

"Birddog Two Five Seven Three Niner, this is Tuy Hoa Tower. What is your situation? Over."

"Tuy Hoa Tower, this is Birddog Two Five Seven Three Niner. Frontseat is wounded and not conscious. Request immediate medivac and a Birddog pilot. Request any assistance you can give me. Over."

"Birddog Two Five Seven Three Niner, this is Tuy Hoa Tower. What is your location? Who is flying the aircraft? Over."

"Tuy Hoa Tower, this is Birddog Two Five Seven Three Niner. This is the observer in the backseat operating the controls. I am not rated. I am heading west to find the shoreline and identifiable features. I hope to find your base. Over."

"Birddog Two Five Seven Three Niner, this is Tuy Hoa Tower. The pilot is carrying a homing beacon. Find it and turn it on. Medivac chopper will soon be airborne and come to you. Over."

Dunn reached into the pocket of the unconscious pilot, who was moaning. He quickly found and turned on the emergency radio beacon. Dunn softly cursed himself for not paying attention to the direction Wails had headed when he made the detour to find the sniper. None of the visible terrain was in the least bit familiar to him.

"Tuy Hoa Tower, this is Birddog Two Five Seven Three Niner. The emergency radio beacon is on. I see the shoreline. When I reach it, I will proceed north until I hopefully approach your location. Over."

"Birddog Two Five Seven Three Niner, this is Tuy Hoa Tower. Roger. Medivac is up. When they pick up your beacon, they will contact you on this channel and give you a new frequency on which to talk to them. Good luck. Over."

Dunn reached the shoreline and slowly turned the plane to the north. He was extremely worried about Jim Wails, who was now conscious but in considerable pain and moaning loudly and incoherently.

Wails will be no help, Joe thought, *and Tuy Hoa Tower offered absolutely no help in how to land. Well, I just have to keep my wits about me. I have witnessed hundreds of landings from the backseat. Each one was a stroll in the park. Right. Then, why am I sweating profusely?*

"Tuy Hoa Tower, this is Birddog Two Five Seven Three Niner. I see a landing strip! I hope it's you. I am lining up to approach for a landing. Oh, no! It's a deserted tarmac. I am going to try to take it down anyway. Over."

"Birddog Two Five Seven Three Niner, this is Dustoff. We have your beacon and should be at your location in less than five mikes. You are heading into the deserted base formerly called Lima Zulu Pony. Switch to Romeo Foxtrot (Radio Frequency) 2145. Over."

"Damn, I dropped too fast, and I need more speed." Dunn was talking to himself out loud, as if his own voice might help calm and assure him. The runway was coming up at him much too fast. "Oh, my God! This is scarier than I thought it would be. I've got to get the nose up. Great God! Well, here it comes!"

The Birddog plane hit the ground with a much, much greater force than any of his preceding landings as a passenger. "We bounced! We bounced at least fifteen feet. I have to keep it in control and put it back down. Another bounce... but smaller. Oh, Christ! Jim, I hope that first bounce didn't hurt you worse! Jim, we made it!" Dunn exuberantly announced coming to a stop.

Quickly, Dunn reached forward to open the cockpit door and flipped it open but did not try to push the front seat forward and squeeze out. Instead, he turned his attention to Wails, who was now fully awake and alert. Dunn grabbed a large bandage from the medical kit and applied pressure to help stop the flow of blood. The point of entry of the bullet appeared to be somewhere between the chest and the left shoulder.

"Oowww!" Wails cried out when Dunn applied the pressure. "You call that a landing! What were you trying to do, get me killed?" He spoke the words slowly and painfully, but with a hint of a smile on his face.

"I've got him," said the medic, who had just run over to them from the medivac chopper that had landed next to them moments later. "We'll take him from here. Did you receive our transmission? You didn't answer. We were worried until we spotted your plane on the tarmac."

"Sorry, I was a little busy. Take good care of Jim Wails. He's one of Uncle Sam's finest."

"We're taking him directly to the hospital at Camh Ranh Bay. There's a pilot from his unit already on a chopper and on his way here now. Can you stay with the plane until they arrive?"

"I'll be fine. Go on! Get out of here. Get him to the hospital. I'll be just fine."

Dunn had to wait another twenty minutes before the chopper carrying the pilot finally arrived. During this time he kept his CAR-15 at the ready since he was alone and in the middle of an open tarmac. While he waited, he inspected the Birddog and was amazed that the two tires hadn't blown from the torture they had to endure from his awful landing.

"Wait a minute," he announced to an audience of one. Any landing in which you survive is a gorgeous landing. So, my landing was a gorgeous landing." Then he noticed another ten new bullet holes in the aircraft and mused to himself, "That sniper never missed."

"Hi, Joe Dunn, my name is Rick Slater. I am the Executive Officer of the Birddog unit." Major Slater walked over from the chopper that planned to wait until he was sure he would be able to lift off in the 0-1. "My friends call me 'Crash.' You are definitely in the category of a friend.

"Tuy Hoa Tower explained you had to fly and land the plane. Quite frankly, I never expected to find either you or the plane in one piece! Tonight, over some drinks on me, you're going to have to tell me how the hell you did it. We called your unit and left word with your TOC that you are going to be our guest for the night. Tomorrow, you can return with the Birddog assigned to support Charlie Rangers in the morning. By the way, can it still fly?"

"Other than a few bullet holes in it, I don't see why not. Your offer sounds awfully good to me right now, Crash."

The flyboys treated him to a feast of steaks, lobster, beer and bourbon that night. At one point in the early morning, Dunn found himself on the cold ceramic floor of the air-conditioned latrine, clutching the commode as the room spun around and around. Oh, how he hated throwing up. But what he despised most was losing control, which is why he rarely allowed himself to get drunk. He didn't have much choice this time, not that he would have chosen anything differently.

The fifteen-minute ride from Dong Ba Tin to Tuy Hoa at 0600 that morning felt like hours to Dunn. His frontseat was non-stop excited chatter for the entire duration.

How can he be so cheerful and talkative this early in the morning? Thank God I'm not scheduled to fly today, thought Dunn. *I pray my head clears enough to let me do some studying. There are only four days left until I leave for Saigon.*

"Hey, Joe!" Rod Winthrop called out in his booming voice, waiting and greeting them when they arrived. "I'm jealous, man. Word is you started the Christmas season early. You stayed and partied with the flyboys in air-conditioned luxury last night. You Hot-Shit Hot-Dog!"

"Yeah, whatever," murmured a subdued Dunn.

"Oh, looks like somebody had too much to drink. A little under the weather this gorgeous morning, are we?" Then, turning to the pilot, Winthrop continued, "We have a busy day, and I have already briefed the chopper pilots. So, what do you say? Let's get a head start, and we can talk when we get airborne."

"Thanks. Hope you guys have an uneventful day," Dunn bid them farewell. He stopped in at the TOC before returning to his billets. The TOC was alive in its normal hectic routine.

"Hey, Dunn," said Phillips, who was leaning over Staples studying a map, "the Old Man said something about you running into a problem in the Birddog. Then, we heard you were going to stay over and party with the pilots. Did you have a good time?"

"Well, you know how pilots are," explained Dunn.

"Yeah, those fuckers let it all hang out in some pretty hairy combat operations when they support us. I imagine they are just as wild when they let it all hang out at a party." Phillips then went back to his serious discussion with Staples. The radios were alive with multiple transmissions.

Dunn had planned on heading to his bunk to rest before tackling any new tasks. However, on passing by the 2nd Platoon area, the Cuban called out to him. "Hey, sir. Look what we found...poor little fellow... we want to try and nurse him back to health and keep him as a team mascot. We call him, 'Chieu Hoi.' Isn't the little bugger cute?"

The Cuban was holding a scroungy, emaciated gray-striped kitten. "Chieu Hoi" was a Vietnamese term meaning, intent to surrender. It also referred to the "open arms" program, promising clemency and financial aid to Viet Cong and NVA soldiers and cadres who stopped fighting and returned to South Vietnamese government authority.

"He has a cute little face but since you can count the ribs on his tiny little body, it looks like he surrendered to you big, mean Rangers in the nick of time. Make certain you keep him away from Team 24's pet python," Dunn advised.

"Right, sir, can't you do something about that? Team 24 lets their damn python roam freely in the billets at night. They claim it keeps the rodents away. It fuckin' freaks me out," the Cuban complained.

"Sorry," replied Dunn, "you'll have to take that one up with the platoon sergeant." Then Dunn proceeded on to his billet where he found two waiting letters from Marie. They were the perfect medicine for his mind, body and spirit. Surprisingly refreshed, he again relished his youthful life with renewed countenance.

Later, that afternoon, Dunn, Lee and Appier were enjoying each other's conversation over a lunch of good, old-fashioned hamburgers and fries when Lee asked, "How the hell did Jack Kent pull a sabbatical leave without it even counting as any time off or as an R & R?"

"I have to give him credit," said Appier. "He was smart enough to get a trip to Japan on Uncle Sam's time."

Suddenly, the TOC loudspeaker again blared an announcement of a team in contact. "Attention in the compound! Attention in the compound! Team 42 is now in contact! I say again, Team 42 is now in contact! All members of 4th Platoon assemble at the TOC ready for immediate deployment as a React. Members of 4th Platoon-it's time to scramble! Sitrep follows: Team 42 is now in contact under heavy enemy fire; one Ranger is wounded in action. Stand by." Then, after a brief pause the voice continued, "The wounded Ranger is John Ruffin. I say again, the wounded Ranger is John Ruffin."

"Holy shit!" said Lee. "I hope he is not hurt too badly. I was just talking to him the other day and he was getting ready to DEROS home. This was to have been his last mission. He was just coming to the end of his second consecutive tour with Charlie Rangers. He is a hell of a nice guy."

"All we can do now is pray he'll be all right and to stay out of the way of the TOC and 4th Platoon. They will be scrambling about now," said Appier.

"I am glad we have the ROK White Horse Division as the principal reactionary force instead of the Ruff-Puff ARVN," added Dunn.

"Attention! Attention! It is my sad duty to report that the Ranger WIA is now a KIA. That is all."

"Goddamn! Son-of-a-Bitch!" screamed Lee, slamming his fist on his own knee. "Those fucking bastards!"

"God rest his soul." fervently stated Appier.

"God help us all," Dunn spoke in a whisper, mostly to himself.

"Lieutenant Dunn! Lieutenant Dunn!" yelled SP/4 Garbo, running toward them.

"What's the matter, Slant?" Dunn jumped up to meet him.

"London sent me to get you right away. Goldstein grabbed his gear and a loaded weapon. He's planning on joining 4th Platoon in relief of Team 42. He's headed for the TOC now!"

Dunn didn't wait for Garbo to finish before he was racing for the TOC. 4th Platoon was loading onto a deuce and a half truck and he managed to jump in front of and face Goldstein, who was preparing to climb aboard.

"No! Goldstein, you are not going in with 4th Platoon," Dunn told him.

"Get the fuck out of my way! You don't fucking understand! John was my best friend in the world. Those fucking... I have to, sir... they killed him! Goddamn it!"

"Give me your weapon, now! Roger Goldstein, you are not part of the relief team." The deuce and a half began pulling away just as the last two members of 4th Platoon were still in the process of climbing aboard.

"You want my rifle? Fuck it! Here! You just don't fucking get it. You have no fucking idea. I loved him; he was fucking family to me!" Goldstein angrily replied.

Dunn's hung-over reflexes were not sharp enough to fully deflect the rifle away from his face and it smarted when the butt struck his cheek and nose. But he grabbed the barrel with his right hand and caught it with his left hand after it ricocheted off his face.

He watched as Goldstein, with tears streaming down his face, slunk back to the 2nd Platoon area, yelling to no one in particular and yet to everyone, of his hurt, anger and frustrations. "He knew it! He told me! He fucking knew he was going to bite a bullet on his last mission. He was fucking crying. He was scared and John was never scared. I fucking tried to get him not to go. I fucking tried! I tried! Happy... fucking... holidays! Why are we doing this? Why can't they either just let us win this fucking undeclared war or let us all go home?"

When 4th Platoon relieved Team 42, they were able to break contact with the enemy and pull everyone out of the bush, including the body of John Ruffin. Rangers never left behind a fallen comrade. It was discovered he ended up bleeding to death from a gunshot wound in the chest and the savage enemy fire had prevented his teammates from traversing the twelve feet to reach him in time to save his life. Shortly after the Charlie Rangers were extracted, the Koreans were inserted to pursue the enemy force.

The following morning, the entire unit not in the field and many of the pilots attended a solemn, short ceremony in tribute to John Ruffin. Lieutenant Rod Winthrop delivered a eulogy, followed by Major Wayne saying a few words of praise. The men openly wept public tears of deep, private grief. John Ruffin had been with Charlie Rangers for nearly two full years. Everybody knew him. Everybody loved him. Goldstein stood stoically with the men in Fourth Platoon. Goldstein's anger gave way to a torrent of tears before the short ceremony concluded.

John Ruffin had been full of humor, wit and Ranger bravado; he was young, charming, good-looking and full of life. He had given them the ultimate gift, and his Ranger spirit would now dwell forever in their hearts.

Dunn spent the remainder of that day and the next on paperwork for the men in his platoon and for the men in the supply section, his additional assigned duty. The Rangers returned to their routine of war in not only a somber and thoughtful mood, but also a vicious one. Team leaders, reflecting the attitudes of their teams, volunteered for combat missions. Either in spite of or because of the approaching holiday season and the tragically and vividly defined real danger, teams volunteered. It was as if each Ranger sought to take on the mission himself to insulate the rest of his Ranger family.

A Leg unit would probably have reacted entirely differently, even opposite. However, the Ranger was a special breed of volunteers. Rangers were the country's Imperial Guard, and they served to protect and to defend. Rangers lead the way.

On December 17th and 18th, Dunn pulled duty flying C & C. The flight scheduled by Staples for him and PFC William Armstrong was not slated to depart until 1830 hours. Thus, he would have less than one hour from the time he returned to the company area until he had to be back on the tarmac.

Billy Armstrong was packed and waiting for him at the TOC a full two hours before Dunn even finished his C & C duty. "Are you ready, Billy?" Ramos, who was taking the two of them to the tarmac in the Major's jeep, asked.

"Are you kidding? I've been packed and ready for the past week! I'm traveling light, just this small bag with some gifts for the family. Everything else I might need is at home." Then turning towards Dunn, asked, "Do you know what kind of plane we are taking to Saigon, sir?"

"Yes, Sergeant Staples arranged for us to fly in style. We are taking a twin turboprop U-21 VIP aircraft, a 'UTE.' It is used to chauffeur around generals and other dignitaries. It happened to be heading back to Saigon empty."

"Really! Wow! That is so cool, sir."

"There it is, right over there. The two pilots appear to be waiting on us, so let's not delay them on our account," said Dunn, as they thanked and waved farewell to Ramos.

As they approached the plane, Dunn did a double take when he recognized the pilot. "Hank Berry! How are you? It sure is good to see you!"

"Joe Dunn! Well, I'll be a son-of-a-bitch! Are you one of the pax going with us to Saigon?"

"Yup! Billy, say 'Hi' to Hank. He is rated to pilot just about anything that flies. Just how well, we are about ready to find out."

"Hi, Hank, uh, sir," stammered Billy.

"Joe, you and I have got to celebrate tonight at the Bien Hoa Officer's Club, just like we did when we first arrived In Country. Only, this time you're paying! We've got a lot of catching up to do. As you can see, I did get stuck temporarily flying dignitaries around in this U-21. My call sign is 'Red Baron' and I am with the 201st AHC. I want to hear what the 'Ultimate Weapon' has been doing for the past five months."

"Sorry, Hank, but I have a heavy duty, cerebral, written exam tomorrow morning at the Education Center in Saigon. Then, I have to make stand-by arrangements to get back here to my unit."

"No way! Tomorrow night we will celebrate on the town in Saigon. Then, I'll bring you back to this hellhole myself the following day. Billy is welcome to join us," Hank promised.

"Billy is leaving tomorrow. He is heading home to CONUS for the holidays on R & R and an additional two-week leave," Joe explained.

Since the Army announced a new change in policy regarding leave trips to the Continental United States, the Major took back the two free additional days he had given Armstrong. So, instead, Armstrong was allowed to take leave in conjunction with his R & R. Therefore, he would be gone three weeks from the unit. His DEROS date, signifying the end of his tour in Nam, would be pushed back two weeks to make up for the leave time.

"Too bad, you lucky bastard, you're going to miss a great time," said Berry. "Well, hop on and let's go!"

"Hey, sir," asked Armstrong, once the two of them had settled into their comfortable seats, "do you know everybody in 'Nam? This cushy plane is just for the two of us? Man, this is really out there! I can't believe I'll be with my family for Christmas. It's only one more wake-up before I am flying home!"

"How many are in your family?"

"I have three brothers and two sisters. I am now the oldest as my older brother died years ago in an accident on our farm."

"I bet they are all really happy you are going home. Your folks must be very proud of you," Joe commented.

"I can't wait to show up in my uniform wearing my Black Beret! I want my mom and dad to be proud of me, because they don't really understand me. They used to worry I was going to run off to Canada as a draft-dodger because I would protest against the war. So, naturally, they were surprised when I hitched up and volunteered for 'Nam. I guess they didn't realize how good a job they did in raising me to love our country."

"They sound like wonderful folks. So, what are you going to do once your tour is finished?"

"First, I want to go to Ranger School in Fort Benning. I want to earn the black and gold Ranger tab, just like you and Sergeant London wear on your shoulder. I am proud that I completed Jump School, and I am very proud I have earned the right to wear the Black Beret. But now, I want to earn the Ranger tab, too. After that, I want to use the G.I. Bill and go to college. I will be the first person in my mom and dad's whole family to ever go to college."

"Do you know what you want to study?"

"Yes, sir! I want to study Political Science. Then, I want to run for office. I think it is important for our politicians to have served our country honorably during time of war. Then, when they speak out against a war like the one we are now fighting in Viet Nam, people will listen. People respect a veteran. Politicians who were veterans of a war won't allow young men's live to be wasted. The demonstrators against the war in Viet Nam are patriotic. It's just that the politicians won't listen to them. Just like my mom and dad, they think protestors are anti-American. My dream is to someday get elected and save our country from fighting in another Viet Nam."

"Keep that dream alive. If you believe and work hard enough, you can achieve a reality from your dream."

"Yes, sir. I am going home wearing the two symbols of my dream-my Black Beret and see what I have here on my dog-chain under my shirt." He showed Dunn his circular bronze medallion that said, "Make Love, Not War."

"I heard you tell the pilot that you were taking a test, sir. What kind of test are you taking?"

"I am taking the Law School Admissions Test."

"Wow! You are an example to me of what can be done. I am proud to know you, and I am really proud to be in your platoon."

"Thank you, Billy. That means a lot to me." Dunn easily understood why the men in his platoon adored this courageous young 18-year-old. Billy had lofty ideals, but his feet were firmly planted in rich soil with deep roots in a mid-American farming family that Billy appreciated and nurtured.

Dunn spent the entire next day taking the exam. Upon entering the test site, he nodded to the Officer-in-Charge of the test, Captain John Edgerson, who returned the nod with a smile. Dunn was one of seven applicants taking the exam. The other six all happened to be clerks stationed right there in Saigon.

While Dunn was struggling with the prerequisite for entrance into a law school, young Billy Armstrong was happily winging his way to a time zone that was twelve-hours later.

Quickly clearing customs with his single, small bag, Armstrong broke into a run. Deftly avoiding and weaving around people, he raced through the corridors of the Travis Air Force Base terminal. Finally reaching the outside, he ran even harder to the designated bus stop for the free shuttle to the San Francisco Airport.

"Sorry, son," said the red-capped porter, "you missed it. The next military shuttle to San Fran Airport is in two hours."

"Is there a place where I can rent a car, sir?" panted Billy.

"Sure thing, son," said the porter, pleased and impressed with the mannerly young soldier, who referred to him as "sir." "It's on the other side of the terminal, back from where you just came."

"Thank you, sir," Billy yelled back as he was already on the run. Soon he was driving out of the air base in a compact car. He was back in the good old U. S. of A. and since he was in uniform, the civilian car rental company had reduced the fee.

The airlines allowed soldiers to fly half-price when they flew standby in uniform, so in order to save money, he had resisted making a reservation. It was only eleven in the morning so if he could get to the airport early enough, he felt he stood a decent chance of getting a stand-by flight home. The girls in the car rental office had been nice and had given him good directions... if only he could remember them. Thankfully, they also gave him a map.

Just as Billy approached an intersection in Oakland, the light turned red and he came to a stop. Through his open window, he recognized the familiar chants of an anti-war demonstration, "Power to the people!" "Fuck the pigs!" "Hell No! We won't go." "One, two, three, four, we don't want your fucking war," and after that they continuously chanted, "Strike, strike..."

Pulling his dog chain so that his medallion was visible hanging out of his shirt, he raised his fist in a salute and tribute to the marchers, who were heading towards his intersection. The light turned green and the car behind him instantly began honking.

Billy also wanted to get across before the marchers arrived so he could get to the airport. However, he pulled out slowly, just in case, as he didn't want to accidentally hit somebody.

"Whoa! Whoa! Hey, muthafucka! Where do you think you're goin'? Look, it's a fucking Baby-Killer! You trying to run us over, you fucking ass-wipe?"

"I saw him shaking his fist at us! He wants to bomb us with his car," screamed another marcher.

"Fuck the Baby-Killer," shrieked a girl. "Show him that Vietnamese people have human rights. Get him!"

"Get the Baby-Killer! Fuck him up!" The crowd drew towards him like slivers of iron to a magnet and they started rocking the car and eventually overturned it. Hands groped at him. Somebody grabbed his dog-chain and suddenly he was being choked and pulled through the open window. Lashing out in self-defense he fought back. A hundred fists and feet pummeled and kicked him.

⚜

"Oh, my baby! Honey, come quick! Billy's eyes are open. The Christ Child has answered my prayers." Billy's mother had not once left the side of his hospital bed. Now, tears of joy replaced the countless tears that had been freely flowing from a deeply wounded mother's worried heart.

"Merry Christmas, son," said his father, gratefully peering into Billy's bewildered eyes. "It's Christmas Day. Your mom and I are right here with you. Everything is going to be fine. You have just given us the best present any proud parents could want. You're awake and with us on Christmas."

"Where am I?" asked Billy. "I remember the marchers attacking me."

"Don't even think about them, son," said his father. "You are safe in a military hospital now. You have to stay here for a couple more weeks. Then, you can transfer closer to home. The doctors say with a few months of physical therapy, you are going to be as good as new."

His mother stopped crying and beamed a genuine smile. "The Army says you don't have to go back to Viet Nam! You can choose a new assignment to finish out your enlistment."

"Mom, when I volunteered to go to Nam, it was to serve my country. This time is going to be different. I am going back. But this time, it's for me. It's what I intend to do for myself. It is who I am and who I want to be. Mom, I want you to bring me that trophy catalog from the top drawer of the desk in my room. I lost my bronze medallion, and I want to order a new one."

17
New Year

O N CHRISTMAS DAY, A CHOPPER CARRYING TWO special passengers, made a surprise visit to Tent City. Two men dressed in complete Santa suits arrived by helicopter toting gift bags. They gave each man a pen and stationery. Also, they gave everybody a much-needed laugh. The sight of the two white-bearded elves in the stuffed red and white suits, struggling to hold onto their caps and beards while they toted their bags as they tried to escape the wind from the chopper blades, was hilarious.

A lot of the pilots decided to forego their own mess and joined the Rangers in the daylong feast of turkey prepared by Pancho. Some Devils and Demons pilots presented the Rangers with a nice frame containing their unit patch and the words: "We will fly to Hell and back to support the C/75 Rangers. 2nd Platoon Slicks."

For a ten-day period, starting two days before Christmas, there were no scheduled combat missions.

During this break, John Greenhouse, a West Point classmate, visited Dunn. Greenhouse had just been assigned to a line unit there in Tuy Hoa and Dunn enjoyed seeing and talking with him.

Dunn also received a letter from "Fuzzy," one of his best friends from the Academy. Fuzzy alerted him he had just gotten his orders that would take him to Nam the following month. While Dunn was glad his tour was already half over, it surprised him that many of his classmates were only beginning to arrive In Country.

Also, during this break, Dunn received a nice letter from COL Shane, the Catholic chaplain who had performed his and Marie's wedding ceremony. That letter opened a floodgate of happy memories for him...

COL Shane had flown in from Ft Ord, California, and insisted on arranging a bachelor party the night before the wedding. It was probably fortunate for Dunn that he did not attend his own bachelor party. Since he was recovering from a mild case of strep throat, he did not want to risk being sick for his own wedding. As it was, during Communion of the Wedding Mass, when Father Shane handed him the chalice and he drank the wine, Dunn thought his vocal chords would rip away from his throat.

Evidently, the ushers had a great time without the groom. They managed at 4 a.m. to awaken most of the guests at the Thayer Hotel with some raucous renditions of songs by the Four Seasons and a West Point ballad entitled, "Benny Havens." The ushers foolishly challenged their host to a drinking contest, in which he literally drank them all under the table and carried them back to the hotel at West Point.

One particularly irritated guest, a visiting retired Brigadier General, demanded an explanation but was summarily dismissed and marched back to his room by COL Shane.

Dunn met Father Shane many years before when his father was stationed with the military in Germany. As a youngster, he volunteered to serve as an altar boy at the early 5:00 a.m. mass for the troops. He invited the priest home for breakfast and to meet his parents after the very first mass. They immediately formed a bond that was to become a long-lasting friendship. Over the years, wherever his father was stationed in the Army, Father Shane was not far behind.

The priest was a convert to Catholicism and therefore, completely unorthodox in his sermons and mannerisms. He loved music and started a vocal trio-group for whom he wrangled an appearance on the Ed Sullivan Show.

While in Germany, he raised enough donations to purchase a Volkswagen to donate to Rome. He did this so he could arrange a private session to personally meet the Pope.

During an earlier tour in Viet Nam, without actual authority, he "requisitioned" material from around the world and "re-assigned" craftsmen to construct a miniature Catholic cathedral in the town of Nha Trang.

His masses at Ft Ord were popular because of the choir that sang rock music and the band that included numerous trumpets.

For months before the wedding, COL Shane waged a private war on behalf of 2LT Dunn. COL Shane wanted to officiate the wedding in the West Point Cadet Chapel, a magnificent edifice that housed the largest organ in the hemisphere. He wrote letters to the Catholic priest assigned to West Point, the Chaplain of the United States Military Academy, the Military Ordinariat and even to the Pope. COL Shane wanted the grand stage of the Cadet Chapel, which was non-denominational and supposedly for all Cadets. He believed that the local Catholic priest feared the loss of revenues if Catholic cadets could select the Cadet Chapel in lieu of the Catholic Chapel for weddings. Since Cadets were not allowed to marry until after graduation, West Point turned into a marriage factory with couples lined up waiting for their turn at the altar.

Actually, Dunn was pleased to have their ceremony at the Catholic Chapel. The number of guests filling the Catholic Church would have made the Cadet Chapel look empty. Plus, he could not imagine the wait he would have had if his bride had to traverse the length of the Cadet Chapel's center aisle.

Despite the recurring horrible nightmare he dared not tell Marie about, he was glad they had married in the Catholic Chapel.

When they had exited onto the hewn stone steps outside the heavy, wide, double wooden doors into the vibrant sunshine, the newly married couple radiated happiness. Dunn's 5'11" frame stood tall and erect with prideful broad shoulders back and head up. Marie was gorgeous and now his wife.

When his eyes adjusted to the bright sunshine, he was amazed to see a line of First Class Cadets on both sides of the sidewalk directly in front of them. They were all "Firsties," seniors, from Cadet Company G-1, his company of the past four years.

"Cadets! Pree-Sent Arch!" barked Cadet Captain Schooner, as all the cadets drew their sabers. Never had he felt so elated as when he stooped, with his beautiful bride on his arm, below the archway formed by the cadet sabers. He wanted to invite the Firsties from his former cadet company to his wedding reception, but their TAC Officer would not allow them to attend because alcohol was being served.

Dunn was glad the photographer stopped them for a shot under the arch but was disappointed when he eventually saw the proof. The picture focused on the couple and did not capture any of the glory of the cadets in their Full Dress Gray Over White parade uniform. They looked so sharp in their white, cross belts adorned with a gleaming brass chest plate and numerous brass buttons on the gray tailed coat over heavily starched white trousers. The gold chevrons on the sleeves as well as the feather plumage on the tar-bucket hats indicated the high ranking of these cadets.

Before departing from the area of the chapel for more picture taking, Dunn made certain to shake the hand and personally thank each cadet. Spare time was a scarce and precious commodity for cadets so preparing and getting into the parade uniform was always a dreaded nuisance to him when he was a cadet. So, he especially appreciated their contribution to him on this special day.

The cadets had royally screwed up one thing, though. Dunn had earlier parked his light blue Oldsmobile Cutlass on the ramp leading up to the Catholic Chapel. His best man, 2LT Matt Wheeler, parked directly behind him. Matt's car was a dark blue Cutlass. Poor Matt. As only cadets can do, they covered what they thought was the newlywed's Cutlass with hilarious decorations. The fact that it was the wrong blue Cutlass made it even funnier.

The wedding party then made its way down to Trophy Point overlooking the big bend in the Hudson River. Trophy Point was just off the Plain, the meticulously kept expanse of grassy field where the cadets marched. In five days, it would be one year ago that he stood on the Plain with his graduating classmates to watch the Corps pass in review. Dunn was glad the photographer took his advice on selecting this site for taking the album pictures, even though the bridesmaids had problems with the wind buffeting their wide-brimmed picture hats. He felt the site was a good omen for their marriage.

The golden Lady of Fame smiled down on them from her white granite perch one hundred feet above the display of cannon balls. This marriage would last!

"Why is the Lady of Fame not fickle, Smack?" an upperclassman barked.

"Because she has been on the same ball and shaft for two hundred years, sir!" responded a Plebe.

⚜

The Christmas downtime meant that Joe would have considerable waking moments in which to miss and daydream about Marie. However, the free time also permitted him an opportunity to talk with and get to know the men in the unit. He spent time talking with all the men, not just the men in his platoon and, surprisingly, it put him in an extraordinarily good mood.

To be fair, though, the numerous sugar reports from Marie helped, too. Besides that, Marie's mom sent him a couple of sheet sets for his cot and they alone produced a relative feeling of exquisite comfort. For some reason, he especially liked the blue set.

He wrote a few long letters to Marie and in one he wrote:

I love you, Marie. I am in a very good mood today, especially after all the sugar reports yesterday! No matter what may come, I know God has blessed me with the most wonderful gifts possible in this life-the gifts of true, mutual love, of health, of freedom and of future.

Perhaps my efforts and time now, will contribute to affecting a peaceful, prosperous existence for our children and their children. I welcome this opportunity to serve my country and to serve our common G.I. in this, the best capacity for which I have been selected, trained and am competent to perform.

My duties are rewarding and satisfying because I am serving a noble purpose, and I have a sense of accomplishment. Our young eighteen, nineteen and twenty-year-old men, the Rangers of 2nd Platoon, may cause me big headaches and numerous little problems continuously, but they are almost without exception the finest, most dedicated men a country could produce, and a leader could develop....

He actually felt the words he wrote and hoped she didn't think he was being too naïve

彡

"Time for Charlie Rangers to go back to work so when the Old Man returns from The World, he'll be proud of us," said Staples, in the first Ops Briefing of 1971. "Until further notice, we will have two ARVN companies as a reactionary force. Tomorrow morning, Lieutenant Jack Kent will depart for Firebase Lucy. Lieutenant Kent, you will coordinate with a Major Crighton to establish artillery support for our teams.

"Firebase Lucy has been built in a spot that provides covering fire for all the sectors in which our teams will operate. He is expecting you. Hopefully, you will have to be there for only a few days.

"Lieutenant Appier, please prepare one heavy team for a ten-day X-ray mission. Two teams from each platoon will be inserted tomorrow. All insertions begin as soon as the recon is completed.

"Platoon leaders let me know which teams you wish to send in first. Lieutenants Lee and Winthrop will handle operations in the TOC. Lieutenant Dunn, you will fly C & C in the fixed wing Birddog.

"Platoon leaders should check with me concerning team sectors, and after the recon I will meet with the team leaders."

Staples continued the briefing, to include delineating the supporting assets, call signs, terrain, weather, intelligence data and enemy dispositions.

The sign of a truly effective company is one that can smoothly operate in the absence of the commander and the operations officer. Charlie Rangers was effective. While briefing his team leaders, Dunn realized he felt as if there had never been a pause in the action during the holidays.

At 0615 hours the next morning, as Dunn walked over to the pilots' ready shack, he was surprised to see the Birddog taxi approach.

"Joe! Hey, Joe Dunn!" Dennis Riley called out. "Are you flying backseat today?"

"Yeah," replied Dunn, "you're stuck with me today, and we have a busy schedule. I'm glad you came in early."

"I wasn't sure you would be the one flying C & C so I came in early because I brought you something, and I wanted to make certain it was delivered to you. It's from Jim Wails. They just shipped him home; too bad it wasn't in time for Christmas. He wanted you to know that he is fine and that he was damn proud to serve with you. He said to tell you that he drew this with his sharpshooter hand."

"Thank you," said Dunn, accepting a two-foot square, heavy-duty parchment. On it was a picture of a Birddog in flight, intricately drawn all in pencil. Below the Birddog was the unmistakable forested, mountainous landscape of Viet Nam. "I'm glad he is okay. Wow! This is really nice."

"I was very careful not to fold or bend it for you. Here, he also gave me this card to give to you."

Dunn opened the business card size, envelope and read the card inside: "From a Damn Fine Pilot, to a Fucking Great Pilot, THANKS (signed) Jim Wails." He smiled.

"I'll be right back. I want to put this incredible drawing in my hooch for safekeeping. Thanks for bringing this to me."

The rest of that day was unbelievably busy as they performed all of the assigned missions. But then the following day was even busier as in addition to inserting an additional five teams, Dunn and Riley were kept busy with the eight teams inserted the previous day.

All the teams signaled to the Birddog with either panels or mirrors and that allowed Dunn to get a fix on each of their locations on the ground. Then, he radioed the coordinates of those locations to the team. Rarely were the teams ever actually lost but it was important to accurately verify their locations.

"Man," said Riley, his frontseat. "I don't know how you do it. How can you tell, in that jungle down there, at what spot the team actually is on the ground? There are no roads, buildings or any other landmarks of any kind...just jungle and mountains that look the same."

"Sure there are," answered Dunn on the intercom. "Each mountain and valley is a separate landmark. You just have to line up the map contours with the features on the ground. It is definitely easier for us looking down from a plane than for the teams on the ground. I appreciate the teams checking with me so they have a verified fix as to where they are. Then they can check their map to see what is around them and how best to execute their mission."

≈

The following day, both Major Wayne and Captain Phillips returned to the company from their two-weeks leave. Rod Winthrop took Dunn's place flying C & C for two days and was followed by Lee the two days after that.

Dunn happened to be in the TOC near the end of Winthrop's seemingly uneventful first day when a call came in about a 1st Platoon team. The point man on Team 14 had inadvertently tripped a booby trap wire on a trail and the subsequent explosion of a fragmentation grenade wounded the following three Rangers, including the team leader. The early radio reports stated that fortunately, none of the three Rangers was seriously wounded. But, at the request of the team leader and with the consent of Phillips, Winthrop called for a team of Devils and Demons to extract Team 14 by rope ladder.

"We had a deja vu situation," said Phillips, opening the Operations Briefing that evening. "Team 14 was pulled out of the bush by rope ladder from a chopper and during the exfil, the ladder snagged on a tree. One man, SP/4 Jake "Cowboy" Heller, was knocked around pretty badly and he has been hospitalized with some puncture wounds. Fortunately, he suffered no broken bones and he wasn't one of the three men who sustained shrapnel wounds from the grenade.

"Unfortunately, a rucksack full of equipment and a weapon went crashing down a rocky, tree-covered slope. First thing tomorrow morning, we would like you, Dunn, to volunteer to go get it. You'll have to rappel in, retrieve the stuff and climb back out by rope ladder."

"Absolutely," responded Dunn enthusiastically. "I will have Sergeant London rig the chopper for me."

"That's what we figured. Take with you whomever you deem necessary."

※

When Dunn briefed London and the team leaders on the requirements for the next morning, they all eagerly volunteered.

"Sergeant Halloway, I appreciate your offer, but you already have made a combat rappel. Tell Slant he had his joy ride dangling below a helicopter and it is time for someone else to get a chance. I know he will want to volunteer when he hears about this but...I would like for you, Professor, to be up in the belly of the chopper with London. Knowing you two guys are watching my back will make me feel much better."

Then, turning to one of his newer team leaders, SSG Tom "Ripcord" Harper of Team 27 Dunn asked, "Ripcord, did you say you wanted to join me and you know how to do the Australian rappel?"

"Airborne, sir! I'm your man. What the fuck? It's just another day at the office," enthused the new team leader.

※

The next morning, Dunn and Harper exited from the chopper about ninety feet up from the sloping ground. Dunn waved the chopper away from them after they reached the ground. The steep slope was precarious enough without the wind generated from the hovering aircraft. Meanwhile, two Devil gunships circled around further overhead.

"Over here," yelled Ripcord, "I found the ruck. Evidently it hit a tree and the fucking shit spilled out all over the place."

The two spent another fifteen minutes collecting the spilled gear and stuffing it back into the rucksack. Then it took them an additional half hour to locate and retrieve the weapon. After that they had to climb back up to a spot where a few boulders provided them a sufficient clearing in order to signal for the chopper to lower them the rope ladder.

I sure wish I had my Fuji movie camera with me, as it is quite a ride dangling on a ladder beneath the chopper. It is sure exhilarating to head back, knowing the mission has been successfully completed and with no further harm to anyone.

On the way back to the base camp and with both men still on the rope ladder, the chopper came to a hover above a river when suddenly. Bam, bam, bam, bam, bam!

"What the hell?" said Dunn, stunned by the sudden eruption of the door gunner's M-60. Then he looked over at Ripcord who also let loose with his M-16. Bam, bam, bam, bam!

Looking down, Dunn saw floating upside down, the largest Cayman he had ever seen. Ripcord cheered and flashed a "thumbs up" at the door gunner, as if dangling below a chopper wasn't exciting enough.

❦

Following the Ops Briefing that evening, Dunn informed Phillips he intended to go back into the bush with Team 21 after its recon.

"No, Joe, you can't. I was coming over to tell you that Goldstein's court martial is convening here tomorrow. His attorney has been here all day and you are scheduled to be a witness sometime tomorrow during the day. Make certain that all the members of Team 23 are available also as none of you are to leave the compound. When the board wants to see you, you must be immediately available. I will be telling Pappy and all of the others who may be called as witnesses.

"You know the Major expects a speedy conviction. He has long suspected Goldstein of being a dope-head and considers this guy's refusal to go into the field a slap in the face to the officers, an insult to the Rangers who perform their mission, and a dishonor to the memory of all who have lost their lives."

"Sir, the members of Team 23 and myself will be available when called upon to testify." Dunn assured Phillips

❦

The next morning, five officers arrived and set up for the hearing in a structure that had been cleaned and set aside for their purposes. The

Chairman of the Board was LTC Charles Latham, himself an Airborne Ranger assigned to the 173rd.

During the long day, a steady procession of witnesses paraded before the Board. In constant attendance, of course, were Goldstein and his attorney, CPT Edgerson. Major Wayne also attended the entire proceeding. Finally, at the end of the day, the Board called its last witness, Lieutenant Dunn.

Dunn was glad to finally be called as sitting around all day just waiting to be called was both vexing and boring. He knew the Board had kept some of the witnesses for over an hour, as they asked detailed questions and collected all sorts of information relating to Goldstein. *I wonder what they will expect of me?*

As if he hadn't had to wait long enough, the Board took a forty minute break right before they called him in to testify.

"State your rank and full name, and then spell your last name for the stenographer," bellowed Lieutenant Colonel Latham, a large-framed man who towered at least 6'1" in his stocking feet.

"Sir, I am First Lieutenant Joseph Dunn, D-U-N-N."

"Did there come a time when Specialist Goldstein informed you that he no longer wanted to go into the field and that he no longer wanted to participate in combat ambush missions?" LTC Latham asked the question harshly and directly right off the bat.

"Yes, sir."

"Did you advise your commander, Major Wayne, of what Specialist Goldstein had informed you?"

"Yes, sir."

"Did Major Wayne direct you to give Specialist Goldstein a direct order to accompany his patrol, Team 23, on a combat mission?"

"Yes, sir."

"Did you in fact give Specialist Goldstein a direct order to accompany his patrol, Team 23, on a combat mission?"

"Yes, sir."

"Are you confident that Specialist Goldstein heard and understood your order to accompany his patrol, Team 23, on a combat mission?"

"Yes, sir."

"Did Specialist Goldstein respond or say anything to you when you gave him the order to accompany his patrol, Team 23, on a combat mission?"

"No, sir."

"Did Specialist Goldstein in fact comply with your order to accompany his patrol, Team 23, on a combat mission?"

"No, sir, he did not."

"Lieutenant Dunn," stated LTC Latham, matter-of-factly, "that is all. You are dismissed."

"Sir," interrupted CPT Edgerson, "with your permission, I have some questions for this witness."

"You do not have my permission," barked LTC Latham, "I have heard enough witnesses to know what happened and to have an exact appreciation of the situation. The Board concurs. Right, gentlemen?" The four other officers of the Board nodded in complete agreement.

"This last witness has confirmed what we already know and have concluded. CPT Edgerson, you and your client are also excused. Please wait outside...Major Wayne, please remain and report front and center."

On his way out, Dunn noticed the lips of Major Wayne curled downwards on one side in a half-smirk to hide the self-satisfaction he was obviously feeling.

A military tribunal is not an impartial trial, thought Dunn. *I don't know what went on all day with all the witnesses, but if that's the way the entire proceeding went, they didn't allow Edgerson to even develop a defense. What a crock!* Dunn thought as he hurried away, not wanting to address either Goldstein or his attorney.

"Major Wayne," began LTC Latham, "the rank of 'Major' generally denotes the position of a battalion staff officer or an advisor. A company commander is nearly always a Captain. But you have been accorded the enviable position of a commander as a Major...an extra feather in your professional career plume, so to speak."

"I am aware of..."

"Do not interrupt me again, Major!" Latham literally barked, erasing the last vestige of the Duke's smirk. "As a more senior officer, you should bring greater experience to your position. This Board is unanimously outraged at the circumstances for which we were convened. Specialist Goldstein has dutifully conducted himself for two years in this unit with honor and valor. Now, your actions have kept him here long beyond the time he should have been transferred home. The order you directed should never have been lawfully issued. Not only are we finding him 'Not Guilty' of violating a direct order, I shall personally see to it that a letter of reprimand be permanently attached to your personnel file. Do you have any further questions or statements to make part of this official record?"

"No, sir, I do not," said the Duke with hidden inner rage.

"One more thing, Major," said the Chairman of the Court Martial Board, "as the commander of a Ranger company, you should know what the Ranger motto is, so please tell us."

"It is 'Sua Sponte,' sir."

"Do you know what that means?"

"Yes, sir. It is Latin meaning, 'Of Their Own Accord.'"

18
Grief

"LIEUTENANT DUNN," BLARED THE LOUDSPEAKER "report to the TOC immediately! I say again, Lieutenant Dunn, immediately report to the TOC!" Joe was re-reading some letters from Marie when the blaring speaker suddenly summoned him. Upon entering the TOC, he approached Phillips and Staples and inquired, "Did you need me?"

"The Major wants to talk to you." They both pointed to the Major, who was chewing on an unlit pipe and reading a sheet of paper.

"Sir, Lieutenant Dunn reporting as ordered." Since the Major obviously knew he was there and was intentionally ignoring him, he figured he had better officially report. He had not felt compelled to report that way since the first day he reported to the unit and the time Goldstein was first advised of his court martial.

After a few additional staged moments, the Major erupted. "I am sic-'n-tarred of you goddamn glory-hungry lieutenants! You ought to be fucking ashamed of yourselves! Lieutenant Dunn, do you know what my fucking policy is regarding officers in this unit being put in for valor medals? Do you?" He practically spit out the last sentence after he drew out his dripping pipe and waved it with his hand.

"Yes, sir. Only enlisted men are to be put in for valor awards, not officers."

"That's goddamn right! Then, why the fuck have you been put in for a goddamn valor medal?"

"Sir, I honestly do not know what you are talking about."

"You don't? You didn't have an aviation unit try to do an end run around me? You didn't think I would find out? As your fucking commanding officer, any goddamn valor award for you has to come through me, I'll have you know!"

"Sir, I still do not know what you are talking about. I did not have anything to do with any valor award from any aviation unit."

"Then, what do you propose I do with this recommendation for you to receive the Distinguished Flying Cross?"

"Sir, you can do whatever you want with it, I really don't care." Dunn didn't wait for any further comment before he turned and walked out.

"Good! 'Cause that's what I planned to do anyway!"

The prerequisites for a Distinguished Flying Cross is set forth as follows:

The Distinguished Flying Cross is to be awarded to any person who, while serving in any capacity with the Armed Forces of the United States, distinguishes himself by heroism or extraordinary achievement while participating in aerial flight. The performance of the act of heroism must be evidenced by voluntary action above and beyond the call of duty. The extraordinary achievement must have resulted in an accomplishment so exceptional and outstanding as to clearly set the individual apart from his comrades or from other persons in similar circumstances. Awards will be made only to recognize single acts of heroism or extraordinary achievement and will not be made in recognition of sustained operational activities against an armed enemy.

Major Rick Slater, the Executive Officer for the Birddog unit of Jim Wails, had submitted Dunn for this particular high award. But Dunn never got to read what Slater had written about him.

"Gentlemen," announced Phillips in the Ops Briefing, "tomorrow we extract X-ray and all the teams in preparation for our next move. The 17th Aviation Group has approved another request from the 173rd Airborne Brigade. We are moving into a tent city back at Ahn Khe, where we should be relatively safe since two Battalions of the Herd will be around us. Otherwise, there will be nothing there, not at all like here in Tuy Hoa-no PX and no clubs.

"Because of the increased ambush activity lately by Charlie over the treacherous pass at Ahn Khe, I have requested gunship support in the air for our convoy. During the convoy, I want Lieutenant Dunn in the fixed wing as an observer. We do not intend to let Charlie use our tactics against us just because we happen to be in a convoy."

Later, Dunn discussed the new plans with his sergeant. "Sergeant London, I have learned 2nd Platoon will not be scheduled for any insertions during the first two days after we are situated in Ahn Khe. Phillips indicated our teams would probably be operating in a different sector from the rest of the company. We will find out more of the specifics later. Anyway, what do you think about tasking all of our team leaders with conducting classes for the entire platoon?"

"That's a great idea, sir. We have a lot of new men who need the specialized training in Ranger tactics and all the men could use a refresher. Plus, this is a chance for all the men, not just the individual teams, to learn from each team leader. Great idea! I will ask each team leader to provide a topic for a class."

"You never need help in this category, but just in case you do require my assistance in securing any training aids or supplies, don't hesitate to task me, too. I plan on attending the classes with you."

"Airborne, sir!" London responded energetically.

Without a hitch, the convoy moved to Ahn Khe. Dunn took some pictures of the Charlie Ranger vehicles moving through the Mang Giang Pass with its many hairpin turns. Fortunately, there were no other shots fired than the ones he took with his camera.

The day after they arrived and set up their tents, they had to move again. This time, they moved only a few hundred meters up on a hill with a few buildings that served as billets for the troops. But London and Dunn, as well as most of the other officers and top NCO, still had to be in tents. As extra precautions, the men dug in and constructed fortifications.

On the third day there, in conjunction with payday activities, the team leaders conducted classes all day for the 2nd Platoon. Naturally, the classes were all outstanding.

"Tomorrow, 2nd Platoon will be opconnned to 3rd Battalion, 173rd Airborne Brigade," briefed Staples as Captain Phillips was away attending a separate briefing with the Herd. "2nd Platoon will be operating in a separate AO from the rest of the company. Lieutenant Dunn shall take one team leader and one other man with him to act as liaison.

"You three will be at Firebase 'Mattie,' which is the location of 3rd Battalion Headquarters and a Battery of 173rd Artillery.

"Lieutenant Dunn, you and your two men will coordinate operations and control the firing of artillery in support of 2nd Platoon teams.

"Sergeant London, you will be in charge of 2nd Platoon and its teams here while Dunn is at Firebase Mattie. The Battalion Commander, LTC Gunderson, requires that an officer from Charlie Rangers be there to clear locations for firing the artillery, to personally brief him and to control the ambush teams. The three of you will be further required to maintain constant radio watch, twenty-four hours a day."

"Sergeant Staples," asked Dunn, "how long will 2ndPlatoon be opcon to 3rd Battalion and how long can the three of us expect to be there?"

"Sir, for all I know, maybe three days or three weeks. Let me know the names of the two men you take with you."

"Sir, whispered London to Dunn, "considering the relative strengths of the teams, I suggest you take SSG Forest and SP/4 William Dayne with you. Forest will keep you entertained and "Wild Bill" Dayne is reliable and excellent on the radio. Wild Bill has a commo MOS."

"Staples, I agree with you about the two men," immediately concurred Dunn.

⚜

Dunn was favorably impressed with Firebase Mattie when the three of them were dropped off by helicopter. The base was being built on a mountain in the middle of nowhere. Just as they arrived, three Big Windy Chinook Helicopters were leaving. They had airlifted in some tractors that appeared to be already at work building and reinforcing the perimeter.

"Hey, sir," said Specialist Dayne, after their welcome briefing, "I think we're going to be pretty fucking safe here, what with the artillery battery, the mortar section and three companies of the 173rd operating around us. The perimeter is heavily manned."

"Guess what?" Dunn said with a smile. "We still have to build a sturdy bunker, which means digging in and making bags."

"Fuck it, sir!" said Buck Forest. "I'll put up with these Legs for whom we are now working. I don't mind living in a poncho hooch and sleeping on an air mattress that leaks. I don't mind that we have no hot meals here. I don't even mind the constant radio watch. But... the worst fucking thing is digging in and filling those goddamn sandbags!"

"No, the worst thing is that mail will be brought out to us only once about every five days," laughed Dunn.

LTC Gunderson, the Battalion Commander that Dunn briefed daily, had been a Tactical Officer for Cadet Company B-1 when Dunn was a Cadet in Company G-1. The briefings were smooth, no-nonsense and professional. LTC Gunderson voiced his appreciation and support of the Rangers.

Also, two of Dunn's classmates with the Battery and another classmate from the Engineers were scheduled to arrive at Firebase Mattie in the next few days.

Dunn enjoyed the new experiences this duty station provided, and the three men learned a great deal working with the artillery units. The three men also shared and worked equally hard as they filled and stacked sandbags.

On their third night there, as they were huddled around the radio, Dunn asked Dayne about the AK-47 bullet that Wild Bill wore on a chain around his neck.

"That's my 'good-luck charm,' sir. I got it with Team 24 on our last mission, the first time we were in Phan Thiet, just before you joined the unit. I was walkin' point on an overgrown trail. We thought it wasn't being used anymore when, all of a sudden, I almost walked right into a fuckin' gook that was walkin' point, too, and we sure scared the hell out of each other. He raised his gun first and tried to fire but, fortunately for me, his rifle jammed. That's when I fuckin' blew him away. The rest of them just di di maued out of there. I crawled over to that dead gook, retrieved his weapon and took the round out of it as this souvenir. I drilled the hole and have worn it ever since."

"Then, that fucking 'good-luck charm' is probably what saved you from yourself on our last night there in Phan Thiet," added Foster.

"Why, what happened then?" asked Dunn.

"I spotted Wild Bill raiding 2nd Platoon's supply of grenades; he took about eighteen grenades. I figured he was gonna do some goddamn fishing with them."

Wild Bill protested, "Hell, no, I was upholding the Ranger honor. Some fucking Marine accused us Rangers of being 'chicken shits." So, I challenged him to a game of 'chicken.' The loser had to pay for a round of drinks."

"Major Holden, our prior commander, heard the explosions and asked me to check it out," continued Buck. "I found Wild Bill here, on the edge of a cliff about a hundred feet above the South China Sea. He was sitting across from this crazy ass, wide-eyed Marine and they were using one of those large, wooden spools that cable is wrapped around, as a table. The bag of grenades was at Wild Bill's feet, so, I asked him what the fuck they were doing. He told me to sit down and have a free drink with him."

"I never fucking lost. I never paid for a single drink," proudly interjected Dayne.

"By this time, Wild Bill was three sheets to the wind," continued Buck, ignoring Dayne. "He reached down, grabbed one of only eight grenades left, pulled the pin and placed the grenade on the make-shift table. I about shit! Wild Bill then sat back and folded his arms. The fucking jarhead finally snatched it and threw it into the fucking sea! Good thing, too, 'cause Wild Bill was so fucking drunk that he missed when he reached to pick up his free drink!"

"I upheld the honor of Charlie Rangers. A fucking commo Ranger showed up a Marine. Of course, I've fucking been on more Ranger missions and in more goddamn contacts than a lot of guys in our unit with an 11-B MOS, fucking Infantry. But, goddamn Woody Woodpecker won't give me the CIB 'cause I'm only a fucking commo guy," Wild Bill complained.

London was right about Dayne and Forest, Dunn thought.

He really enjoyed being with the two guys. Wild Bill was quite a character and Buck especially kept him in good humor with his war stories and his tales about women. However, he was glad when word came for him to return to Ranger Hill, and operational control of 2nd Platoon was back with the TOC.

On his first day back at Ranger Hill in Ahn Khe, Dunn was Duty Officer again and his entire platoon was on bunker guard. Each platoon was now required to rotate and spend four days on twenty-four hour bunker guard, a genuine haze. The men adamantly maintained they would rather go out into the field on a combat mission.

Since the evening was quiet, Joe was beginning a letter to Marie, when suddenly the silence was shattered. Kaaabooom!

"What the fuck!" Gregorov shrieked as he jumped up from his radio. "Hey boss, what was that explosion?"

In a flash, Dunn raced outside the TOC and noticed a bit of debris floating down from the top of the hill. Instantly, he ran toward the top of the hill where a bunker position was stationed.

"Sorry, sir," babbled Specialist Neil Hedon, an FNG, Fucking New Guy, in Team 21, "it was an accident! I swear it was an accident!"

"What the fuck happened?" Pappy yelled from the 3rd Platoon conex, where a large group of Rangers had gathered to drink.

At the same time someone else yelled, "What's going on?"

A lot of Rangers were definitely shaken up and another voice called out, "Goddamn it! What in hell happened?"

Dunn calmly announced to the compound, "Nobody was injured. Everybody relax and go back to whatever you were doing. The excitement is over." Then, turning to "Hammer" Hedon he said, "Tell me what happened."

"Sir, I was up in the tower of the bunker, and I accidentally knocked over the clacker of a claymore mine and it fell off the tower. Although the clacker was in the 'safe' position, the claymore exploded. Sir, I really am sorry!"

"'Hammer' is a good nickname for you, Ranger."

As he walked away Joe wondered and muttered out loud, "Why is it that my platoon always seems to be the one that has a 'happening'?"

When Joe returned to the TOC to finish writing his letter to Marie, he was soon in a very nostalgic mood as it had been exactly one year ago on Valentine's Day that he had proposed to Marie. He remembered how happy her parents, Mr. and Mrs. Russo, had been when they learned of his intentions to marry their daughter.

Dolly Russo was genuinely ecstatic and not at all surprised Joseph Dunn chose Valentine's Day to ask her daughter, Marie, to marry him. Mrs. Russo accused him of always being so brash, so self-confident.

"But, a wedding in only three and a half months?" she had said to him. "Impossible! Well, Marie loves you. Heck, the whole family loves you, and we have known you for only one year. Pop has a picture of each of our three children in the hallway, and now he has hung two pictures there of you. Pop is so happy.

"We love all three of our children dearly, but Marie is Pop's pet. He adores her and has always wanted the best for her. You were so smart and considerate to formally ask for Pop's consent before you proposed to Marie. I wonder if you truly appreciate how happy and proud you made Pop by first seeking his blessing? I hope you know Pop loves you as if you were one of his own sons."

When he thought about Pop, Dunn chuckled to himself as he remembered that day... Pop hadn't looked very happy when he spotted them near the end of the reception trying to unload their suitcases from the elevator. He hadn't even offered to help them but just stood and looked as if someone were stealing from him and there was nothing he could do about it. Pop hadn't wanted the night to end, plus he was obviously worried about them jaunting around the world on their honeymoon.

Dunn was glad Pop hadn't been home when he first introduced Dolly to his friend, the priest, Father Shane. After they first met, Father Shane followed Dolly into the kitchen and exclaimed, "God has endowed you with such wondrous bounty!" as he cupped both her breasts. Then, he simply continued talking as he walked back into the dining room.

In the kitchen, Dolly had been left shocked, stunned and almost speechless. "How could a priest do such a thing?" she said out loud. She never imagined a Catholic priest such as him. Priest or no priest, it was a good thing that Pop hadn't witnessed the way Father Shane blessed her "bounty."

Nevertheless, after the wedding, Dolly said, "I think he gave a very touching sermon at the wedding."

Also, Dolly remarked to Dunn, "You were smart and wise about another thing, too. Pop would never have allowed Marie to fly to Hawaii to spend a week with you, on your R & R vacation from Viet Nam, if you were not married."

Joe wondered, *Does Pop realize how lucky he is? After all, who else would have married his daughter and then given her back to him for a year?*

Dunn finished writing his letter to Marie. In it he had asked her to be sure and give each of her parents a big hug and kiss from him.

ⓦ

Four days later, at the Ops Briefing, the men were advised of a major change in policy affecting assets in support of Charlie Rangers.

"There has been a shake-up of our aircraft support," briefed Phillips. "We no longer have our own designated choppers and 0-1 fixed wing Birddogs. Instead, when we have a specific mission during the day, we are to request what we need for that specific mission only. Then, if someone else isn't using the aircraft, we get them for the duration of the mission. It's more involved, but that is the general idea. Obviously, TOC now has greater pressure in arranging the necessary support. We promise this dramatic change will not affect your teams and will guarantee to secure the assets when and where they are needed."

"My God," Dunn remarked out loud, "I wonder if this is all part of the 'Vietnamization' process. All the assets are slowly being turned over to the South Vietnamese. Support better damn well be there when a team is in trouble and needs it."

The next morning Dunn was aboard a chopper with two of his team leaders on a visual reconnaissance flight. As the 0-1 fixed wing Birddog hadn't been ordered until noon, he would be flying in it later in the day as C & C. After checking out the sectors of the Area of Operation in which the two teams were operating, the chopper started to head back and then just hovered.

Something is wrong, thought Dunn.

"Look!" yelled SSG Parvis, tugging at Dunn's sleeve and pointing off in the distance. "An artillery firebase is firing its guns. Check out the smoke rings."

Crouching forward, Dunn poked his head into the area of the cockpit and yelled above the roar of the whirling blades, "What's wrong?"

"Our radio network is out! No commo! We have no way of checking which way the firebase is firing artillery!" responded the pilot who was turning ashen white.

"Let's go! Let's go!" Dunn yelled and waved with his arms in case the pilots couldn't hear him over the noise of the craft. "No sense waiting here like sitting ducks in the event the firebase shifts fire in this direction."

Flying by that same firebase in a Birddog later that day, Dunn noticed how peaceful and serene it looked in contrast to the morning. Only an hour earlier, it probably had been smoking again, since he called upon them for two separate fire missions.

Within two hours time, he presided over two contacts, each with an artillery fire mission and gunship support, and three team extractions.

"Basestealer 28, this is Avenger 13. Over." The gunship who worked so effectively earlier was calling him on the radio."

"This is Basestealer 28, go ahead. Over."

"Basestealer 28, this is Avenger 13. Just thought you might show us where the next bus stop is located while we wait for our sister ship, Ghostrider, carrying the hitchhikers. Over."

"This is Basestealer 28. Roger that. Follow us. Over." Dunn could see the pilot and the peter-pilot clearly under the left wing of the plane and directed his frontseat to fly over the designated landing zone to be used for the clandestine insertion of the Ranger team.

"Avenger 13, this is Basestealer 28, bus stop is coming up at eleven o'clock and is pear shaped. Over." As the Birddog flew directly over the target LZ, Dunn's frontseat dipped his wings a couple times.

"Basestealer 28, this is Avenger 13, got it in sight, thank you. We're going to head back to rendezvous with our sister ships, which should be near. Over."

"Avenger 13, this is Basestealer 28. Roger, out." Dunn's frontseat made a banking turn to head in the same direction as the departing gunships. The two Avengers were already far ahead and preparing to link up with the other two distant choppers.

"Basestealer 28, this is Ghostrider 41, we have a special delivery package and ready to go to the deck. Over."

"Ghostrider 41, this is Basestealer 28. Roger, I have you in sight. Good. You are now just below me, and one click out. Please turn ten degrees right. You are eight hundred out and closing. Please come another five degrees right. You..."

"Wwhheww. Wwhheww." Dunn blew into his microphone... but nothing. He lost all transmission capability. Switching to intercom, he discovered it, too, was out. The radio was dead. Looking down, he helplessly watched the choppers fly past the LZ and off into the blue. Tapping on his frontseat's shoulder, he yelled, "The radio is out!"

His frontseat shrugged and raised up and out both of his hands as if to indicate, "There's nothing I can do."

The Avenger "gunnie" covering the Ghostrider called him back and vectored him into the proper LZ for Dunn. Fortunately, Dunn had shown the gunship where the LZ was before the chopper with the team arrived.

※

"Sir," said Ramos, who met him as soon as he had deplaned the Birddog, "the Major wants to see you right away."

"Do you know what this is about?"

"Nope. But he's waiting in the parking lot with that new guy, Velasquez, who joined the unit yesterday and was assigned to your platoon."

"Seems like your man, Velasquez, got himself into some trouble in Nha Trang before he joined our company," bellowed the Old Man. "Come on in here. I want to show you this."

Heading into the TOC, the major handed Dunn an MP report. He read that Velasquez had been taken into custody unconscious and in his possession were nineteen, hand-rolled, marijuana cigarettes and fifteen Binoctal tablets, a drug banned by the International Narcotics Control Board in their list of psychotropic substances under international control.

"You will personally investigate this entire incident and report your findings back to me. Leave immediately for Nha Trang, and take Velasquez with you. He claims he was drugged in the fucking bar where he was taken by the MP. Also, he claims $650.00 was taken from his person and that the goddamn drugs were planted on him. I want you to find out the goddamn truth!" bellowed the frustrated major.

"Come on, Ramos," called out Dunn, "turn it around and take the two of us back to the tarmac. If we hurry, there is a chopper heading to Qui Nhon, the nearest place I know where we can get a flight into Nha Trang."

\(\mathscr{C}\)

Two days later, Dunn was back and immediately reported to the Old Man. "Sir, I have every reason to believe that Velasquez was, in fact, drugged and probably lost hundreds of dollars. However, to be fair, Velasquez did voluntarily visit a place that was specifically 'Off limits.'

The bar, Suzie's Place, has a reputation for the drugging and robbing of GI's. It is also known for selling a large assortment of drugs.

"In my opinion, sir, they would not have planted that many expensive drugs on a mark they drugged and robbed. That part makes no sense to me. I am sure Velasquez lost money, but he had no business being in a bar I am sure he knew was 'Off Limits' and also a drug lair."

During the two days that Dunn was investigating the matter with Velasquez, Dunn got Velasquez to do a lot of talking about many different subjects, including a pretty good explanation of what really happened. Velasquez practically confessed to using drugs.

The Old Man gave SP/4 Velasquez an Article 15 administrative punishment and a reduction in rank before he shipped him out of the unit.

\(\mathscr{C}\)

On 21 February 1971, Dunn was briefing the pilots and crews supporting them that day from the 71st Assault Helicopter Company (Rattlers and Firebirds). Daniel Sharkey, his frontseat in the Birddog, was present and sitting in on the morning briefing. Dunn was glad Dan was his fixed-wing pilot, because he liked Dan's easy-going personality that was coupled with Dan's serious, all-business approach to his flying mission.

"Guys, I know this is the first time you have supported Charlie Rangers. However, most of you have indicated a familiarity with LRRP and Special Forces operations. Our six-man patrols set up ambush sites in similar fashion. Presently, we have nine teams operating in separate sectors to the north of this mountain range. See here on the map... this section is about 45 kilometers west of our present location. I have written the various call signs and frequencies you might need on the briefing board. Make sure you have those. There are..."

Wwhheeeeeeee!

"Scramble Siren! Team is in contact! Rattlers, go on ahead! Don't wait for us. Dan and I will catch up in the Birddog," Dunn immediately ordered.

Since they were too far out to pick up transmissions from the team in contact or to do any good when they first lifted off, Dunn was forced to simply monitor the Rattler frequency. He could monitor all five radios but could only transmit on one at a time. First of all, however, he wanted to find out which team was in contact.

"X-ray, this is Speedball 28. Birddog is up. Sitrep. Over."

"Speedball 28, Team 44 in contact! Need gunnies! Small arms. Unknown size. Over."

"Roger. On the way. Tell Four Four to pop smoke now! Speedball 28. Out." Dunn then switched to transmit to the gunship. "Rattler 7, this is Speedball 28. Team in contact is in the southern most part of the sector. Smoke is out. Over."

"Roger. Two Eight, crossing over the mountain range now. Rattler 19, you got anything, Jim?"

"Negative, Rattler 7. Team on the ground says the bad guys are south of their smoke, about 100 meters away. I don't see it yet."

"Got it! There! At your 2 o'clock... to the east. Tell the team we iden- tify goofy grape."

"Roger! Going hot!"

"Follow us in!"

"You've got lead. We're right behind. Watch for flashes. Now! Right below you now."

"Movement! I've got movement!"

"Flashes! Small arms! Flashes! Green tracers! Green tracers!"

"There! They're trying to flank!"

"I see 'em!"

"Come back around! Come around!"

"Roger. Coming around!"

"Yeehawww! Die! You bastards! Yeehawww! Gottcha now!"

"Good guys are moving north. They should be clear. Setting up for rockets. Rockets away!"

"One more run with minis! Good guys say they are in the clear!"

"Speedball 44, this is Speedball 28, when you reach the Lima Zulu, pop another smoke. Over." Dunn was now on station.

"Speedball 28, this is Four Four. Roger. Smoke is out! Tell the gunnies that was fucking great shooting. Over."

"Speedball 28, this is Firebird 27. I identify purple passion and ready to accept passengers. Rattlers standing by to prep the Lima Zulu. Over."

"Speedball 44, this is Speedball 28. Identify purple. Keep your heads down. Gunnies are prepping before your pickup. Over."

"Airborne! Roger that! This is Speedball 44. Over."

"Rattlers and Firebirds, be advised I am calling Red Leg Black Rain on Charlie's last location to your south. Out."

The firebase was located to their west and would be firing to their south. For the return to base, the choppers took a circuitous route. Joyously, the team was winging its way back to base with a gunship escort by the time Dunn arranged for an artillery barrage on the ground the enemy had occupied.

"It's amazing how quickly the entire episode can be over," remarked Dan Sharkey, his Warrant Officer frontseat pilot, over the intercom. From the time the Rattlers fired their first shot, until you completed the artillery barrage, was less than fifteen minutes. Do you think that will be the extent of our excitement for the da..."

"Contact! This is Speedball 23. Contact! I say again, contact! Over." The radio transmission from the Professor's team answered Sharkey's interrupted question.

"Dan," said Dunn over the intercom," fly north and slightly east."

"Two Three, this is Two Eight, I understand "contact", Send sitrep. Over."

"This is Two Three, we initiated contact on four and have two confirmed. We are now under heavy fire from at least a dozen more unfriendlies. They are eighty to one hundred Mikes to our east. Stand by for Zulu." Dunn recognized the voice of Halloway, who was obviously excited, yet calm and deliberate in his transmission. "Charlie is firing mortars. One friendly 'Whiskey India Alpha' in the face! Need immediate evac! Get us some support, Two Eight. Hurry! Over."

"Speedball 28, this is Rattler 7. We monitored and will be there in less than two minutes. Over."

"Joe," said his frontseat excitedly over the intercom, "I spotted the enemy mortar and am lined up for a shot with rockets."

"Do it!" Dunn called for another fire mission from the artillery as Sharkey put the plane in a dive and fired two rockets. "Black Rain 3, this is Speedball 28. Fire Mission! Over." Dunn watched the two flashes from the rockets fired by Sharkey out the front window of the plane.

"Holy Shit!" Sharkey exclaimed over the intercom, "The ground below us is a series of flashes! There's a fucking war going on down there! I'm going around for another shot!"

"Speedball 28, this is Black Rain 3, send co-ordinates. Over."

"Speedball 28, this is Two Three. We have another friendly 'Whiskey India Alpha' right leg, two rounds. Over."

"Two Three, roger. Help is on the way. Pop smoke. Over"

"Black Rain 3, this is Speedball 28, one round, Hotel Echo, at Papa Quebec One Five Seven Niner Hotel Golf Two Four Eight Seven. Over."

"Rockets away!" Sharkey fired a second set of rockets from the plane.

"Speedball 28, this is Rattler 7 ready to go hot. Identify lime green smoke. Over."

"Rattler 7, this is Speedball 28. Roger. Engage from the east side. Incoming Black Rain Red Leg. Over."

"Speedball 28, this is Black Rain 3. Shot! Over."

"Two Eight, this is Speedball 23. Tell the gunnies to shoot closer to us. Get closer!"

"Speedball 23, this is Rattler 19. I monitored. Get your heads down. Yell if it's too close. Over."

"Black Rain 3, this is Speedball 28. Splash! Add Five Zero; Right Five Zero, one round, Hotel Echo. Over."

"Rattler 19, this is Speedball 23. Yes! Yes! Yippee! Again! Hit those fuckers again! Over."

"Speedball 28, this is Black Rain. Shot. Over."

"Speedball 23, this is Rattler 7, get down! Making another pass. Over." The second gunship quickly followed the first with raking fire upon the enemy, who were caught in the open as they were aggressively trying to close in on the team.

"Black Rain 3, this is Speedball 28. Splash! Right Five Zero; Foxtrot, Foxtrot, Echo! Over"

"Speedball 28, this is Speedball 23, I think we can break contact and move to a Lima Zulu. Over"

"Speedball 23, this is Speedball 28. Negative. Take cover for incoming Red Leg. Do you copy? Over."

"Speedball 28, this is Speedball 23. Willco! Over."

"Speedball 28, this is Firebird 55, ready to take on pax. Over."

"Firebird 55, this is Speedball 28, be advised that two of the six pax are casualties requiring immediate aid. Over."

The ground below them began to erupt with a methodical series of explosions. Volcanic splatters of dirt and earthen debris shot upwards at their point of detonation. Visible shockwaves reverberated outward and overlapped in circular patterns in the jungle trees.

"Speedball 28, this is Rattler 7. We and Rattler 19 are making passes to mop up. Over."

"Speedball 28, this is Firebird 55. Roger. We are clear to dust off directly to hospital. Over."

"Speedball 28, this is Black Rain 3. Fire Mission complete. Over."

"Rattler 7, this is Speedball 28, request cover for the Tango to move west to a Lima Zulu. Over."

"Firebird 55, this is Two Eight. Stand by. Over."

"Two Eight, this is Rattler 7. Have the Tango move. We will cover. Over."

"Speedball 23, this is Speedball 28. Move now to Lima Zulu less than one hundred to your west. Over."

"Speedball 28, this is Speedball 23. We are moving. Both Whiskey India Alpha are beau coup serious! Get the chopper in right away! Over."

"Speedball 23, this is Speedball 28. Pop smoke as soon as you are there. Firebird is ready to directly dust off. Over."

"Two Eight, this is Two Three. Smoke out. Over."

"Identify sunflower yellow."

"Firebird 55 is on final. This is Rattler 19. Seven and I have got you covered! Over."

"Black Rain 3, this is Speedball 28. Be advised the friendly element has been extracted. Your fire destroyed three enemy mortar and unknown number of enemy personnel. Thank you for speedy and accurate support. Out."

"X-ray, this is Speedball 28. Secure Romeo Charlie from every Papa, and tell them to Charlie Mike. Over."

Dunn almost wished the teams would remain in groundhog for a while longer as two slicks had been used to evacuate the two teams in contact. Since one of the slicks was now on its way to the hospital, it was not available. Also, both gunships needed to re-stock their armaments after providing hellacious covering fire with both rockets and minis. Even his frontseat had fired six of the eight rockets hung under the Birddog's wings. Now would not be an opportune time for another contact.

"What do you say, Joe," inquired Sharkey over the intercom, "should we also head back to refuel and get some more rockets for this afternoon? It's early yet for lunch, but I am hungry after all that excitement. How about you?"

"Dan, if you don't mind, I'd like to monitor all the commo checks by the remaining teams in the field. They have all been listening in to the transmissions from the first two contacts and some are already reporting they have evidence of activity and expect action themselves. Let's stay on station for another half hour."

"Contact! This is Speedball 12. Contact! Contact! This is Speedball 12. Contact! Over." Sure enough, the half hour was not nearly over before the call came in, alerting them to yet another team in contact.

"Speedball 12 this is Speedball 28. Sitrep of contact. Over." He knew that Staples would arrange for supporting aircraft to be dispatched without being asked. The TOC monitored his transmissions even though they could not hear the teams on the ground.

"Speedball 28, this is Speedball 12. Two confirmed plus one trophy. No incoming and no further activity. Request extraction. Over."

"Speedball 28, this is Speedball 3. Be advised that Rattler 29 and Fireball 11 up and enroute your location. Over."

"Speedball 12 this is Speedball 28. Are you at a Lima Zulu? Over."

"Speedball 28, this is Speedball 12. Negative. We will be there in five Mikes. Over."

"Speedball 12 this is Speedball 28. Roger. Your taxi is on the way. Over."

"Speedball 28, be advised that Rattler 29 is on station and ready to go hot. Over."

"Rattler 29, be prepared to prep Lima Zulu before Fireball One One goes in for the hitchhikers. Wait to identify smoke. Over."

After Team 12 was successfully extracted, Dunn checked out of the communication net with X-ray and bid Sharkey to RTB, Return To Base.

Sharkey dropped him off before taking the plane to be refueled and re-armed. Prior to eating or doing anything else, Dunn tried to get any information he could about the injured on Team 23. The Professor's team had not yet returned from the hospital and no definitive word had been sent back to the TOC. Because he was worried, he did not have much of an appetite. He ate a little but had to wait for Dan Sharkey, who ate enough for the two of them.

"How can you not want to stuff yourself? Sharkey asked him between bites. "The delectable aroma alone is enough to make a blind man's mouth drool. You've got to keep up your strength. I bet I lost ten pounds expending nervous energy alone this morning. The war will wait. Have some of this delicious chicken."

"Thanks. I'm fine. When you're ready, let's go back up. I have a feeling we're going to be busy again this afternoon."

He was right. Two more teams, both from 4thPlatoon, got into contact. He used up two full loads of munitions on two sets of supporting gunships, called in two additional artillery fire missions and fired all eight of the rockets below the wings of the Birddog. Fortunately, no Rangers were wounded. A total of seven confirmed enemy soldiers were killed that afternoon and three weapons captured by the 4th Platoon teams. By that evening, Dunn and his frontseat were both exhausted, more from mental fatigue than from physical exertion.

"I plan on submitting you for a valor award for the actions you took flying Command and Control today," said Sharkey to his backseat when they were finally finished for the day. "You did one hell of a job on all five contacts. You kept your cool and definitely saved some lives of the guys on the ground."

"No, Dan," pleaded Dunn, "please don't do that. The guys on the ground deserve all the glory. Besides, my commander won't approve it. He does not allow officers in our unit to be put in for any valor awards."

The day had already been one of the most event-filled and taxing days that Dunn would spend in 'Nam.

"Then, that guy must really be an asshole if he doesn't appreciate what you officers do for him."

"Yeah, I suppose he really is. You know, it's strange, but the men on the ground don't even always know or appreciate what we do for them. Of course, they're the reason we're here and do what we do. It's enough I appreciate what I am doing. I gotta tell you, I sure as hell appreciate what the men on the ground are going through."

"Hell, yes. The highlight of my tour is definitely working with you Rangers. I will never forget the bravery and professionalism displayed by your 'kids.' And I say that with true affection. I don't think I could have ever even imagined such dedication as I have witnessed."

The twilight sounds of the routine in the Ranger camp that evening aroused a sense of foreboding that made Dunn uncomfortable and tired. The awful war waged relentless on the boys in the bush. Today had been tiring for him, but it had been hell for the Rangers on the ground.

⚜

"We have decided not to infill any additional teams tomorrow," announced Phillips in the Ops Briefing. "The four remaining teams in the bush are pretty damn skittish. All five contacts were fucking hairy today, and they listened in to the transmissions detailing all the activity.

"Dunn, you did a nice job, calling in the artillery, controlling the supporting assets and maintaining commo with both the teams and us. You must have done something right for Staples to comment. He even gave you a word of praise today.

"It's really too bad about your two men. SP/4 Gabriel lost an eye and Sergeant Peterson had to have his right leg amputated below the knee. Joe, I'm glad you have already written up recommendations for valor medals for both of them and for their team leader, as well. It might be hard to get him a Silver Star, but from what you wrote, the TOC agrees Team Leader Halloway deserves a shot at it. He kept his cool in a terrible situation and risked his own life to get both of those men out of the line of fire and back to safety. SSG Halloway is a hell of a Ranger!

"Tomorrow, we don't have a Birddog. So, Joe, you'll have to fly C & C from inside a Firebird chopper."

⚜

The next day happened to be a Monday. Probably none of the men in the bush knew exactly what day of the week it was, as one day was pretty much like any other day. They didn't measure the days by any name as part of a week or by any date as part of a month. Instead, they measured them in hours or in how many consecutive nights they remained in the bush. Lars Swenson and his Team 24 were on day three.

Mid morning of that day found Lieutenant Dunn performing Command and Control duty high above them in the belly of a Firebird chopper when suddenly, "Contact! Contact! This is Beanball 24. Contact! Contact! Over."

"Two Four, this is Two Eight. I understand, 'Contact.' Sitrep. Over."

"I don't know! We have one killed. Scotty Edwards is dead. The team is in the middle of hooches! We should get the fuck out of here! Over."

Scotty Edwards had been on his cherry mission. He arrived In Country exactly thirty days before and had been with Charlie Rangers only one week before this mission. He was barely eighteen years old.

"Beanball 24, this is Beanball 28. Put the Swede on the horn. Let me talk to the Tango Lima. Over." Dunn was stunned and wanted to speak only with the team leader.

"He's firing up the fuckers! We're fucking pulling back! Wait one. Over."

For some reason, when Team 24 chanced upon the thatched hooch, Swenson uncharacteristically ignored a basic principle of sound Ranger tactics and divided his team into two elements. Then he sent three men, including Scotty, around one side, and took the other two men with him around the other. As PFC Scotty Edwards stepped around the hooch, shots suddenly exploded. Two rounds penetrated his chest, one through his heart killed him instantly. From the other side of the hooch, where The Mad Swede was leading his split element, the team leader charged out alone in an angry rampage, firing at the far woods and screaming for the team to fire.

"Fire! Fire! There! Kill those fucking gook bastards! Fire! Fire!" The rest of the team instantly complied as they dropped in place and fired blindly at the jungle in the same direction, as had their team leader.

"Call in a contact! Scotty's dead! A fucking Gook shot him!" The Mad Swede yelled to his RTO.

"Fall back! Fall back! Get the fuck outta here!" The team leader didn't have to tell his team twice for them to retreat, even though they never drew fire.

"Two Eight, this is the Two Four Tango Lima. Get us the fuck out of here now! Scotty Edwards is dead! I am not going back in there for him. He's dead! Get us the fuck out! Over!"

"Two Four, this is Two Eight. Pop smoke! The trees are too thick. I don't know where you are. Over."

"Two Eight, smoke is out! Which way to a fucking LZ, Lima Zulu, to get us the fuck out of here? Over."

The Ranger Creed flashed through Dunn's mind: *I will never leave a fallen comrade to fall into the hands of the enemy and under no circum-*

stances will I ever embarrass my country. Joe knew Swenson lived the Ranger Creed. *That's not like The Mad Swede! Obviously he's not telling me everything; therefore it has to be really bad down there.*

"Beanball 24, this is Beanball 28. Listen to me carefully. I am coming down to you. I am climbing down to you. I will personally take you to the closest Lima Zulu. Wait for me. The chopper will then take us all out, including Edwards. Do you understand? I am climbing down. Over."

Dunn did not wait for an answer. He switched to his intercom, "You are going to pick up the team at that large clearing sixty meters due north... right there!" he instructed as he pointed to the clearing.

The pilot nodded that he understood and said, "Roger."

"But, first, I am jumping out! Take this chopper down on top of that red smoke. Get the right skid as close to the top of the trees as possible so I can jump onto it from the skid on the side with the door gunner. Do it now!" ordered Dunn. As he took off his flight helmet, he handed his CAR-15 rifle to the shocked door gunner and calmly stepped out onto the skid. The pilot did as he instructed, slightly dipping his side of the chopper thus providing Joe a better angle from which to jump.

Without even thinking, Dunn jumped and went right through the small branches until he finally caught one that slowed and eventually stopped his descent. Branches slapped at him and one even punched him under the chin. But nothing really fazed him as he continued to climb, drop and fall down as quickly as he could, as if he were rappelling without ropes. When he reached the ground, the entire team was huddled around the base of that tree and two of the Rangers had already retrieved Edwards' body.

The woods were strangely quiet.

"Which way? This shit is so thick, you can't see five feet through the fucking brush!" screamed The Mad Swede. His face was quite flushed and his eyes appeared rather wild.

"Give me a hand," Dunn said as he motioned for two Rangers to help lift Edwards' body onto his back. The limp weight of the lifeless 6'2" body was far heavier and more awkward than Joe could have ever imagined.

"That way! Due north, only sixty meters," pointed Dunn.

Oppressive heat burned away his adrenaline. Compressed lungs screamed for fuller inflation that never came from short gasps of steaming, hot air through a dry, parched mouth. Robber vines were like the hands of a hundred thieves tugging and fighting him for possession of his burden. Each step was a separate, determined struggle, like the Stations of the Cross. Yet, somehow, the physical hardship was a welcome penance that helped mask the torture in his heart and the maddening in his mind.

Finally reaching the waiting chopper, the entire team had to help lift the burden from him and load it. They even had to help hoist up their lieutenant, whose arms had utterly given up-heavy, numb, powerless and even unable to lift up in the surrender position.

"No!" Joe screamed at the Firebird pilot through the intercom. "You will not return to base until I have called in a Fire Mission."

"Please, sir, let's just go," calmly requested the pilot. All the men of the team were crying, especially Swenson. They were balling like helpless babies while the body of Edwards lay face down, the blood from his still body staining the gray steel floor of the chopper a deep shade of crimson.

"This god damn place is responsible for the death of one of my men!" responded a vehement Dunn. "I am not leaving here until I cover this ground with an artillery barrage!"

As Dunn suspected, there were no secondary explosions. They all felt an extraordinary grief, especially Swenson.

19
Big Windy

"MANY OF YOU DID NOT KNOW SCOTTY," READ Sergeant Johnny Eagle from the epitaph written by Dunn. Chief stood next to a small table that was covered with a white cloth. Alone, in the center of the table, sat a lone, Black Beret. The American Flag was planted on a staff behind the table. "He knew all of you and like you, had volunteered. For only seven days he was one of us before going out on his first mission-so, you might not have gotten to know him very well.

However, he knew all of you. He knew the officers and trusted them... trusted them with his life. Also, he knew the sergeants and relied on them... relied on them to take care of him. He knew the men of Charlie Rangers and loved you. He looked up to you as an example of what he wanted to become. More than anything, he wanted to be a Ranger... entitled to wear the Black Beret.

"He tried so hard, but five days ago, Scotty reported in to our Patron of Soldiers, Archangel Michael, at his new assignment in heaven. The Archangel Michael issued Scotty a new uniform of a white robe and he traded in his airborne wings for a pair of glistening white wings and awarded Scotty a golden halo.

"Afterwards, Scotty made only one request and the Archangel Michael answered, 'Yes, Scotty, you earned it. You may wear the Black Beret in heaven.'

"Scott Edwards is our hero. He gave his life for his country and will forever be in our hearts and minds to help us persevere."

Chief did a perfect job of reading and many openly cried. Swenson was inconsolable; pushing away any who tried to approach him.

"Lieutenant," said Major Wayne to Dunn after the Memorial was completed, "that was the most beautiful service I have ever witnessed."

Then, turning to Chief he commended, "Sergeant Eagle, your words were well spoken and touched us all."

Earlier, the Major met privately with Swenson for a lengthy talk. Swenson refused to talk to anyone else. The rest of the men from the team simply would not talk among themselves or with either their platoon sergeant or platoon leader about that fatal mission.

After a lunch that had been designed, specifically, to provide a savory cheering, but before the men of the unit were anywhere near ready to return to routine, the ugly and unfair brutality of war rudely interrupted again.

"Team 33 in contact!" bleated the loudspeaker. "One Ranger KIA. Kyle Rose is the KIA. I say again, Kyle Rose is KIA." Then, after a short pause, "The entire Team 33 has been extracted and is presently inbound."

"Goddamn, sir," said Gregorov to Dunn just outside the area of the mess, "the company went so long, over eight months, without losing a man. Now, on the same day as Scotty's memorial service, 3rd Platoon also loses a man in combat! That was such a beautiful ceremony for Scotty. This is really terrible. I wish I were back in 2nd Platoon, boss, so I could take a team back out to avenge their deaths."

"Thanks, Rusky, but you are too valuable to all the men doing your present job in the TOC."

"I know, and I appreciate what I have learned working with Staples. But I want to do something... I need to do something! I could arrange for some 'Arclite' B-52 strikes or anything to strike at the Communists. I do not understand your country sometimes... but, of course, now it is also my country.

"I don't understand how they can demonstrate against the war? Don't they realize they are just helping the enemy? They think that Scotty and Rose are victims of an unjust war. They are not victims. They gave their lives defending their country and should be treated as heroes.

"When I escaped to your country and got to enjoy all your freedoms, I felt I owed a tremendous obligation. That is why I knew it was my duty to volunteer to come here to Viet Nam to fight the Communists," explained a frustrated Gregorov.

"How old were you when you escaped your country?" asked Dunn.

"I was only nineteen years old when I escaped from Bulgaria, my country. Do you have time? Do you want to hear how I escaped?"

"Absolutely."

"I was working as a diver with my best friend, who was also nineteen. Two freighter ships, both owned by Onassis, I think, but both with Italian crews, were in the port at Varna. After the one ship left, I learned the sister ship was leaving the next day. So, I convinced my friend to help me steal scuba gear and swim out to the ship before it left. I used an oxygen re-breather apparatus that has an exhaled air catchment bag. This bag periodically must be cleared and one must not dive below ten meters in order to avoid poisoning.

"In the port, the Communists deployed buoys with radar so as to prevent boats and swimmers from escaping. I didn't realize they were so sensitive that they could locate us just by triangulating our position in the water. The Communists sent two naval submarine chaser/hunter cutters out to get us. I tried to get my friend to use my bag to hide his bubbles, but instead, he surfaced. When he did, they killed him with a machine gun and then blithely fished his body out of the water.

"Normally, they send in divers, but I was lucky, boss...they just left. So, I swam to the ship and begged to speak to the captain of the ship."

"Can you speak Italian?

"Yes, boss. I speak a few different dialects of Italian, can speak six other languages fluently, and am conversant in a half-dozen more. I lied to the captain and called to him I had family in southern Italy. He told me he had to get 100% of the crew to agree to hide me before he would allow me to board. That took some time and I had to wait in the water for over an hour. By then I was turning blue. Evidently, every single crewman agreed to hide me because they let me come aboard and hid me in the boiler room. They all told me to go to America, which is what I finally did."

"That's an amazing story, Rusky. I have always been favorably impressed with you. Just don't let the Old Man catch you impersonating an officer when you arrange for us to get priority on the B-52 strikes," Dunn warned with a smile.

Sheepishly Rusky explained, "I know you've heard me in the TOC at night, but sometimes it's the only way to get us advanced allocations. Besides, sometimes it actually works, as the Old Man doesn't hear me. He and Staples and the rest of them drink every night so don't pay much attention to me. The Old Man has threatened to court martial me a dozen times, but Staples always protects me.

"Did you know that Staples protects you, too, boss? He's always running interference for you. That's why he arranged for you to go to Firebase Mattie when he did. That was when the Duke was hot about losing the Goldstein court martial and blamed you. The way the major talks, he obviously hates all VMI, Citadel graduates and West Pointers... it's strange that he picked you guys to work for him. Well, I'm on duty tonight, so I better go try to get some shuteye," concluded Rusky as he headed for his quarters.

Dunn continued on into the TOC, where he walked in on a very heated conversation. "The only reason I told you he has a secondary MOS of an 11B Infantry is so that you would fight to get him promoted, sir!"

Staples was evidently arguing with the Major on behalf of a soldier in the unit.

"Yeah, but now I find out our goddamn cook served a prior tour in 'Nam with the Special Forces, and earned both the Airborne and Ranger tabs, even though he never wears the goddamn tabs on his uniform!" practically shouted the Major.

"That's because he then went to school to become a cook," Staples explained as he threw up his arms and let them fall back to his side. "He volunteered to come here as a cook... not to run ambush missions."

"If I'm short men to run a mission, then it's goddamn straight that I will use Pancho to go into the bush! He's in this goddamn unit and he is Infantry qualified." the Major adamantly insisted.

"He is more important to you and this unit in the mess hall, where he puts out fantastic meals. Based on his cooking skills in the mess only, he deserves a promotion! Hell, we are always taking his men who are only cooks and putting them out on X-ray. They and the commo guys all deserve to be put in for a secondary MOS of Infantry based upon their on-the-job performance so we can award them all the Combat Infantryman Badge," persisted a very determined Staples.

"Goddamn it, Staples," exploded Wayne, "we've already been over that issue! I will not award the C.I.B. to some commo guy or cook. As long as I am Commander, that award is reserved for true Infantrymen in this unit. What we are talking about here is a goddamn Airborne Ranger, Senior NCO with Special Forces training and experience as a goddamn Infantry grunt. Somebody like that can lead an ambush team and save lives."

"Sir, when you talk to him, remember, you may not be able to force him to go into the bush on ambush missions. Instead, you might end up losing a great cook." warned Staples.

"Tommy, you've been goddamn quiet. What do you have to say about this?" asked the Major.

"Sir," answered Phillips, who remained seated, "I tend to agree with Staples. If the shit were ever to really hit the fan... then everybody would pitch in and volunteer. Until then, it probably would be best to keep the status quo. Remember, because of Pancho, you have the unit with perhaps the best mess in all of 'Nam. Keep him here and happy as long as possible... at least wait till next month before approaching him about it. My DEROS is in a couple weeks and after that I don't care since I'll be home. Until then, I think he is much too important in the mess to go 'messing' with him, sir."

"Hey, Lieutenant Dunn," Staples greeted him as he changed the subject, "that was a very nice memorial service for PFC Edwards. Say, why don't you join us this evening for a drink and a game of Hearts?"

"I think I'd like that," Joe replied.

"Goddamn right," interjected Wayne. "We, two officers challenge you and Pappy to a card game of Hearts tonight right after the Ops Briefing. Dunn and I will take on all comers."

The Ops Briefing was rather short and full of bad news. Phillips opened the meeting with a detailed accounting of the contact initiated by Team 33 and the subsequent events that resulted in the tragic loss of a Ranger life.

Strange, thought Dunn, *there never was an after-action report or detailed accounting of the action in which Scotty was killed.*

"Now, for some more bad news," continued Phillips. "Most of the sectors we will now be working in have been designated as 'No Fire' zones. The majority of our missions for the time being will be for the sole purpose of gathering intelligence. The teams will observe and report all activity they witness. Whenever possible, the teams will be encouraged to capture prisoners for interrogation.

"Until now, Charlie Rangers has always operated in 'Free Fire' zones, meaning that any and all indigenous encountered were automatically deemed enemy personnel. Teams operating in a 'No Fire' zone are now not allowed to initiate an ambush. A 'No Fire' zone means you are not allowed to fire your weapon unless you are fired upon first and are returning fire only. This policy comes from the very highest level of command. The men are going to find this policy difficult to comprehend and you must make certain they understand and obey. I know they will be angry, especially after today, losing our second man in just five days."

Later, when Dunn briefed his team leaders, an incredulous Parvis decried, "What stupid fucking politician decided on this policy? We're not allowed to go into North Viet Nam; we can't bomb Hanoi; and the enemy has free refuge in Cambodia and Laos. Now we have to whistle at them so they can fucking shoot at us before we are allowed to kill them!"

"Just make sure any trophies have been fired first before you fucking bring them back in," said Forest.

"The real challenge is to bring back some live POW's, said London. "You're also going to be expected to spend a full four days in the field. For some of you bad-ass Rangers, that's going to be a first!"

Since none of his teams were scheduled for insertion over the next few days, Dunn suspected there would be some heavy drinking and pot smoking that night. He headed back to the TOC.

"About goddamn time," barked the Major. "Staples already poured you a drink of fine goddamn Jim Beam. The cards are shuffled and ready for you to cut, Lieutenant."

Surprisingly, he and the Major made a good team, beating all challengers and easily winning most hands.

"Thanks for the drink," said Dunn, "but now that I have finished it, I must retire to my cot. I have been putting off writing to my wife, and I am way overdue in sending her a letter. Sir, it was fun." He didn't really want to be there and felt the Old Man was being nice simply because of Scotty's death.

"You play a goddamn good game, Dunn," said the Major, now on his third drink. "We make a hellava team!"

When Dunn got back to his cot, he started a letter to Marie. Generally, he avoided discussions of the war in his letters, but now he needed to share his grief:

My Darling Marie,

Tonight I've been drinking a little bit, but I'm not drunk. I'm sad and I hurt inside. I want to cry but I can't seem to. I love you. When I get back to the World, there is something I must do. Please write down the following address and put it in the safe-box. I have to visit the Edwards to tell them personally of their son...

I lost a boy from my platoon and just today, the 3rd Platoon also suffered the loss of a Ranger.

My main goal-the thing I wanted more than any awards or decorations-was to be able to brag I had not lost one single man. Oh, Marie, I feel so bad. The boy was only 18 years old and wanted so much to be a Ranger. He tried so hard. He died like a soldier, but Christ, what a sacrifice!

Oh, Marie, I don't like to write anything to you about this war. I usually try not to, but I need you and love you. Put this in your heart and never mention it to anyone. When we are together, we will love and hold each other. Please never hide anything from me. You and I are one and our love means to share everything. Marie, I love you more than anything. I'm sorry if I make you sad, but I have never hurt like this...

૰

The following day found Dunn irritated and irritating. He jumped all over London for dropping the ball on a few minor duties and then felt he had to lecture two of his team leaders for not performing what he felt was their best.

"Sir," pleaded London, "we have never let you down before. Go read some letters from your wife and then send her an upbeat, happy letter. She could probably use one, and you probably haven't sent her a fucking 'happy' letter in some time.

"What do you say? You are fucking chewing everybody a new asshole. My ass is all bloody from the ass chewing you have been giving me. I can take it, but the guys are down and right now, they really don't need you on their case. Let me take care of things... are you fucking hearing me, sir?"

"Loud and clear, Sergeant London, thanks. I guess sometimes I need a two-by-four across my thick head. Thanks for not using one, even though I obviously deserve it. I am going to take your advice right now, Platoon Sergeant."

"Airborne, sir! We know how you feel. Remember, we feel the same way."

Dunn retreated to his tent and took out his treasure chest of past sugar reports from Marie. He was just getting ready to write a letter to her when a big wind practically knocked down his tent.

"What the...?" Shielding his eyes from the flying dust and debris, he struggled outside against the wind.

"Heads up! Look out!" one Ranger yelled.

"Holy Fuck! Look out!" another yelled.

Wooosh! Rrrriiiiippp! Riiip! A piece of steel, about ten feet long, two feet wide and a quarter inch thick came hurling through his tent, ripping out one side. A few other steel sheets, which had been placed against sandbags, had flown as far as thirty meters. Everything inside the tent was strewn all over the hill. Afterwards, Joe was picking up items, including letters, seventy-five to a hundred meters away.

"Look," shouted a Ranger from 3rd Platoon, "that huge Skycrane helicopter is hoisting a fucking radar unit onto the top of our small Ranger Hill!"

"Nobody warned us it was coming, goddamn it," shrieked Pappy. "Anybody hurt from the fucking flying shit?"

"That does it," shouted Dunn to anybody who might be within earshot, "I will find out who is responsible. When I do, I'm going to rip somebody a new asshole! Nobody, no matter what his rank, is going to stop me and right now, I'm in the perfect mood to rip into somebody!"

He didn't even have on his shirt when he went storming up to the radar site where some first lieutenant had just arrived and was checking the radar unit.

"Who is in charge here?" bellowed Dunn.

"I am, sir."

"And just who are you?"

"1LT Doughty, 180th Assault Support Company, sir."

"Do you realize you nearly destroyed our base camp and some of my men could have been killed from the steel sheets that hurled through the air as a result of your negligence? Do you?"

"Yes, sir. I mean, 'No, sir!' I'm sorry, sir."

"Who is your commander?"

"Sir, my commander is Major Gary Laughlin."

"He's going to hear from me!" Dunn promised before he then wound his way down to the TOC, still fuming and intending to reach the 180th Assault Support Company on the landline.

Before he could find their number, a Major entered the TOC and said, "Excuse me. I am Major Laughlin, commander of 'Big Windy.' I came to apologize. We didn't realize the hill was occupied or we would have given you advance warning. I fully intend to chastise the pilot and

crew, who should have noticed your presence and aborted until you were advised. Are you Major Wayne?"

"No, I am Lieutenant Dunn, but I accept your apology. 'Big Windy' is certainly an appropriate call sign. Your bird wrecked havoc on our camp." Although he was still mad, the Major's apology to him sounded sincere.

"Well, if there's anything we can ever do for Charlie Rangers, then give us a call. We have also been known to do a lot of good for guys on the ground. Your unit has a great reputation. It would be an honor to work with you guys, so if something comes up where you need us, give us a call and use my name."

"That's good of you, sir," interrupted Staples. "I'm adding your information to our list of assets. Here, take my information in the event Charlie Rangers can help your unit out. I am the NCOIC, Non Commissioned Officer In Charge, of the TOC. You never know when you might need us."

"Thank you, Sergeant Staples, I'll do that."

After Major Laughlin left, Dunn went back to collecting love letters that were scattered all over the hill. Before he got back to his cot, the men of his platoon had removed the torn tent and erected a new one. Some kind souls had even gathered many of his letters and placed them neatly on his cot. After venting his anger on Big Windy and witnessing the kindness from his men, Joe's hurt subsided considerably.

The following week brought a return to normalcy, if there was such a thing during wartime, to the events on and around Ranger Hill.

"Gentlemen," announced Phillips at the beginning of the Ops Briefing, "it is my distinct pleasure that I present to you my replacement, Captain Raymond McDonough, your new Operations Officer. You see, I am so short I won't write another letter because I'll beat it home. I'm so short my feet don't touch the ground!"

"Wise Ass," chuckled Pappy, "you're so short, Mama-San said she had to use a magnifying glass to find your pecker, sir!"

"The platoon sergeants should have gotten the word out," announced Staples, "but just in case any of you have not heard, in one hour at the mess, we are having a 'Short-Timer Jungle Juice Party.' Everybody is welcome to contribute anything, preferably alcohol, to the barrel. When Phillips wakes up from his party, he'll be so short that he will have missed the fact that he already left!"

Two days later, when everybody had finally gotten rid of the Jungle Juice in their system, Staples opened the Ops Briefing. "The 180th Assault Support Company has requested the assistance of Charlie Rangers concerning a downed helicopter. Sometime earlier today ground fire caused the crash of a Big Windy CH-47A Chinook helicopter in the mountain range inland from Tuy Hoa.

"All the crewmen, including one deceased, were safely evacuated from the site. What they want is for us to send in a team to make certain there are no useful radios or any sensitive equipment left that might be of value to the enemy. They are quite certain there are no munitions or weapons and think everything of value was destroyed in the crash. They just want us to make certain.

"The helicopter crashed on the side of a mountain and so far, there has been no indication that Charlie has been able to get to it...probably due to the heavy air traffic all day around it. Where the downed chopper is located is also going to be a little tough to get to.

"Tomorrow, a heavy team led by Major Wayne, will be inserted into a level clearing three quarters of the way up from the base of the mountain. They should be able to reach the downed chopper the same day but most likely they will spend the night on the mountain and be extracted the following day from the spot of insertion.

"The team will have to carry a 292-radio antenna to insure communication when they are on the mountain. While they are on the move, we will insure aircraft are present to maintain constant commo for them with the whip antenna. The heavy team will be comprised of all of Team 31 plus additional individuals from 3rd Platoon. The VR of the AO is set for 0830 hours."

"Why is the VR so late?" asked Kent. "It should be at 0530 or 0600 hours, at the latest. Otherwise, it will cut into the operation time."

Staples politely explained, "The Old Man has to make some calls and won't be available till then."

"Let the team leader of Team 31 make the VR along with the C & C. They can then report the results to the TOC and thus to the Old Man," Kent tried to bargain.

"No. The Major is the team leader and is very adamant about going on the VR himself in order to observe the situation first hand."

"Where's the Old Man now?" asked Kent.

"He's meeting with the commander of the 180th Assault Support Company, but he should be back any moment," replied Staples.

"LT Dunn, sir, the Old Man wants you to fly C & C. You'll have to do so from a chopper since we didn't get a Birddog for tomorrow."

"Sure thing, Sergeant Staples," Dunn acknowledged.

The next morning was very leisurely and a most welcome change from the generally hectic, even frantic pace of most of the mornings in which he flew C & C. During breakfast, Dunn even allowed himself time to chat with some of the men from the 3rd Platoon's heavy team that was to be inserted.

"This should be interesting," said SSG Tom "Shark" Clemmons, team leader of Team 31. "I don't think Woodpecker has ever been to the bush with a team before. I wonder what the fuck I did to deserve such a treat!"

"We really should go over our hand signals and our signs with the Major," said SGT Matthew "Hard Core" Penny, his assistant team leader, who would also served as the heavy team's Radio Telephone Operator.

"Absolutely!" Shark agreed. "Nobody fucking gets on the insertion choppers until all of us, including the goddamn Major, go over and understand the 'Standard Operating Procedures' for the field. No fucking team that I go into the bush with will be unprepared, even one with 'Woody Woodpecker' as my team leader."

"Hey," remarked Dunn, "it's nearly 0830 hours. Time you and your ATL join me and head for the TOC to pick up Duke for the VR." Dunn got a kick out of the way the men openly referred to Major Woodrow H. Wayne as "Woody Woodpecker."

Outside the TOC, the Major's driver was sitting on the jeep while talking with Staples. "You guys might as well hang around out here," he told them as they approached. "The Major is on the phone and will be for sometime yet. But, I'll let him know you are ready."

"Fuck!" Shark showed his annoyance. "I don't like late day insertions. By the time we get there and finally do get inserted, it's going to be fucking late in the day!"

Fifty minutes later, Duke appeared carrying a new CAR-15 rifle and wearing a floppy, booney hat and a web belt with an H-harness over his cammies. "Come on, Ramos! Time's a wastin'. Let's go so we can take a look at a goddamn crashed Chinook."

It was past 1130 hours when they finally touched down on the tarmac after the VR flight. The Major had the pilot circle the crashed helicopter and the landing zone for the insertion three or four times before he was satisfied. They could see the large, crashed helicopter was inverted on a cliff on the side of the mountain. It was split nearly in two at just about the middle of the craft, but otherwise appeared to be surprisingly intact. However, pieces of wreckage were visibly spewed around the mountainside. Fortunately, there were no indications of any hostiles present.

"Based on the thick triple canopy, the distance and the climbing required, I figure it will take the team at least four hours to reach the downed helicopter," Dunn remarked after he and Staples finished enjoying a lunch of fried chicken, corn and French fries. "I spoke with the Devils and Demons from the 134th AHC and they sounded really happy to be working with us again. Devil 8 is the lead gunnie. They will be on stand-by for us throughout the entire duration of the mission, just as you requested."

"You know, sir, you will remain on C & C in the air until the team establishes communication from their static site with a two-niner-two?" asked Staples.

"No problem," replied Dunn. "If it gets too much later before they're finally inserted, I won't be up all that long as it is. It's already 1330 hours."

"The team is on the tarmac. We're just waiting on the Major. Here he is now."

"Airborne, sir!" Rusky greeted the Major after he strode into the TOC. "I hear you're taking a team into the bush. I'll keep you entertained on the radio tonight, boss."

"No need. We're gonna get in, do our job and get out before Charlie knows we were ever there. So, goddamn, how do I look? Do I need more camouflage stick on my face?" the Major struck a pose as if he were snooping in the brush.

"Where's your rucksack, sir? Aren't you taking extra munitions?" Rusky asked.

"Quick, get yours! Let me take it. You say yours is always packed and ready to use. Didn't you tell me you store it right here in the TOC? Yeah! Great! Give me a hand. Strap it on my back. Okay!"

"Be careful, boss, there are short fuse phosphorus grenades inside," warned Gregorov.

"Got it! Come on, Dunn. There's a team waiting on us. Ramos, let's get going." They sped off for the tarmac, where they found the entire team lounging practically under the helicopters to take advantage of the little shade they provided.

"Time to wake up," announced the Major. "Climb aboard so we can get these choppers airborne. Let's go to work!"

"Hold on, sir," interrupted Shark, "we have to go over procedures first. We have guys who have never worked together before, so this is essential."

"Goddamn! Whey didn't you do it while you were waiting for me?" bellowed the Major.

"Sir, as the team leader, you also have to know the hand signals and the procedures for control of the team in all situations."

"Goddamn it! How long is this gonna take?" asked the exasperated Major.

"At least a half hour. Sir, we usually spend a couple hours on this material before each mission," Shark patiently explained.

Dunn walked over to his C & C ship, which was empty. When he glanced back at the heavy team, he noticed Duke hastily removing the rank insignia from his uniform. Then he strode over to the Ready

Shack, where the crews had been hanging out all morning and hung with them for the forty minutes it took before they finally were airborne and inbound towards the downed Chinook.

"Spitter 28, this is Spitter 31. Commo check. Over." Dunn recognized the voice of "Hard Core" Penny, who was following proper procedure by checking in with him as soon as the team was on the ground.

"Spitter 31, this is Spitter 28, Lima Charlie, how me? Over."

"Spitter 28, this is Spitter 31. I read you 5 by 5. Out."

"Spitter 28, this is Devil 8. Packages delivered. Be advised that Devils and Demons are Romeo Tango Bravo. When uninvited guests drop in, give us a call. You hire, we fire! Great to be working with you again. Out."

The two slicks that had inserted the heavy team and the accompanying gunships returned to their home base of Tuy Hoa. From there they could quickly respond if needed.

Dunn looked at his watch; it was nearly 1530 hours. "The team will probably have to forget about the downed aircraft for today," he said to his chopper crew over the intercom. "They are going to have to Charlie Mike to the high ground to set up the two-niner-two radio antennae while there is still enough daylight. They need direct line-of-sight to communicate with the TOC. Otherwise, Staples will have to pull out his bag of tricks to arrange periodic fly-bys to check in with the team during the night."

"Spitter 28, this is Spitter 31. Over."

"Spitter 31, this is Spitter 28, go ahead. Over." It was now just past 1600 hours, so Dunn figured the RTO was making the normal hourly radio communication check.

"Spitter 28, this is Spitter 31. We, ahh... request choppers for an extraction. Over."

"Spitter 31, this is Spitter 28, say again. Over." Dunn wanted to make certain he heard the RTO correctly.

"Roger, Spitter 28. Please send in the choppers to extract Spitter 31. Over."

"Spitter 31, this is Spitter 28. Sitrep! Is there a problem? Over."

"Spitter 28, this is Spitter 6. Send in the goddamn choppers! Over."

"Spitter 6, this is Spitter 28. Do you have a medical emergency or is there a problem? Please provide a sitrep. Over."

"This is Spitter 6. Goddamn it! This is Major Wayne on the radio. I want a helicopter, and I want it now! Over."

"Spitter 6, this is Spitter 28. Roger. I copy. You want a helicopter. Do you need gunships? Are you taking fire? Are there casualties? Any medical requirements? Sitrep, please. Over."

"Goddamn it! There is no sitrep! This mission is over. Just send me a damn helicopter! I am not spending the night out here. This is Major Wayne, and I demand a helicopter come in and get me out of here! I am not staying overnight! Do you understand me? I will not be left out here overnight! Over."

"Spitter 6, this is Spitter 28. Roger. Stand by. Over."

"You better goddamn understand that I will not be left overnight out here in this goddamn jungle. I have to get back to the TOC before night-fall, goddamn it, so give me an ETA, Estimated Time of Arrival, for my chopper," he demanded.

"Devil 8, this is Spitter 28. Over."

"This is Devil 8. Over."

"Devil 8, this is Spitter 28. Request immediate pick-up of element from same Lima Zulu and return to point of origin. No sign of any unfriendly. I say again, no sign of any unfriendly. Over."

"Spitter 28, this is Devil 8. Roger that. Be advised that Devils and Demons are now enroute. Over."

"Spitter 6, this is Spitter 28. Please be advised that choppers are on their way. Over."

"Spitter 28, this is Spitter 31. Roger. Will that be for one passenger or the entire tango? Over."

"Spitter 31, this is Spitter 28. The entire tango; I say again, the entire tango. Do you copy? Over." Dunn didn't hesitate to pull the entire team. The downed helicopter, the considerable air activity over the past two days, the repeated use of the same Landing Zone, the late hour of the afternoon and the restricted radio communication were compromising factors that made his decision easy.

"Spitter 28, this is Spitter 31. Willco. Ready to pop smoke on your command. Over."

After the team had been safely extracted, Dunn instructed the aircraft commander of his chopper to return him to Ahn Khe. When the team landed on the tarmac, the Major quickly jumped in the jeep with Ramos and sped away, leaving Dunn to rode back on the deuce and a half with the team. Nobody spoke. Maybe it was because Dunn was not a member of 3rd Platoon and thus an outsider, or maybe it was because they were upset at not having been allowed to complete their mission. Probably, it had a lot more to do with him being an officer, because right now they were not too happy with their officers.

When they arrived at the company area, Dunn noticed the new Operations Officer, Captain McDonough, outside the TOC beckoning to him and said, "We still have a mission to complete. Sergeant Staples tells me you and some of your men in 2nd Platoon are the best we have to rappel in to complete the job. We have already lined up supporting assets. Could you be ready first thing tomorrow morning?"

"Airborne, sir, I'll let you know who will rappel with me at the Ops Briefing." Dunn didn't want to give any names until he had solicited for volunteers. He knew this mission would be dangerous, as by now

Charlie would most certainly be planning a welcoming party for any further excursions to the downed helicopter.

"I'm your man, sir," emphatically stated Halloway, after Dunn fully explained his impression of the mission. "This is not a question of sharing a damn experience. You are going in again; therefore, so can I. Next to you, I am the best-qualified Ranger for this job. Besides, you and I make a great team together. I'll even let you be the team leader this time!"

"Nobody from my platoon goes without me doing the rigging," said London.

"I'll join London in the chopper," said Chief, "with my cut-off M-60 and plenty of belts of ammo!"

Dunn felt he could not have hand picked a finer team. Actually, the entire platoon begged to go. However, he picked these three, who he was mighty glad were also the first to volunteer.

"When you two rappel in," stated McDonough at the Ops Briefing, "be sure you have plenty of C4 plastic explosives, blasting caps and incendiary grenades. After you make certain there are no weapons, radios or other retrievable items, we want you to destroy it so Charlie can't make use of it. The chopper will be revved and ready to lift your team off at 0700 hours on the tarmac. The same two Devil gunships from today will be with you."

Dunn agreed there was no need for a separate C & C. Besides, now that Phillips had left, there was nobody in particular he would feel too comfortable with in Command & Control.

The rest of the Ops Briefing was just general information. The weather was supposed to be brutally hot again and Dunn prayed he and his men were also not in for a hot reception from Charlie.

✦

"Don't waste any time trying to find items to retrieve," cautioned London early the next morning. "Set up the explosives, pull the pin on a grenade and then get the fuck out of there. I want to see your ass on the rope ladder less than a minute after you rappel in."

"Sounds like good advice to me," agreed Halloway.

"I learned a long time ago not to ever argue with my platoon sergeant," said Dunn. "That's exactly what we're going to do. By the way, when I briefed the flyboys, our chopper pilot gave me the same advice. Except, he threatened to send you two down after us if we weren't back on the ladder in thirty seconds."

"Hey," smirked Chief, "I only volunteered to go along for the damn ride, not to go chasing after your butts."

"The egg beater is cranking up! Ready?" asked Dunn.

"Airborne, sir!"

When the four choppers arrived at the site above the downed Chinook, the slicks hovered high while the two gunships slowly circled at a lower level. The gunships were looking to draw gunfire. After a few uneventful moments, their slick began to descend to the predetermined height of fifteen to twenty feet. The two Rangers were going to rappel in onto the side of the rock-faced mountain cliff slightly higher than the downed aircraft.

"Get ready!" London shouted.

Dunn and the Professor each grabbed a rope and dropped an end out of the helicopter. Holding onto the rope close to the end tied onto the chopper, they climbed out and stood upon the skids. They faced the chopper. Holding the rope with their right hand, they used their gloved left hand to snap the rope through their D-ring and then to gather the rope behind their back. The D-ring was at their waist on a six-foot piece of rope London had expertly tied like a diaper around each of them. All eyes were fixed on the dangling ends of the ropes flicking ever closer to the ground.

By the time London yelled, "Go!" the two Rangers were already airborne in a single bound from the chopper to the mountain.

"Let's do it, sir! Look! Nothing's been disturbed. Charlie hasn't been here, yet. Hot damn!" the Professor said as he quickly set about the task of strategically placing the explosives.

Dunn quickly scoured the area for evidence of items to retrieve. Finding none, he assisted Halloway.

"Pulling the pin!" yelled Dunn. "Go! Go for the ladder!" The operation took slightly more than a minute from the time their feet simultaneously landed on rock.

BLAMM! BLAMM! BLAMM! Large caliber fire! BLAMM! BLAMM! BLAMM! Both large caliber and automatic .51 caliber were fired! BLAMM! BLAMM!

"Climb!" Dunn yelled at the chopper above him, at Halloway and at himself. However, the two Rangers did not climb; they held on to the oscillating rope ladder for dear life as the chopper bucked, lurched and began to rise.

The door gunner and Chief responded with M-60 machine gun fire, green coming up, red going down. All hell broke loose and the gunships responded.

Just then there was a loud, KA...BLAMM! The downed Chinook exploded, splitting into pieces and going careening further on down the mountainside.

Bam! Bam! Bam! Small arms fire whizzed by the dangling Rangers.

"The chopper's hit! Smoke!" Halloway yelled. "We're gonna crash!"

"No," Dunn yelled back, over the staccato roar of the churning rotor blades, "the pilot still has control. Look! He's heading for that clearing. Get ready to jump and roll!"

The chopper was dropping quickly, too quickly, towards a large sloping field. Black smoke billowed from the engine above. "Now, jump!" ordered Dunn. The momentum slammed the bodies of the two Rangers into the slope. But having curled into balls, they actually rolled uphill for a ways.

The forward motion of the helicopter carried it another forty feet past the two dazed Rangers as they watched the attitude of the helicopter to cause one of the large blades to strike the ground. Instead of rolling, the helicopter continued to beat itself to death into its earthen grave.

"Holy shit!" exclaimed Halloway.

"Come on! We've got to help them!" shouted Dunn as he raced towards London and Chief, who had been thrown out of the helicopter.

"We're okay," said London, trying to struggle to his feet. "Help the crew."

"Yeah, I'm all right," said Chief. "Come on. I'll give you a hand."

"Help the door gunner," Dunn yelled to Halloway, as he pried open the cockpit door.

"Thank God you're safe," said the startled and groggy pilot. "The other Ranger..."

"He's fine," interrupted Dunn, "he's helping your door gunner. Here. You're harness is unfastened. Let's get you out of there."

"Help him first," said the Aircraft Commander, pointing to his Peter Pilot. "I think he's hurt."

"Sergeant Eagle is helping him now," responded Dunn. "Come on out so you can assist us," he urgently insisted because he realized the fire in the back of the helicopter was quickly spreading.

"His nose is broken and he is complaining that he cannot see well." Chief directed the AC to care for his Peter Pilot. "Guide him away from the aircraft." Both pilots had been cut up from the flying Plexiglas.

"Chief! Grab the machine gun from the mounts," yelled Halloway. "Sir, I need your help as the door gunner is badly wounded." The impact pulled the gunner's seat belt mounts out of the bulkhead, further injuring him when he was slammed into his mounted gun.

London reached Halloway before Dunn. The three of them lifted the wounded man in a makeshift sling of arms and carried him away from the burning chopper. The crippled aircraft was splattered with blood as well as bullet holes. A large caliber bullet passed through the door gunner's upper right leg and ripped away a portion of his left gluteus maximus. His mangled flak jacket testified to having saved his life from other bullets.

"I have to go back! I have to scramble the radio frequencies," suddenly shouted the pilot.

"Oh, no! We've got it." Dunn stopped the pilot and then called to Halloway. "Professor, how many incendiaries do you have left? We're not coming back to destroy any more downed helicopters so let's take care of it now!"

The two Rangers hurried back through the black smoke and into the stench of the spilled and burning jet fuel to put the wounded bird permanently out of commission.

Right after the Rangers destroyed their second helicopter, the gunships arrived and whisked them safely away. The remaining slick carried the crew of their sister ship directly to the hospital.

As he did after every mission involving one of his teams in contact, Dunn took time to submit each combatant, except himself, for a valor medal. He reserved the highest recommendation for the pilot.

20
Captain

TOMORROW, I FINALLY LEAVE FOR R & R," SAID Halloway. "I just wanted to drop by and let you know the guys in my Team 23, would feel honored if you take them into the bush as team leader while I'm gone." The Professor waited until after his platoon leader finished briefing the team leaders and they were alone. Team 23 was scheduled for an upcoming mission in a couple days.

"Thanks, I'd be honored to go on the mission with your team. So, where are you taking your R & R?" asked Dunn.

"I am meeting my wife in Hawaii. She's really excited and has always dreamed of going there. She is from Germany and I married her a little more than three years ago when I was stationed in Frankfurt," Halloway replied happily.

"Where is your wife living now?"

"She stayed in Columbus, Georgia. My last assignment was there at Fort Benning where I was an instructor in Jump School. I was known as a 'Black Hat.' Airborne instructors wear black baseball caps. So, I guess I'm just partial to black headgear. After 'Nam I hope I can return to Benning, this time as an instructor in Ranger School. I'd be proud to continue to wear the Black Beret."

"I wish you both a grand time in Hawaii. When you get back, you'll have to give me some pointers on things to see. I am also meeting my wife there next month to celebrate our first anniversary," Dunn volunteered.

"We're staying in the government hotel on the beach near Waikiki. Where are you staying, sir?" asked Halloway.

"We're staying in the same place as you for the first and last nights. The rest of the time we're staying at a place called, The Coco Palms, on the Island of Kauai."

"One more thing, sir, I'd appreciate it if you would take my ATL on the VR tomorrow. Sergeant Philip Keeler is a bit of a newbie, and it would be good for him. The guys call him, 'Slick.' He's a terrific Ranger."

"Absolutely, I was already planning on taking him. You just go and have a wonderful R & R," Dunn instructed.

"Airborne, sir!"

◖◗

The VR the next day was uneventful, as were the following four days that Dunn spent in the field with Team 23. The team did discover a deserted Viet Cong Base Camp and after scouting around, the men found six, separate entrances to an interconnected tunnel complex. Each entrance was barely big enough to permit a small man access through a hole fortified with logs and earth. The entrances were always below or flush with the surrounding ground and frequently adjacent to large rock boulders. Also scattered about the deserted camp were tall, woven bamboo and wicker baskets containing watermelons and gourds of all sizes, shapes and colors. There was no evidence, such as fresh fires or any smells that indicated recent occupancy.

◖◗

The middle of the following month, Dunn had another opportunity to go into the field, this time with Team 24, and they had similar, uneventful results. Lars Swenson, the Team Leader of Team 24, was on R & R in Bangkok when Dunn took that team into the bush.

Performing reconnaissance in lieu of ambush missions is certainly safer for the men, he thought. *The chance of sustaining casualties is a lot less if the men are not executing contact, but merely observing and reporting their sightings.*

"So, I imagine that was your last Ranger mission to the field with us, sir," said Staples to Dunn on the night after he returned from the four days out with Team 24. "How did you like working with Swenson's team?"

"They are most competent and professional. But they are more quiet and reserved than I expected, not at all like their team leader, The Mad Swede. Of course, he was never the same after the mission in which Scotty was killed. He became withdrawn and often paranoid. I wish I could have found out the truth of what actually happened that day," Dunn said.

"Let it go, sir. Just let it go."

"You're right, but I'll never be able to forget it."

"Did you know the Old Man has been trying to talk Swenson into applying to OCS, Officer Candidate School?"

"No. Really?" Dunn was surprised.

"Yeah. The Old Man has taken a shine to him. I think the Major sees a lot of himself in Lars. I'll bet you didn't know that the Old Man was an NCO and went to OCS himself. As a Buck Sergeant, he and Pappy both once worked for me in Europe. We actually made a pretty proficient team. That's why the Major requisitioned both of us to join Charlie Rangers and now work for him."

"Well, one thing the Old Man did that was really good was to get you to work in the TOC for Charlie Rangers. You are the absolute best for our guys in the field," Dunn complimented.

"The Old Man did another good thing when he got you, too," said Staples. "It has been a real pleasure working with you. You are a consummate professional and a tribute to the Ranger heritage. I think you pulled more C & C airtime and more missions in the field than any other officer we have ever had in Charlie Rangers."

"Thank you, Sergeant Staples. Your words mean more to me than any medals."

"Think you'll remember these times, sir?"

"I'll never forget this past year with Charlie Rangers. Who knows, maybe someday I'll write a book about our experiences here in 'Nam," joked Dunn.

"Nobody would ever believe the truth, sir!"

"Yeah, you and I lived it and sometimes I don't even believe it, myself."

"Well, you're not quite finished," piped in McDonough. "The Old Man wants you to serve one last time as Pay Officer. So, you'll be flying around the country for a few days, visiting our liaison sergeant at the Replacement Depot, the hospital at Qui Nhon and the Convalescent Center at Camh Ranh Bay.

"Then, when you finish with that, you are set to be a member of the Promotion Board for selection of men to be promoted from E-5 Sergeant to E-6 Staff Sergeant. Different unit commanders, including ours, will be referring applicants to the Board, which will convene in Tuy Hoa. The Major was considerate in that he figured it would be easier for you to leave directly from there on your way to your R & R."

◊

After making his rounds to pay all the men, including the infamous lad in Saigon's LBJ stockade, Dunn still had one final stop to make. He needed to pay the men at the static X-ray site.

However, the weather did not cooperate and for a couple of the last few days he was there, Ranger Hill was caught in another typhoon. The rains hit Ahn Khe hard, which for Dunn the worst part was no mail moved in or out for a couple days. Fortunately, the weather again cleared before he was scheduled to leave.

On his last day in the company, he flew out of Ahn Khe in a helicopter to pay the men on the eight-day X-ray mission. Team 27 was part of a heavy team securing the X-ray site. Enroute to the site, the chopper pilot advised him that TOC had an emergency situation. A sniper had wounded a cherry from Commo Platoon. Paymaster became "Dustoff." Dunn enjoyed watching a pair of "Delta Troop," 1/10 CAV Cobra helicopters obliterate the sniper's hiding place.

"The mighty Cobra," remarked his chopper pilot, "slim and trim, but deadly!"

"What happened?" asked Dunn as he rushed out of his helicopter to help the two Rangers who were carrying the wounded man to his chopper.

"The kid stood up to take a leak, and Sir Charles put two rounds in his shoulder. The poor kid's only been with the unit a week or two." SGT Don Carp from Hawaii was the team leader on the X-ray site.

"Does TOC plan on relocating you?"

"No, I think Captain McDonough is pulling my team and replacing us with two teams... Chief's team and a team from 3rd Platoon."

When Dunn returned to the TOC, he strongly asserted to both Wayne and McDonough the X-ray site was compromised and should be relocated, not strengthened. He further pointed out the mountaintop of the existing site was a grassy knoll, which afforded no protection for the men.

"Commo is good from that location," retorted Wayne. "The Cobras blew away that fucking sniper. There won't be any more goddamn problems. Besides, Lieutenant, this is not your goddamn problem anymore."

Team Leaders "Chief" Eagle and "Shark" Clemmons relieved the X-ray support detail and took B-40 fire that night long after Dunn had left, both team leaders and a couple of others were wounded. Rusky got Spooky up, and they stayed all night till the teams got out. Chief got another Bronze Star with Valor out of that one.

Dunn had hoped to spend the last full hour with his platoon before he was to depart to sit on the Promotion Board in Tuy Hoa. Instead, Major Wayne called Dunn into his tent for a private conference.

"Goddamn, Lieutenant Dunn! We've accomplished a hell of a lot together this past year. Seems like it was just a short time ago that you were a goddamn geek and wet behind the ears. Now, you are an experienced Ranger and about to be promoted to the goddamn rank of Captain. You know that when you are promoted, you no longer have a position in Charlie Rangers.

"I have arranged for you to be sent to our command element, the 17th Aviation Group. Their Combat Headquarters is in Tuy Hoa where you will be filling a Captain's slot in their Operation Center. That's why I assigned you to the Promotion Board. When you leave, you can take all your gear, since you won't be coming back. When you report back from R & R as a Captain, you will already be there in Tuy Hoa."

Dunn listened but did not respond, so the Major continued the conference. "I am also required to go over your OER with you and give you a copy. Since I had to rate you, I decided to rate all the lieutenants. I gave all of you a goddamn good report. You were really all right there together, but, of course, somebody had to be at the top and somebody had to be at the bottom. I rated Lieutenant Kent, 3rd Platoon Leader, at the top, and you happened to be at the bottom. But, this won't hurt your goddamn career. It really is a good report. As you can see, I gave you the highest possible goddamn ratings for job and duty performance. Any questions?"

"No, sir," was Dunn's steely-eyed response. Dunn couldn't help but notice Major Wayne raped him in all the subjective categories, such as "Loyalty, Character, Trustworthiness and Honor."

I will not allow this coward to upset me, thought Dunn. *His opinion of me in the scheme of life is irrelevant. I certainly no longer value his opinion. If the Army actually figures otherwise, then I will deal with whatever develops. But, right now, the most important thing is celebrating my first anniversary in Hawaii with my wife. Nothing is going to spoil my happiness.*

Before Dunn left, Staples presented him with a plaque bearing the unit scroll and patch, a silver map of Viet Nam, the C.I.B, interlocking flags of the USA and Vietnam and a silver plate inscribed with the words, "Presented to LT Joseph Dunn for Outstanding Service from the Officers and NCO's Company C Ranger 75th Infantry Airborne." For an even more treasured memento, Dunn collected all the available men in 2nd Platoon and captured their gruesome and glorious presence in a posed picture.

※

Four days later, Dunn stepped upon U.S. soil in the cooler warmth of the Hawaiian sunshine. Quickly scanning the group of women who had been escorted to greet his plane, he tried in vain to spot Marie. Suddenly, out of somewhere heavenly, she was there, wrapping her slender limbs around his neck and snuggling into his arms that instinctively pulled her supple body close to his.

"Mmmm, I missed you," she purred into his ear, kissing his neck and his cheek and finally giving him a sensitive, deep kiss on the mouth. Pulling her head back slightly, she looked directly in his eyes and smiled. "Oh, how I missed you!"

Her porcelain face glowed with unbridled happiness that he felt and shared. Her white skin contrasted sharply with his now deeply tanned body; however, they were the perfect couple. The paradise setting of the Hawaiian Islands only complemented the harmony of the two souls reunited in love and pleasure.

On their second night together, shortly after the sound of the shower stopped, Marie stepped out wearing a loose-fitting shirt that barely covered her below the waist. Marie was a near perfect "10," had a devilishly cute face, long dark hair and a body to die for. She had deliberately left the bathroom door ajar, thus bathing the room in a comfortable light. Sighing audibly, she slid in beside him under the sheet and onto her stomach. Turning her head toward him, she whispered, " Would you mind rubbing the back of my neck and shoulders? My muscles are so tight and I know it would help me relax."

Dunn rolled out of the sheet and straddled Marie, still under the sheet, with one knee on each side of her waist. His strong hands gently cupped her shoulders as his thumbs carefully started to caress the back of her neck.

"No. Do it underneath, on my skin," Marie smiled as she lifted her head and reached back with her right hand to pull her shirt toward her head. Dunn looked down and when he lifted up the sheet, he was greeted with the sight of a beautifully rounded bottom that shone virgin white as if spotlighted. The precise line of her barely noticeable tan intersected her back a good inch above the beginning of the beautiful separated white mound. Dunn swung his left foot onto the floor on the right side of the bed and simultaneously assisted her in pulling the shirt over her head. He gently but firmly grasped her right hand as she drew her arm out of the sleeve.

"Allow me to give you a 'complete' massage," he leered as his soothing voice instantly drew a knowing smile from Marie.

I want this to last, he thought. *I want to create a million memories for my private replay.*

He caressed her fingertips and stroked each finger before he expertly massaged her right hand. Then moving up her right arm, he alternately rubbed, stroked, probed and caressed with just the right amount of pressure and touch.

When he reached her shoulder, she thought, *I hope he stays there a little longer as it feels so good. I'm ticklish under my arms and don't want to be tickled because this was so relaxing. But...there he is, working under my arm, down my side, and it feels so heavenly, almost erotic. How could he have found an erogenous zone under my arm?*

Next, he kneaded her right buttocks and worked his way down her leg until he reached her right foot, which he massaged, stroked and caressed as expertly as he did her right hand.

Kneeling on the bed, he switched over to her left foot and proceeded to attend to her entire left side. When he finally reached the fingertips of her left hand, she was anxious to turn over. But he again straddled her with his knees and began to give her the best shoulder massage she had ever felt. She was so relaxed as he did the most wonderful things to her neck and back that she was afraid she would really fall asleep.

Suddenly, he was back on the floor at the right side of the bed. She had not realized her arm was still hanging limp over the side of the bed. He began caressing each finger in his mouth, rolling his tongue and sensually sucking them one by one. As he worked his way up to her right shoulder, she realized he was duplicating the complete massage he had just given her with his strong hands by now using his talented tongue. Her body writhed uncontrollably and she gasped at each new sensation she felt.

It felt like a thousand tiny pins of velvet when his tongue darted under her arm and alternately between her arm and her side. By the time he reached her toes, she was more than ready, but she did not want him to stop. By the time his mouth had worked its wonderment around her body and found her left index finger, she thought she would finally turn over.

However, he again straddled her back with his knees. When he bent over to massage her neck with his tongue, he teased her with his swelled and hardened weapon pressed against her. Instantly she arched her back and leaned her head back to give his mouth a deep kiss. Too late... his tongue had already traveled down her spine, causing her to shiver with heated delight. His hands were now upon her bottom as his tongue slid down her backside. Instinctively, she thrust her rear upwards as she simultaneously rose to her knees. Then his tongue found her sweet spot and his slippery finger slid in and out of her. Unable to stand it any longer, in one swift movement, she turned around, threw him back on the bed and as she straddled him, took his full and throbbing cock deep inside of her. Up and down she rode as hard and as fast as she could until they both climaxed together and collapsed into a sated jumble of limbs.

They had both been sleeping soundly for about four hours when she awoke him with a tender but strong massage of his neck and shoulders. It was now his turn to be driven crazy and her turn to play.

⚜

It seemed like only an instant before the seven-day Hawaiian honeymoon was over and Captain Dunn was back in Tuy Hoa. Only now he had private, air-conditioned quarters in wooden barracks, daily maid service and a regular eight-hour workday. Gone were his cammies and Black Beret and in their place he wore standard issue fatigues and an OD baseball cap. His place of duty was a desk, and his weapons of choice were a telephone and a pen.

"You are going to learn a tremendous amount about running a large organization," briefed Captain Bill Hammonds, one of the two other officers with whom he would closely work over the next two months in the Operations Center. "You and I have the job of prioritizing and allocating substantial assets to all the subordinate units on a daily and sometimes hourly basis. Believe me, we have dealt with Staples and Gregorov often enough for me to appreciate what you have been through the last ten months with Charlie Rangers. I hope to instill an equal appreciation of the conscientious requirements of your present tasks. Our many subordinate units count on us."

Bill Hammonds welcome briefing proved prophetic. Dunn was surprised and actually amazed at how much he appreciated the experience of working in the Operations Center for the 17th Aviation Combat Group. He wrote to Marie that he felt guilty he was not required to work harder and more hours, but that his superiors, especially LTC Fred Albertson, the unit Executive Officer, constantly praised him.

"The Fourth of July party, originally planned to be a fish luau at the commander's trailer complex, will most likely be canceled," announced Albertson. "Instead, we're trying to see if we can get the Command Mess to put together a festive menu in its place. The Viet Cong destroyed the bridge outside the base that leads to the town where the local fish market is located. Everybody is afraid to go off base, and the commander does not want anyone to risk their life for a party."

"Sir," interrupted Dunn, "I was looking forward to the luau, especially the rock lobster out of the South China Sea. I'll gladly go to the market. Just give me a jeep and a list of what you need."

"Are you certain, Captain Dunn?"

"Absolutely, sir. There's no need to alter the plans for the commander's party."

Saturday morning at about 0900 hours Dunn and Specialist Carver, one of the enlisted men from his office, went into the town of Tuy Hoa to buy fish and lobsters. Dunn took his camera and snapped a dozen pictures of the local people and places, including the destroyed bridge.

Carver knew one of the Vietnamese girls who had a day off from working at the Enlisted Mess Hall. She met them and took their money to pay for the lobsters and fish. It cost less than $25.00 for 33, unbelievably large lobsters. Dunn took them back alive to the Officers' Mess to prepare for the commander's affair that evening. They were back before 1245 hours.

"Hey, sir, I read about you in the Army Times. You were in a Ranger unit, right?" asked Carver.

"Yeah. What are you talking about?"

"Oh, I always check the listing of medals awarded... you know, just in case my name might appear. No, really, you were listed as having been awarded ten Combat Air Medals. Wow! You must have seen a lot of action and done some heroic things, sir."

"No. That just means I logged a lot of hours in support of combat missions. The men on the ground and the pilots at the controls deserve all your respect, not the backseat passengers just along for the ride like me."

"Yea, well I'm still mighty impressed, sir."

Dunn took off his OD baseball cap and wiped the sweat from his forehead with his forearm as he said, "Damn! It's hot!"

"How about a refreshing can of iced-cold soda, sir?" Carver said as he handed him a can of Coca-Cola he had picked up from the Officers' Mess. "That visit to town was 'Number One.' It was kinda cool seeing how the Vietnamese people actually live. The fish market was beau coup busy! At first I was nervous 'cause everybody is so scared to go off the base. But, I wasn't afraid at all. Sir, let me know if you are ever going back into town and want somebody to go with you."

"I'm so short I won't have time to make another trip." Dunn raised the can of soda to his lips to drink. He took one sip but could not drink any more from the can. When the metallic can touched his mouth, it tasted like it was rusty, like the cans of hot beer that had been delivered to Charlie Rangers by Big Windy.

Aluminum cans were not supposed to rust. But, the Rangers had all greedily punched open the cans and chugged the hot beer. Evidently, the pallets of beer had been stored for months in the hull of a ship and sat in ocean salt water. Maybe aluminum cans were not supposed to rust, but they sure tasted awful with a corroded metallic taste. He was sure he would never again drink from a can without recalling that bitter tasting memory.

🍃

"I want to pay tribute to a young officer who made this headquarters' event possible this evening at my patio," announced COL Daniel Merryweather, the commander. The party was a picnic-style "Hail & Farewell" ceremony of surf & turf. "Captain Dunn has been with us for under two months but has already performed more beneficial tasks than many of my staff are able to accomplish in triple that amount of time. Come up here, Dunn. So you don't forget us, I want to present you with this handsome hand-carved plaque from the Philippines. See the intricate carving of our 17th Aviation crest? Also, I am pleased to announce award to Captain Dunn of the Bronze Star for his spectacular job performance both with Charlie Rangers and with us while here in 'Nam!"

"Thank you, sir," said a surprised, yet humble Dunn, shaking the Colonel's right hand and accepting the plaque with his left.

"Captain Dunn," called out LTC Albertson, "may I speak with you for a moment? I want to personally thank you for the superior job you have done for us. In the short time you have been with us, you have made significant contributions and a most favorable impact. All our units benefit from the simple, but brilliant method you designed to reallocate unproductive air assets. Since you are such a 'Short-Timer,' and as your Rating Officer, it is my pleasure to give you your copy of this Officer Efficiency Report from me.

"I have met some mighty fine officers in my career. But this is by far the finest OER I have ever given. It has been an honor to have you work for me. Also, congratulations on the Bronze Star. You certainly earned it!"

"Thank you. Thank you, sir."

"By the way, we just received a request that the Bronze Star, with 'V' Device for Valor, be approved for award to Major Woodrow Wayne, the Commander of Charlie Rangers. It was put in for him by CPT McDonough, his new Operations Officer, based on his leading a team into the field to recover some sensitive items on a downed CH-47 Big Windy Chinook. Do you know anything about that mission?"

"Yes, sir, there are a number of Rangers and helicopter crewmen that, in my opinion, deserve valor medals for that mission."

"Really? Well, okay, then. There is one more thing I must ask you. We are not favorably disposed to granting Major Wayne's request to be extended as Commander of Charlie Rangers. Would you be interested in extending over here to become Company Commander of Company C, Ranger, 75th Infantry, Airborne...a job usually for a senior Major? I could get you a special extension approved from Washington DC and orders cut immediately."

"I am elated that you think so highly of me." He was stunned.

"I have done my homework. Colonel Merryweather and I agree you are the best man to command Charlie Rangers. This is a prime combat command position, as you well know. What do you say?"

"Sir, it is an honor to be asked. However, I must decline. The war on this front would be tame compared to the one at the home front that would erupt if I extended." Dunn did not hesitate to decisively respond and was relieved to note LTC Albertson accepted his declination without further argument.

If I were single, Dunn thought, *I would have extended for a full year in a heartbeat. To command the men of Charlie Rangers would be the ultimate honor and the best damn job in the Army. As it is, on 27 July I intend to be on that big beautiful freedom bird. I only want to go home to Marie and stay by her side.*

Dunn gazed out the small window of the plane at the land called, Viet Nam. He felt like cheering a farewell.

He was returning home a year older, but he was no longer the same person. The motto of his beloved Military Academy, "Duty, Honor, Country," now had a much deeper connotation for him because he had lived and knew the meaning, and sometimes the bleeding and sorrow behind those words. He was leaving behind family, brothers in arms, brothers of the Black Beret, and some forever.

Also, he intended to leave behind his memories of the war. He knew it would be a long time, if ever, that he would be able to speak or write of them, as he knew a cheering public would *not* accord Vietnam Veterans the triumphant welcome home they justly deserved. Someday, perhaps the American people would recognize and rejoice those unsung heroes of the country's longest conflict. Perhaps the American people might also someday discern to condemn the horrible war but be able to praise its worthy warriors. Hopefully, in the near future, the American people of their own volition might be able to get past their present, infantile and immature ideals, and with maturity and wisdom brought on by retrospect, learn to genuinely celebrate and even champion those wonderful and extremely courageous men who valiantly answered a cause more dear than life-like the Rangers who served-*of their own accord.*

But for now, he was simply content to be going home to his Marie and their future together, whatever that might be.

◖

"Gentlemen," announced the voice of the pilot over the loudspeaker, "as we taxi towards an imminent take-off, it is my distinct pleasure to declare right now, you are the 'shortest' men in all of Viet Nam!"
"HOOAHH. HOOAHH. AHHOOGAA!"

AFTERWORD

The Vietnam War divided our nation on a scale not witnessed since the Civil War. Its long duration and tragically high number of dead and wounded broke the will of the American people and turned them against the war itself, and in many ways, the men and women who fought there. As a result, these disenfranchised veterans were never accorded the recognition and appreciation their sacrifice deserved. An entire generation of American veterans have been dishonored and mistreated because of a collective national policy that failed from its inception. Yet, no generation before them can claim to have fought with more dignity or more valor than these maligned soldiers, sailors, marines and airmen. Their sense of duty, equal to that of their fathers and grandfathers, can never be challenged.

Their stories were late in coming due to the unpopularity of the war. Early apologists and anti-war authors fed into the national psyche that the victory had been lost and our young warriors had failed. The truth was suppressed to support the populist embarrassment over a final withdrawal that smacked of defeat. It took more than a decade after the war had ended before its veterans, proud of their achievements, began telling what had really happened in the jungles, rice paddies, and mountains of South Vietnam. Only then did we discover that valor and honor were as common in this war as they had been in every war before it.

Hundreds of America's finest young men and women have since tossed off this veil of shame forced upon them by an ungrateful nation. Proud of the job they did, they unabashedly told their stories in countless biographies-gut wrenching, heart-pounding stories of deadly combat, ambushes, and booby traps that defy description. They have painted vivid pictures of mayhem and destruction that the uninitiated can never imagine. In sharing their experiences, they have preserved forever the trials and tribulations of America's longest war, and the affects it had on its participants. Once and for all, our nation can understand and accept what it had previously denied-that our young men and women who served in Vietnam had upheld the finest traditions of our military heritage.

Gary Dolan, a platoon leader with Company C (Airborne), 75th Infantry (Ranger), has opted to tell his story in a form unusual for combat veterans of the Vietnam era. *Of Their Own Accord* is his masterful novel of a year in the life of an Airborne Ranger platoon leader during the height of the war. Although this author has elected fictional device, let me assure you that the story you are about to read is based almost entirely on actual events. During his year in the deadly Central Highlands of South Vietnam, this young West Point graduate defied conventional doctrine and made the decision to lead by example and not by privilege of rank. He personally led numerous 6-man long range patrols deep into enemy territory, not for personal glory, but because he could not... would not...send his men into mortal combat without sharing the peril with them. His story is both revealing and hard-hitting, and runs the full gamut of emotions from abject fear to unqualified heroism, from tender love and devotion to unbridled loyalty to a very special brotherhood of warriors. Dolan reveals the truism that only a combat veteran understands-that it is not patriotism that inspires young men to such bravery, but their love and devotion to their comrades.

Although hidden behind the overt shield of fiction, do not be fooled for a moment. His tale rings as true as any biography that this author has read. I am in deep admiration of his ability as a writer, yet I am even more impressed with his accomplishments as a leader of America's finest warriors. The Vietnam era LRP/Rangers and their brethren in the Navy SEALs, Force Recon Marines, and Special Forces wrote the book on U.S. special operations. The success our special operations forces enjoy today is a direct result of lessons learned in the green hell that was Southeast Asia.

I am proud and honored to have been asked to write the introduction to this outstanding work. Gary Dolan has written an unqualified tribute to his men and to his nation, a success story in an unsuccessful war. It should be required reading for every young, aspiring officer entering the military today

Gary A. Linderer
F Co., 58th Inf. (LRP)
L Co., 75th Inf. (Ranger)

Glossary

AFB: Air Force Base

AK-47: Standard Infantry rifle of the North Vietnamese and Viet Cong soldier

AK-50: Improved enemy Infantry rifle with a triangular bayonet

AO: Area of Operations

Ao dai: Traditional Vietnamese woman's formal long gown with slits on either side

ARVN: Army of the Republic of Vietnam; a South Vietnamese soldier; our Allies

ATL: Assistant Team Leader

AWOL: Absent Without Leave

B-40: A shoulder-fired, rocket-propelled grenade launcher carried by North Vietnamese and Viet Cong soldiers

B-52: "Stratofortresses" have been the backbone of the manned strategic bomber force for the United States. The B-52 is capable of dropping or launching the widest array of weapons in the U.S. inventory. This includes gravity bombs, cluster bombs, precision guided missiles and joint direct attack munitions.

0-1 Birddog: Two-seater, single propeller, fixed wing airplane built by Cessna; used by FO and C & C

Blooper: Nickname for the M-79 grenade launcher; also known as the "Thumper"

Bush: The enemy terrain in which the Rangers operated; the "Field"

C & C: Command and Control; the exercise of authority over a combat situation

C.I.B.: Combat Infantryman Badge, automatically awarded to any soldier in combat with a Military Occupation Specialty of "Infantryman."

Cammies: Camouflage Jungle Fatigues

Charlie: Nickname for the Vietcong based on the phonetic alphabet, letter "C" (Charlie)

Cherries: First-Timers; those who have been in Viet Nam for the first time less than three months; also known as "FNG-Fucking New Guy" and "Newbies"

Chopper: Helicopter

Conex: steel storage/shipping container about 8 cubic feet with doors that make up one side of the container

Cow: The nickname for a West Point Cadet in his third year as a student

DEROS: Date Eligible Return (from) Overseas

Deuce and a half: Two and a half ton Army truck

Didi mau: To run quickly

Dinky Dau: (Vietnamese, dien cai dau); to be crazy; "off the wall"

Drag: The last man in the march of a Ranger patrol; responsible for rear security and elimination of tracks

Dustoff: Nickname for helicopter used in a medical evacuation

Firstie: The nickname for a West Point Cadet in his final year as a student

FNG: First-Timers; those who have been in Viet Nam for the first time less than three months; also known as "Cherries" and "Newbies"

FO: Forward Observer to direct artillery or air support

Fragging: Troops killing their own officers with fragmentation grenades

G.I.: U.S. Soldiers; "Government Issue"

Gooks: Slang term for the enemy or any oriental person; passed down from veterans of the Korean War; Korean for "person"

Groundhog: To hide and avoid any contact with the enemy

Ground-pounder: Slang term for an infantryman

Gunship: Heavily armed attack helicopter

Hatchet: A Ranger ambush

Herd: Nickname for elements of the 173rd Airborne Brigade

Hootch: Any permanent or temporary dwelling

KIA: Killed In Action

Kit Carson Scouts: Former enemy soldiers who assisted and partici-pated, frequently as the Point, in Ranger patrols

Leave: Military vacation time accrued at two and a half days per month

Leg: A derogatory term applied to non-Airborne soldiers; LEG (Lack Enough Guts)

Lifer: Generally a derogatory term to describe a person committed to a career in the military

Lima Charlie: Loud and Clear transmission

LRP: Long Range Patrol, such as the ambush patrols performed by Charlie Rangers

LRRP: Long Range Reconnaissance Patrol; also the freeze-dried rations in packages carried by patrols

LZ: Landing Zone

Maverick Convoy: A convoy of trucks from different military units

Medivac: Medical Evacuation of wounded or ill

NCO: Non Commissioned Officer

Newbies: First-Timers; those who have been in Viet Nam for the first time less than three months; also known as "FNG-Fucking New Guy" and "Cherries"

Non bai tho: An elegant looking conical palm hat traditionally worn by both Vietnamese men and women; literally, "a hat with poetry written on it"

Nuoc mam: A fermented, spicy fish head sauce, which the Rangers called "armpit sauce"

NVA: North Vietnamese Army regular soldier; the enemy

OD: Olive Drab color

OER: Officer Efficiency Report; evaluation of junior officer by superior and used by the Army for consideration of promotions and assignments

Opconned: Placed under the operational control of

Papasan: G.I. term for a Vietnamese man

Point: The lead position in a Ranger patrol; responsible for frontal security

PX: Post Exchange; retail mall on a military base

R & R: Rest and Recreation; 7 days of vacation time not counted against accrued leave time

Red Leg: Artillery

REMF: Rear Echelon Mother Fucker; derogatory term to describe the majority of soldiers in a support role and not in combat

Ring-Knocker: A graduate of the United States Military Academy

Rock N Roll: To set a weapon's safety on "fully automatic"

ROK: Republic of Korea soldier

ROTC: Reserve Officers Training Corps

RTO: Radio Telephone Operator

Short: Having only a short time remaining to serve in Vietnam

Sitrep: Situation Report

Slick: UH-1 helicopter used for transporting troops in tactical air assault operations. The helicopter did not have protruding armaments and was, therefore, "slick"

Spec-4: Specialist-4 (ranked one grade above PFC and one below a Sergeant E-5)

Strac: the best the military had to offer

Tango: A word beginning with the letter, "T," such as Team or Trail

TOC: Tactical Operations Center

V.I.P.: Very Important Person

VR: Visual Reconnaissance

CHARLIE RANGERS
75th INFANTRY AIRBORNE

"Take a man - Make him a RANGER
Put him alone with 5 of his own
Empty his heart of all but the blood
And make him live in sweat and mud
This is the life us RANGERS must live
And our souls to the devil we give
And you peace children back home don't care
You don't know what its like over here
You have a ball without really trying
While over here men are always dying
You burn your draft cards and march until dawn
And put your signs on the White House lawn
You want to ban the deadly bomb
And you say there's no war in Viet Nam
Keep on using your drugs and have fun
And keep on refusing to lift a gun
You say there's nothing in it for you
And at the same time we're supposed to die for you
Peace children I'll hate you until the day I die
Whenever I hear my buddy's cry
I will see his body a bloody shred
I hear his friends say this one's dead
It's quite a price he had to pay
Down his life he did lay
He paid the price, but what did he buy
Your life, Your Freedom, upon him you relied"

About the Author

Gary Dolan received a B.S in Civil Engineering from the United States Military Academy in 1969 and a J.D. from New York Law School in 1977. Dolan is an attorney licensed in the State of New York, a public accountant and a Certified Trade Broker. Dolan's distinguished 5-year military career includes a one-year tour of duty in Vietnam in 1970 with Company C (Ranger), 75th Infantry (Airborne). While in the service, Dolan was awarded the Airborne, Ranger, Jungle Warfare Expert and Combat Infantryman Badges as well as ten Combat Air Medals, the Bronze Star and numerous other achievement medals. He served as President of Company E (Long Range Patrol), 20th Infantry (Airborne) and Company C (Ranger), 75th Infantry (Airborne) Association, Inc.

In 1996, Gary Dolan founded and served as CEO of eBarter, the world's first online, interactive barter exchange and predecessor to Bigvine, Inc., of which he is the Founder. Bigvine was the premier online barter exchange and was funded with $60 Million by the world's leading investors, including Kleiner Perkins Caufield & Byers, the partners of Kohlberg Kravis Roberts & Co., American Express, NBC and Sanford Robertson (founder of Robertson Stephens & Co., LLC.).

Prior to starting eBarter, Dolan owned an accounting practice and taught courses throughout New York on how to start and run a profitable small business. From 1978 to 1990, Dolan practiced general law as managing partner of Alonge & Dolan in the state of New York. In addition, Dolan served as consultant to the United States Small Business Administration's (SBA) Small Business Development Center at the State University of New York at Farmingdale. He also served there as an adjunct professor for 14 years, teaching business law and accounting. Dolan currently works as an attorney in his own practice.

In his spare time, Dolan enjoys traveling, skiing and has been a New York high school baseball umpire for 5 years. He and his wife, Linda, live in Farmingdale, New York. They have three grown children.

To view pictures of the actual people, places and events that inspired Dolan's writing, please visit http://oftheirownaccord.com.